Photoelectron Spectroscopy

AN INTRODUCTION TO ULTRAVIOLET PHOTOELECTRON
SPECTROSCOPY IN THE GAS PHASE

SECOND EDITION

Photoelectron Spectroscopy

AN INTRODUCTION TO ULTRAVIOLET PHOTOELECTRON
SPECTROSCOPY IN THE GAS PHASE

Second Edition

J. H. D. ELAND, MA, DPhil
Fellow of Worcester College, Oxford

Butterworths
London   Boston   Durban   Singapore   Sydney
Toronto   Wellington

7134- 2990

First published 1984

Butterworth & Co (Publishers) Ltd, 1984

British Library Cataloguing in Publication Data

Eland, J.H.D.
  Photoelectron spectroscopy.—2nd ed.
  1. Photoelectron spectroscopy
  I. Title
  535.8'44   QC454.P48
  ISBN 0–408–71057–8

Library of Congress Cataloging in Publication Data

Eland, J. H. D.
  Photoelectron spectroscopy.

  Includes index.
  1. Photoelectron spectroscopy.   I. Title.
  QC454.P48E38   1983   543'.0858   83-14386
  ISBN 0–408–71057–8

Typeset by Scribe Design, Gillingham, Kent
Printed and bound in Great Britain by the Camelot Press Ltd.,
Southampton

Preface to the second edition

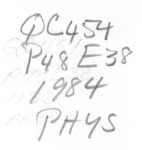

The expansion of photoelectron spectroscopy foreseen in the preface to the first edition has indeed taken place in the ten years since 1972. Besides the ever expanding applications of the technique in different branches of chemistry, there have been considerable advances in our understanding of the photoionization process and of the ion reactions that follow it. Progress has been stimulated by improvements in experimental technique, particularly by the emergence of lasers and electron storage rings as new sources of ionizing radiation. At the same time theoretical chemists have learnt how to calculate ionization energies in a much more sophisticated and reliable way, by going beyond Koopmans' theorem and the orbital model. These developments have prompted the preparation of a second edition.

The purpose of the book remains unchanged, being to equip advanced students and researchers starting in photoelectron spectroscopy, or turning to photoelectron spectroscopy from their own specialities, with a complete account of the subject at a practical level. All parts of the book have been revised and major changes have been made in Chapters 2 (Experimental Methods), Chapter 3 (Ionization) and Chapter 7 (Reactions of Positive Ions). New sections on such topics as multi-photon ionization, synchrotron radiation and rotational effects have inevitably added to the length of the text, but some other topics, which have proved after the passage of time to be of less pressing interest, have been omitted. The references throughout the text are again intended to be useful rather than archival, and to any authors who might feel aggrieved by lack of reference to their vital work, I can only point out that they are undoubtedly cited indirectly. If there is a bias it is towards those authors who have sent me their reprints and to whom I express my thanks most heartily for thereby lightening the task of preparation.

John H.D. Eland

Preface to the first edition

The photoelectron spectrometer will soon take its place in the laboratory beside the mass spectrometers, optical spectrometers and radio-frequency spectrometers that have become routine tools of the chemist and physicist. A new form of molecular spectroscopy naturally requires an incubation period in the hands of specialist physicists and physical chemists before it becomes useful in wider fields of chemistry, and photoelectron spectroscopy is now emerging from such a stage in its development. Sure signs of this emergence are the burgeoning of chemical applications of the technique and the availability of commercial photoelectron spectrometers with very high performance. At the same time, there is a lack of any textbook that covers the new technique at an advanced undergraduate or first year research level, and this I have attempted to provide. My aim has been to cover, at least qualitatively, almost all that a chemist needs to know in order to interpret a photoelectron spectrum with which he is confronted. The treatment is experimentally based and non-mathematical, but assumes some familiarity with other spectroscopic techniques and with the chemical applications of Group Theory.

The importance of photoelectron spectroscopy in the study of molecular electronic structure is now widely appreciated; its relevance to mass spectrometry and unimolecular reaction rate theory deserves more attention than it has hitherto received, and I hope that the inclusion of Chapter 7 on ionic dissociation will go some way to rectify this. Chapters 1 to 6 form a progressive introduction to photoelectron spectroscopy, and they are intended to be read sequentially, with a few possible exceptions. The more difficult topics in Sections 1.4.2, 3.4.3, 3.5 and 4.6 could be omitted on a first reading and Chapter 2, on experimental methods, may be referred to separately from the main text. The final chapter contains accounts of some selected applications of photoelectron spectroscopy in chemistry, and includes a sufficiently full reference list for these topics to be followed up in detail. Shorter reference lists are provided for all the other chapters and should serve as a key to the literature, but they are by no means a complete bibliography; often only the most recent papers on a particular subject are cited. In a rapidly advancing field such as this, it is impossible to write a completely up-to-date book, and the inclusion of new material had to stop at the end of 1972.

In preparing this book I have been helped by discussions with several scientists, and I should like to thank Dr. B. Brehm, Dr. M.S. Child, Dr. C.J. Danby, Professor E. Heilbronner and Mr. A.F. Orchard in particular. Dr. Brehm and Dr. Danby also read parts of the manuscript in draft and made suggestions for several necessary improvements. The typing was undertaken by Mrs. M. Long, and I am most grateful for her speed and cheerfulness in dealing with a difficult manuscript. Finally, I want to thank my wife, Ieva, for the immense amount of help she has given at every stage of the work.

John H.D. Eland

Contents

1
Principles of photoelectron spectroscopy

1.1 Introduction

When light of short wavelength interacts with free molecules, it can cause electrons to be ejected from the occupied molecular orbitals. Photoelectron spectroscopy is the study of these photoelectrons, whose energies, abundances and angular distributions are all characteristic of the individual molecular orbitals from which they originate. The experimental singling-out of individual molecular orbitals is the outstanding feature of photoelectron spectroscopy, and one which distinguishes it from all other methods of examining molecular electronic structure.

The quantity measured most directly in photoelectron spectroscopy is the ionization potential for the removal of electrons from different molecular orbitals. According to an approximation known as Koopmans' theorem, each ionization potential, I_j, is equal in magnitude to an orbital energy, ε_j:

$$I_j = -\varepsilon_j \tag{1.1}$$

This is an approximation additional to those inherent in the molecular orbital model for many-electron systems, but it is a good and a very useful one. It means that the photoelectron spectrum of a molecule is a direct representation of the molecular orbital energy diagram. Furthermore, the spectrum also shows, from the detailed form of the bands, what changes in molecular geometry are caused by removal of one electron from each orbital. These changes reveal the character of the orbitals, whether they are bonding, antibonding or non-bonding, and how their bonding power is localized in the molecules.

The photoelectron spectroscopy discussed in this book is based on photoionization brought about by radiation in the far ultraviolet region of the spectrum. It was invented early in the 1960s independently by two groups, one led by Turner[1,2] in London, the other by Vilesov[3] in Leningrad. Siegbahn[4] and his group at Uppsala had evolved a similar technique a little earlier, but they used X-radiation instead of ultraviolet light and at first concentrated more on the study of solids than on free molecules. Both ultraviolet and X-ray photoelectron spectroscopy have been extensively developed and have found many applications in chemistry and physics. This book is an attempt to present an up-to-date view of ultraviolet photoelectron spectroscopy, and reference to X-ray work is made only when it expands upon or illuminates aspects of the valence electronic structure of molecules or ions.

1.2   Main features of photoelectron spectra

In a photoelectron spectrometer, an intense beam of monochromatic (monoenergetic) ultraviolet light ionizes molecules or atoms of a gas in an ionization chamber:

$$M + h\nu \rightarrow M.001 + e \tag{1.2}$$

The light used is most commonly the helium resonance line He I at 584 Å (58.4 nm), which is equivalent to 21.22 electronvolts (eV) of energy per photon. This energy is sufficient to ionize electrons from the *valence shell* of molecules or atoms, that is, from the orbitals that are involved in chemical bonding and are characterized by the highest principal quantum number of the occupied atomic orbitals. In each orbital, j, of an atom or molecule, the electrons have a characteristic binding energy, the minimum energy needed to eject them to infinity. Part of the energy of a photon is used to overcome this binding energy, I_j, and if the species is an atom the remainder, $h\nu - I_j$, must appear as kinetic energy (KE) of the ejected electrons:

$$KE = h\nu - I_j \tag{1.3}$$

The ejected photoelectrons are separated according to their kinetic energies in an electron energy analyser, detected and recorded. The photoelectron spectrum is a record of the number of electrons detected at each energy, and contains a peak at each energy, $h\nu - I_j$, corresponding to the binding energy, I_j, of an

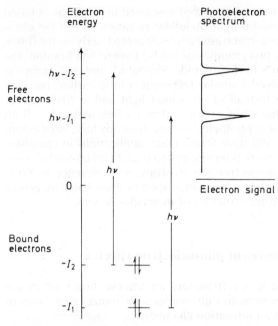

Figure 1.1   Idealized photoionization process and photoelectron spectrum of an atom

electron in the atom, as illustrated schematically in *Figure 1.1*. If the species is a molecule, there are the additional possibilities of vibrational or rotational excitation on ionization, so the energies of the photoelectrons may be reduced:

$$KE = h\nu - I_j - E^*_{\text{vib, rot}} \qquad (1.4)$$

The spectrum may now contain many vibrational *lines* for each type of electron ionized, and the system of lines that corresponds to ionization from a single molecular orbital constitutes a *band*.

Apart from Koopmans' theorem, there are two approximate rules that make the relationship between photoelectron spectra and molecular electronic structure especially simple:

(1) Each band in the spectrum corresponds to ionization from a single molecular orbital.
(2) Each occupied molecular orbital of binding energy less than $h\nu$ gives rise to a single band in the spectrum.

Because of these rules, the photoelectron spectrum is a simple reflection of the molecular orbital diagram, as illustrated in *Figure 1.1*. The rules are a simplification, however, and there are three reasons why there may, in fact, be more bands in a spectrum than there are valence orbitals in a molecule. Firstly, additional bands are sometimes found that correspond to the ionization of one electron with simultaneous excitation of a second electron to an unoccupied excited orbital. This is a two-electron process, and in the ionization potential region below 20 eV the bands produced in the spectrum are much weaker than simple ionization bands. Secondly, ionization from a degenerate occupied molecular orbital can give rise to as many bands in the spectrum as there are orbital components, because although the orbitals are degenerate in the molecule they may not be so in the positive ion. The mechanisms that remove the degeneracy are spin–orbit coupling and the Jahn–Teller effect. Thirdly, ionization from molecules such as O_2 or NO, which have unpaired electrons, can give many more bands than there are occupied orbitals in the molecule, and in such instances neither Koopmans' theorem nor the simple rules apply.

In order to introduce these main features of photoelectron spectra, it is convenient to take practical examples, starting with the spectra of atoms and proceeding to those of more complicated molecules. The spectroscopic names of atomic and molecular electronic states are constantly needed when describing the spectra, and any readers who are not familiar with them may find it helpful to consult Appendix I.

1.2.1   Atoms

The photoelectron spectrum of atomic mercury excited by helium resonance radiation is shown in *Figure 1.2*. The vertical scale in this and all other photoelectron spectra is the strength of the electron signal, usually given in electrons per second. The absolute intensities have no physical significance because they depend on physical and experimental factors, which, although constant throughout the measurement of the spectrum, are not precisely known. The relative intensities of different peaks in the spectrum are meaningful, however, as they are equal to the relative probabilities of photoionization to different states of the positive ion, which are called the relative partial ionization cross-sections. Three horizontal scales are given in *Figure 1.2* to illustrate the relationships between measured electron energy, ionization potential and the internal excitation energy of the ions, including

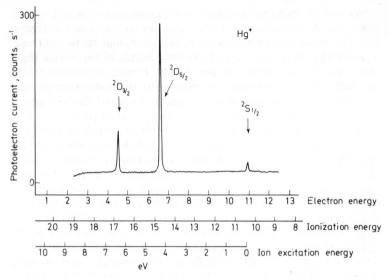

Figure 1.2   Photoelectron spectrum of mercury excited by He I (584 Å) radiation

electronic excitation energy. Although volts (V) are the units of potential and electronvolts (eV) are units of energy, it is a usage hallowed by tradition to speak of ionization *potentials* as energies and to quote them in units of electronvolts. Nevertheless, when energy quantities are being compared, the phrase 'ionization energy' is used frequently in this book, and henceforth the only horizontal scale given for photoelectron spectra will be one of ionization energy in electronvolts. The SI units of energy, joules, are very inconvenient in this field and are not used by spectroscopists; conversion factors for the important units are given in Appendix II.

The spectrum of mercury in *Figure 1.2* was obtained with a spectrometer in which electrons of only one energy at a time were able to reach the detector; it is called a *differential* spectrum. Spectra are sometimes encountered in *integral* form, taken with spectrometers in which all electrons of more than a certain energy can reach the detector simultaneously. The spectrum of mercury measured in such a spectrometer is shown in *Figure 1.3*, where its integral relationship to the spectrum in *Figure 1.2* is apparent. Both spectra show that Hg^+ ions are formed by photoionization in three electronic states, with ionization energies of 10.44, 14.84 and 16.71 eV. The states involved are well known from the atomic spectrum of mercury and have the designations $^2S_{1/2}$, $^2D_{5/2}$ and $^2D_{3/2}$, respectively. The neutral atom has the electron configuration $5d^{10}6s^2$ in the outer shells and the designation $^1S_0$. The $^2S_{1/2}$ state of Hg^+ is produced by the ejection of one of the 6s electrons, but both of the ^2D states are produced by the ejection of 5d electrons. A useful notation for describing these ionization processes is to write the name of the orbital from which the electron is

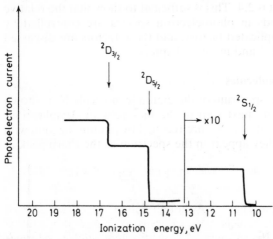

Figure 1.3   Integral photoelectron spectrum of mercury excited by He I radiation. (After Frost, D.C., McDowell, C.A., Sandhu, J.S. and Vroom, D.A., in Kendricks, E. (Editor) *Advances in Mass Spectrometry, Vol 4*, Institute of Petroleum, London, 781 (1968))

removed with the superscript $^{-1}$. Thus the first ionization process is $6s^{-1}$ and the second and third both correspond to $5d^{-1}$. The energy difference between the $^2D_{5/2}$ and $^2D_{3/2}$ states arising from $5d^{-1}$ ionization represents a breakdown of the rule of one band per orbital, in this instance owing to spin–orbit coupling. A similar splitting is possible whenever an ionic state has both orbital and spin degeneracy. The rare gas atoms, for instance, have as their outermost orbitals completed p shells, and ionization yields p^5, a ^2P state which splits into $^2P_{3/2}$ and $^2P_{1/2}$ and gives two peaks in the spectra. Because of the breakdown of the rule of one band per orbital, Koopmans' theorem cannot be used directly to derive the orbital energy for 5d electrons in mercury or for the outer p electrons of the rare gases. A weighted mean of all the energies for ionization from a single orbital must be taken, where the weights are the statistical weights of the ionic states produced. For atoms, these are equal to 2J + 1, so the state $^2P_{3/2}$ of a rare gas in ion has a weight of 4 and the state $^2P_{1/2}$ has a weight of 2. In theory, the intensities of the bands in the photoelectron spectrum should be proportional to these statistical weights, and indeed the rare gas ionizations give peaks with intensity ratios near 2:1. The $5d^{-1}$ ionization of mercury, however, should have an intensity ratio for $^2D_{5/2}$ to $^2D_{3/2}$ of 6:4, but in fact the ratio given by the step heights in *Figure 1.3* is about 6:2.4. This is sufficient to show that the relative intensities of bands in photoelectron spectra are controlled by several more complicated factors, and these factors are discussed again in Section 1.3 and in later chapters.

1.2.2   Diatomic molecules

The photoelectron spectrum of the diatomic molecule N_2 is shown in *Figure 1.4* as the next step in the hierarchy of complication. Three electronic states of N_2^+ are reached by photoionization with 584 Å light, and they appear in the spectrum as the sharp peak at

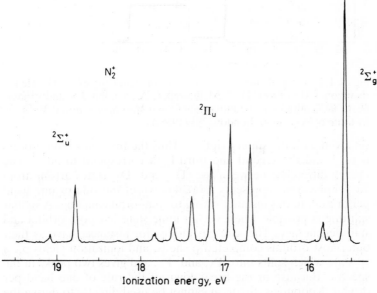

Figure 1.4   Photoelectron spectrum of nitrogen excited by He I radiation. At higher resolution peaks of the $^2\Pi_u$ band are partially resolved into doublets: see the review of A.F. Orchard in Book 3 of the general bibliography (Section 1.5.1). (By courtesy of Professor W.C. Price)

15.6 eV, the group of peaks between 16.7 and 18 eV and the weak peak at 18.8 eV. Each electronic state actually gives a group of peaks in the spectrum because of the possibility of vibrational as well as electronic excitation. Every resolved peak in the spectrum of a molecule is a single vibrational line and represents a definite number of quanta of vibrational energy in the molecular ion.

As was the case for mercury, the ionic states of N_2^+ seen in the photoelectron spectrum are well known from optical spectroscopy. They have the designations $X\ ^2\Sigma_g^+$, $A\ ^2\Pi_u$ and $B\ ^2\Sigma_u^+$ in order of increasing ionization potential, and correspond to the ionization processes σ_g^{-1}, π_u^{-1} and σ_u^{-1}, respectively. It is clear that the three bands in the spectrum are very different both in the spacings of the lines within the bands, which give the sizes of the vibrational quanta in the ions, and also in the intensities of the vibrational lines. The spacings of the lines depend on the vibrational frequencies in the ions, since for the vibrational excitation energies E_{vib}^*:

$$E_{vib}^* = (\upsilon + \tfrac{1}{2})h\nu \tag{1.5}$$

Here υ is the vibrational quantum number and ν the frequency. The frequencies depend on the strengths of the N–N bond in the different electronic states, since for a harmonic oscillator we have

$$\nu = \frac{1}{2\pi}\left(\frac{k}{\mu}\right)^{1/2} \tag{1.6}$$

where k is the force constant and μ the reduced mass, $m_1m_2/(m_1 + m_2)$, for a diatomic molecule. If a bonding electron is removed, the bond becomes weaker and the force constant is less in the ion than in the neutral molecule, so the vibrational frequency is lower. This is exactly what happens in the π_u^{-1} ionization of N_2, where the frequency drops from 2360 cm^{-1} in the molecule to 1800 cm^{-1} in the $A\ ^2\Pi_u$ state of N_2^+. This reduction in frequency by a factor of 1.3 shows that the π_u electrons of nitrogen are strongly bonding in the molecule. The changes in frequency on formation of the $X\ ^2\Sigma_g^+$ and $B\ ^2\Sigma_u^+$ states of N_2^+ are very much smaller, and indicate a very weak bonding character. Any antibonding character of the electrons removed on ionization would be revealed by an increase in frequency, and an example of this is the π_g^{-1} ionization of molecular oxygen, shown later in *Figure 1.6*.

The relative intensities of the vibrational lines in an ionization band are also related to the bonding powers of the electron removed. Strong vibrational excitation, such as that shown in the π_u^{-1} ionization of N_2 is associated with a change in equilibrium bond length on ionization, and the relationship between them is

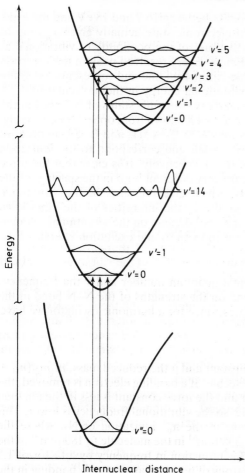

Figure 1.5   Potential energy curves showing the form of the vibrational wave-functions to illustrate the origin of vibrational excitation in electronic transitions

illustrated in *Figure 1.5*. Ionization itself is a rapid process, about 10^{-15} s being required for the ejected electron to leave the immediate neighbourhood of the molecular ion. This time is so short that motions of the atomic nuclei that make up vibrations and proceed on a time scale of 10^{-13} s are effectively frozen during ionization. The internuclear distance therefore remains constant during the transition, and the process can be represented by a vertical line on a potential energy diagram. This is true of electronic transitions in general, and is known as the Franck–Condon principle.

It is a consequence of the uncertainty principle that the bond length in the molecule does not have a single precise value, but can lie within a certain range with a probability at each point given by the square of the vibrational wave-function. Vertical transitions can proceed from any point within this range, according to the instantaneous position of the nuclei at the moment of ionization. Molecules are almost all in their vibrational ground state at normal temperature, and if there is no change in bond length on ioniza-tion, the single transition from this state of the molecule to the vibrational ground state of the ion is most probable, and a single line appears in the spectrum. The reason for this effect is that the probability of each individual transition between a vibrational level in the molecule and a vibrational level in the ion is pro-portional to the overlap between the vibrational wave-functions in the initial and final states. The forms of the wave-functions are shown in *Figure 1.5* for different values of the vibrational quantum numbers v'' of the molecule and v' of the ion. If there is no change in bond length between molecule and ion, the overlap integral between the $v'' = 0$ level of the molecule and the $v' = 0$ level of the ion is large, but all overlap integrals between $v'' = 0$ and higher vibrational levels of the ion are small because positive and negative contributions cancel out. When a change in bond length occurs, the largest overlap integrals arise for transitions from the vibrationless molecule to excited vibrational levels of the ion where the wave-functions have large amplitudes at the molecular internuclear distance. Several vibrational levels of the ion can be reached and a series of lines appears in the photoelectron spec-trum.

When applied to the photoelectron spectrum of nitrogen, these ideas imply that the π_u^{-1} ionization is accompanied by a change in the N–N bond length, but the σ_g^{-1} and σ_u^{-1} ionizations are not. Although the direction of the change in bond length cannot be deduced from the vibrational intensity pattern, it is clear from the decrease in vibrational frequency following π_u^{-1} ionization that the bond becomes longer. Both the change in frequency and the change in bond length on ionization reflect the character of the electron removed from the molecule, and if the electron removed is bonding, an increase in bond length and a decrease in frequency are to be expected. The photoelectron spectrum of oxygen in *Figure 1.6* illustrates these effects again, and here the first band is a π_g^{-1} ionization, the removal of an antibonding electron. There is a

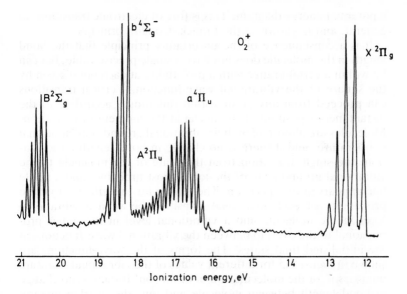

Figure 1.6   Photoelectron spectrum of oxygen excited by He I radiation

shortening of the O–O bond and an increase in the vibrational frequency, visible in the spectrum as strong vibrational structure with wide vibrational spacings. The second band represents the removal of an electron from the π_u orbital, which has the same character as in N_2, and the long vibrational progression and narrow spacing again reflect its bonding properties.

Oxygen is an open-shell molecule with a triplet ground state, and as a result the number of bands in the spectrum is greater than the number of orbitals. The electron configuration of the molecule is

$$...2p\sigma_g^2\ 2p\pi_u^4\ 2p\pi_g^2\ ...^3\Sigma_g^-$$

The ionization of lowest energy, π_g^{-1}, gives a single state of the molecular ion, X $^2\Pi_g$, and a single band in the spectrum. The second ionization, π_u^{-1}, gives two states, a $^4\Pi_u$ and A $^2\Pi_u$, the third ionization, σ_g^{-1}, gives two states, b $^4\Sigma_g^-$ and B $^2\Sigma_g^-$, and similarly all ionizations from filled orbitals give two states, one a doublet and the other a quartet. In the photoelectron spectrum, the bands for a $^4\Pi_u$ and A $^2\Pi_u$ overlap and give the second band the appearance of being single whereas it is, in fact, double. There are five bands altogether in the photoelectron spectrum taken at 584 Å, although only three molecular orbitals are involved. In fact, the electron configuration $\pi_u^3 \pi_g^2$ reached in the π_u^{-1} ionizations gives rise to five different electronic states, but only a $^4\Pi_u$ and A $^2\Pi_u$ can be reached by one-electron transitions. The others, $^2\Phi_u$ and two $^2\Pi_u$ states, have only a weak effect on the photoelectron spectrum[6], because the electron correlation that is necessary to make two-electron transitions intense is weak in O_2 (see Chapter 3, Section 3.2).

1.2.3   Triatomic and larger molecules

The spectra of molecules with more than two atoms are naturally more complex, because there are generally more molecular orbitals from which ionization can take place and many different modes of vibration that may be excited on ionization. One important principle is that the vibration that corresponds most closely to the change in equilibrium molecular geometry caused by a particular ionization will be the one that is most strongly excited. In the ammonia molecule, for instance, the occupancy of the nitrogen lone-pair electron has a strong effect on the bond angles, and when one lone-pair electron is removed the NH_3^+ ion becomes planar. The corresponding band in the photoelectron spectrum contains a long progression of lines that show excitation of the umbrella bending vibration υ_2, in which the molecule can move from the pyramidal to the planar configuration. Similarly, the first band in the spectrum of acetylene (*Figure 4.5*) is a π^{-1} ionization, which weakens the C–C bond and makes it longer, and so the band contains a progression of vibrational peaks that show excitation of the C–C stretching vibration. The second and third bands, on the other hand, represent ionizations from σ orbitals with both C–C and C–H bonding character, and these bands have a more complicated vibrational structure in which two vibrational modes are involved. In a band that shows excitation of several modes, it can easily happen that the vibrational structure is so complex that the individual lines cannot be resolved and a continuous contour is seen. Such unresolved bands are, in fact, much more common than resolved bands in the spectra of all molecules with five or more atoms.

Apart from the complexity of overlapping vibrational structure, one reason for the presence of continuous bands in the spectra is a short lifetime of the ions in the molecular ionic states in which they are initially formed. If a molecular ion in a particular state has a lifetime τ before it dissociates, radiates away its excitation energy or loses its identity by internal conversion to another electronic state, each level in the original state will have an energy width ΔE, given by the uncertainty principle:

$$\Delta E \approx \frac{\hbar}{\tau} \tag{1.7}$$

The energy uncertainty causes a broadening of all the spectral lines and may make the band continuous. This cause of broadening can occur even in the photoelectron spectra of diatomic molecules, and is considered in detail in Chapters 5 and 7.

Bands with resolved vibrational fine structure are often found in the spectra of very large molecules, despite these possible complications. They represent the ionization of electrons that are very weakly bonding, or whose bonding power corresponds closely and exclusively to a single mode of vibrational motion. Factors that are particularly favourable for the appearance of such bands are high symmetry, especially linearity or planarity, the presence of multiple bonds or rings and the presence of heteroatoms with non-bonding lone-pair electrons. Vibrational fine structure is most often to be found in the first band at the lowest ionization potential in the spectrum of a complex molecule because the outermost electrons are least likely to have strong bonding character.

1.3   Intensities of photoelectron bands

We have so far considered the energies of photoelectron bands and lines and the intensities of lines within the vibrational structure of a band. The intensities of the bands themselves also give useful information, which is needed in order to be able to analyse the photoelectron spectra of molecules whose ionic states have not already been identified. The areas of photoelectron bands in a spectrum are approximately proportional to the relative probabilities of ionization to the different ionic states, but experimental factors are also involved. Practical aspects of this problem are discussed in Chapter 2; suffice it to say that the relative ionization probabilities, called relative partial ionization cross-sections, can be derived from the measured spectra, and it is to these derived quantities that the following considerations apply. For resolved bands, the intensity is obtained by summing the intensities of all the vibrational lines.

1.3.1   Limiting rules for relative intensities

The relative partial cross-sections for photoionization to particular ionic states are sometimes also called the branching ratios in ionization, and the most important factors that determine them can be expressed in three approximate rules, as follows.

Rule 1. The partial cross-section for ionization from a given orbital is proportional to the number of equivalent electrons that are available to be ionized. Ionization from an orbital that contains four electrons is twice as probable as ionization from an orbital that contains only two electrons, and all ionizations from orbitals that contain two electrons should give bands of the same intensity. This rule is most nearly valid when the comparison is made between ionizations from molecular orbitals that are made up from the same set of atomic orbitals, but despite this restriction it is extremely useful as it is the only rule needed when interpreting the band intensities in the spectra of closed-shell molecules. As an example of the application of this rule, part of the photoelectron

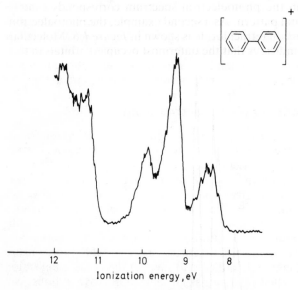

Figure 1.7   Partial photoelectron spectrum of biphenyl, showing the π electron ionization region

spectrum of biphenyl is shown in *Figure 1.7*, where it can be seen that the relative intensities of the first three bands, allowing for some overlap, are approximately 1:2:1. There is evidence from the spectra of other aromatic compounds that the low ionization potential region includes only π electron ionization bands, and the spectrum can therefore be compared with the π electron configuration expected on the basis of Hückel molecular orbital theory. The predicted π orbital pattern for biphenyl is

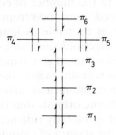

Of the outer π orbitals, π_4 and π_5 are degenerate and form a degenerate orbital that contains four electrons; the intensity pattern seen in the photoelectron spectrum corresponds exactly with the π orbital pattern. As a second example, the photoelectron spectrum of carbon tetrachloride is shown in *Figure 1.8*. Molecular orbital theory indicates that the outermost occupied orbitals in this

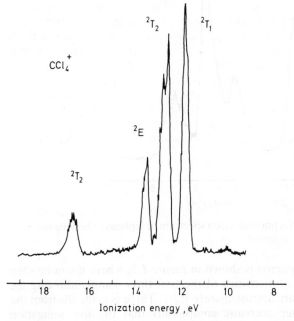

Figure 1.8   Photoelectron spectrum of carbon tetrachloride

molecule are made up from the non-bonding chlorine p atomic orbitals. In tetrahedral symmetry, these orbitals combine to form the molecular orbitals t_1, t_2 and e, of which the first two are triply degenerate and the third doubly degenerate. The relative areas of the first three bands in the spectrum are 1.9:2.6:1.0; this is sufficient to give a strong indication that the e^{-1} ionization is the third band, although the relative areas are rather far from the predicted ratio of 3:3:2. Comparisons with other spectra and with calculations confirm this assignment, and show that the bands represent t_1^{-1}, t_2^{-1} and e^{-1} ionizations, respectively.

Rule 2. The partial ionization cross-section is proportional to the statistical weight of the ionic state produced. In ionization from closed-shell molecules, this rule is equivalent to Rule 1, but for the ionization of atoms and open-shell molecules it is more extensive. The $^2P_{3/2}$ and $^2P_{1/2}$ states of the rare gas atomic ions arise from ionization from the same orbital but have statistical weights of 4 and 2 respectively, and the two peaks in the spectrum have an intensity ratio of 2:1. The ionization of molecular oxygen produces ions in both quartet and doublet states, and the bands due to the quartet states should be twice as intense as those for doublet states that arise from the same orbital ionization. Both Rules 1 and 2 apply to ionization from the closed shells of an open-shell molecule such as O_2. The total cross-section for ionization from a filled orbital, measured as the summed intensities of all the bands that correspond to the resulting electronic configuration of the ion, should be proportional to the number of equivalent electrons in that orbital. The relative intensities of the bands that correspond to a single electron configuration of the ions should be proportional to the statistical weights of the different ionic states, that is, their spin–orbital degeneracies. Nitric oxide, for example, has the electron configuration

$$\ldots 4\sigma^2 \, 5\sigma^2 \, 1\pi^4 \, 2\pi \, \ldots {}^2\Pi$$

The nitric oxide ion produced by $1\pi^{-1}$ ionization has the configuration $4\sigma^2 5\sigma^2 1\pi^3 2\pi$, and this configuration gives the six ionic states $^3\Sigma^+$, $^3\Delta$, $^3\Sigma^-$, $^1\Sigma^-$, $^1\Delta$ and $^1\Sigma^+$, all of which are seen in the photoelectron spectrum[7]. The relative intensities of the photoelectron bands are approximately in agreement with the statistical weights of 3, 6, 3, 1, 2 and 1, respectively. Similarly, the ionization $5\sigma^{-1}$ gives $^1\Sigma$ and $^3\Sigma$ states with statistical weights, and also relative intensities in the spectrum, of 1:3. According to Rule 1, the total intensity of all the $1\pi^{-1}$ ionization bands together should be double that of the summed $5\sigma^{-1}$ bands, but this is not borne out in the spectrum.

Rule 3. In ionization from the open shell itself of an open-shell molecule, the relative band intensities are, in general, proportional to the coefficients of fractional parentage[8]. This rule is due to Cox and Orchard[9], who also first enunciated Rules 1 and 2 as they apply to open-shell molecules. In instances when the molecular configuration generates only one term, Rule 3 is equivalent to Rule 2, and this is so if the open shell contains either a single electron or one electron less than the number required for a complete shell. For the ionization of molecules that have more than one open shell, a further and more complex rule has been given[10].

1.3.2   Band intensity and orbital character

The three limiting rules given above are based purely on statistical considerations; they take no account of any differences in ionization cross-section that are dependent on the character of the orbitals. Relative band intensities in photoelectron spectroscopy depend on the nature of the molecular orbitals, particularly on their atomic orbital character, and on the wavelength of the light used. In the He I photoelectron spectrum of atomic mercury, the $6s^{-1}$ and $5d^{-1}$ ionizations have an intensity ratio of 1:21 (*Figure 1.3*), whereas the orbital occupancies predict a ratio of 1:5. Fortunately, the deviations are not often so large, and the partial cross-sections for ionizations from molecular orbitals that are made up principally from the same atomic orbitals are usually more nearly in accordance with the limiting rules. This includes many of the most important practical instances, and when deviations occur they can also be useful as they may indicate participation by a different atomic orbital in the formation of the molecular orbital concerned. In the spectrum of CCl_4 (*Figure 1.8*), for example, the first three bands all arise from chlorine 3p-built molecular orbitals, and their relative intensities are roughly as expected. The fourth band is much weaker, despite its assignment to a triply degenerate orbital, because this bonding orbital contains a considerable contribution from carbon 2p in addition to chlorine 3p. This is an example of a general rule that in photoionization by 584 Å light, the cross-sections for ionization from the valence orbitals are higher in heavy atoms than in light ones, and there is a large increase in cross-section between atoms of the first and second (full) rows of the Periodic Table. Thus the outer p orbitals of sulphur have a higher cross-section than those of oxygen, the chlorine p electrons have a higher cross-section than those of fluorine, and both sulphur and chlorine p^{-1} ionizations give stronger bands than carbon p^{-1} ionization. This trend is at least partially reversed, however, when light of shorter wavelength, particularly the 304 Å line of helium, is used for ionization. A second generalization is that as the Periodic Table is crossed from left to right, the cross-sections for ionization of atomic s-type orbitals decrease relative to those for p-type valence orbitals in the same atoms[11].

When light of very short wavelength is used for ionization, as in X-ray photoelectron spectroscopy, the characteristic atomic orbital cross-sections are very different from those encountered in ultraviolet photoelectron spectroscopy. In the valence region, ionization from s-orbitals gives stronger bands than p- or d-orbital ionization, and light atoms often exhibit larger ionization cross-sections than heavier ones. These effects can be understood as due to more effective overlap between the X-rays (wavelength $\simeq 1$ Å) and the smaller orbitals. A tendency in the same direction is clearly seen at 304 Å compared with 584 Å, but it must be emphasized that other effects may vitiate a straightforward interpretation. Some atomic cross-sections go through maxima and minima at particular wavelengths, which may accidentally fall at 584 Å or 304 Å, and at the shorter wavelengths two-electron ionization may become significant. These complications are examined in Chapter 3; they rarely affect the He I photoelectron spectra of organic compounds.

1.4   The analysis of photoelectron spectra

The analysis of a photoelectron spectrum consists in the assignment of each band in the spectrum to a particular electronic state of the molecular ion and, where this is meaningful, to ionization from a particular orbital of the molecule. The first step is to ascertain, using a molecular orbital model, which orbitals are occupied and whether they are bonding, antibonding or non-bonding, degenerate or non-degenerate. The exact order of the orbitals and ionization bands in terms of energy is not reliably predicted by qualitative molecular orbital models although an indication is given; the main task in the analysis is to determine this order. The characters of the orbitals are shown in the photoelectron spectrum by the vibrational structures and intensities of the bands, and these are the first points to be compared with the theoretical model. It is also very helpful to make comparisons with the photoelectron spectra of related molecules, whether the spectra have been analysed or not, in order to establish if there are common features or regular trends that can be of help with the assignments. If possible, photoelectron spectra can be taken at a variety of wavelengths. Finally, there is sometimes evidence from outside photoelectron spectroscopy that can assist with the assignments, generally from other forms of spectroscopy. In the next section examples of the analysis of photoelectron spectra on the basis of internal evidence are presented, and sources of external evidence are afterwards discussed in the final section of this chapter.

1.4.1   Examples

Mercury(II) chloride

Mercury(II) chloride is a linear molecule that contains 16 valence electrons of which four are in chlorine 3s orbitals with too high a binding energy to be ionized by 21.22 eV photons.* According to the molecular orbital model, the remaining 12 electrons are accommodated as follows:

$$\sigma_g^2 \ \sigma_u^2 \ \pi_u^4 \ \pi_g^4 \ \dots \ ^1\Sigma_g^+$$

The σ_g orbital is made up from two chlorine 3p orbitals bonding with the 6s orbital of mercury, and is expected to be the main bonding orbital. The π_g orbital, on the other hand, is an out-of-phase combination of chlorine 3p orbitals of π symmetry, and is purely non-bonding in the absence of d orbital participation. A strongly bonding orbital is likely to be deeper lying than a non-bonding orbital, so it is safe to predict from the model that σ_g^{-1} requires a higher ionization energy than π_g^{-1}. The bonding properties of σ_u and π_u are more problematical, as they involve the participation of the unoccupied mercury 6p orbitals, which are of high energy: no prediction of the relative energies of the σ_u^{-1} and π_u^{-1} ionizations can be made.

---

*The $5d^{10}$ electrons of the mercury atom can also be ionized with 21.22 eV photons, but as analysis of the $5d^{-1}$ bands involves some complications it is dealt with later in Chapter 4.

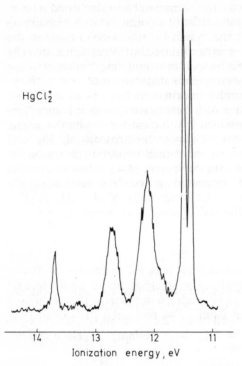

Figure 1.9   Partial photoelectron spectrum of mercury(II) chloride

The photoelectron spectrum of mercury(II) chloride in the valence region is shown in *Figure 1.9* and contains four bands with relative areas of 2.1:2.0:1.1:0.3 in order of increasing ionization potential, which match the four valence orbitals in number. According to the limiting rules for intensities, the first two bands must be the two π^{-1} ionizations from degenerate orbitals and the third and fourth must be σ^{-1} ionizations. The fourth band probably represents ionization from an orbital with strong Hg character because of its deviant low intensity, and this can only be σ_g. The first band in the spectrum consists of two sharp peaks that show the non-bonding character of the orbital ionized, and of the two π orbitals this must be π_g. The two peaks arise from spin–orbit splitting of the $^2\Pi_g$ state into $^2\Pi_{3/2g}$ and $^2\Pi_{1/2g}$, and they are of equal intensity as the two states have equal statistical weights. This is because in a linear molecule angular momentum is quantized only along the molecular axis and all Π, Δ or Φ states have an orbital degeneracy of two, irrespective of the value of Λ. The π_u orbital is an in-phase combination of chlorine 3p with mercury 6p orbitals and is bonding; the breadth of the second band in the photoelectron spectrum is in accordance with this character. The $^2\Pi_u$ state must also be split by spin–orbit coupling, but the splitting is obscured by the unresolved vibrational structure.

With mercury(II) chloride, information from band intensities and band shapes, together with qualitative considerations of the form of the molecular orbitals, is sufficient for an analysis of the spectrum to be made. That the bands represent π_g^{-1}, π_u^{-1}, σ_u^{-1} and σ_g^{-1} ionizations, in order of increasing ionization potential, is confirmed by comparison with the spectra of the other mercury(II) halides and the other 16 electron linear triatomic molecules CO_2 and COS. The four states of $HgCl_2^+$ can be labelled $\tilde{X}\,^2\Pi_g$, $\tilde{A}\,_2\Pi_u$, $\tilde{B}\,^2\Sigma_u^+$ and $\tilde{C}\,^2\Sigma_g^+$, and the task of analysis is complete.

Water

The H_2O molecule is bent and has only C_{2v} symmetry, so that it has no degenerate orbitals. The analysis of its photoelectron spectrum (*Figure 1.10*) can be made on the basis of the vibrational structure of the different bands. The molecular orbitals of H_2O

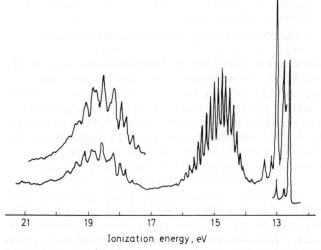

Ionization energy, eV

Figure 1.10   Photoelectron spectrum of water excited by He I light. (From Potts, A.W. and Price, W.C., *Proc. R. Soc. Lond.*, **A236**, 181 (1972), by courtesy of the Council of the Royal Society)

with binding energies less than 21.22 eV are essentially formed from the three p orbitals of the oxygen molecule. One p orbital rises out of the molecular plane; it has b_1 symmetry in C_{2v} and is completely non-bonding. The next p orbital is in the plane and bisects the HOH bond angle; it has a_1 symmetry and, although it is weakly O–H bonding, its most important characteristic is that its occupancy determines the HOH bond angle. The third p orbital is in the plane and perpendicular to the other two orbitals; with the hydrogen 1s orbitals, it forms the main O–H bond. The first band in the photoelectron spectrum, with its single sharp peak and weak vibrational structure, is clearly ionization from the non-bonding orbital b_1. The second band consists of a very long progression in which the first few vibrational intervals are about $900 \, \text{cm}^{-1}$. The O–H stretching vibrations, v_1 and v_3, have frequencies so much higher than this that the mode excited can only be the bending vibration, v_2, whose frequency in the neutral molecule is $1595 \, \text{cm}^{-1}$. A triatomic molecule has only three vibrational modes, so there is no doubt about this vibrational assignment. The band assignment follows at once, as only the a_1 orbital has the angle-determining character that could cause such strong excitation of v_2 on ionization. It is found, in fact, that in the $^2A_1$ state which results, H_2O^+ is linear in the equilibrium position. The optical emission spectrum of the H_2O^+ ion, which was first seen in the spectrum of comet Kohoutek, corresponds to the transition $^2A_1 \rightarrow {}^2B_1$, and fully confirms this assignment[12]. The third band in the spectrum must be assigned to ionization from the remaining orbital, b_2, and its vibrational structure is in accordance with this. It shows excitation of the O–H stretching vibration, v_1, probably with v_2 also excited. The reduction in frequency of v_1 on ionization and the shape of the band both indicate the ionization of a strongly bonding electron. The interpretation of the vibrational structure of the bands therefore leads to the identification of the three states of H_2O^+ as $^2B_1$, $^2A_1$ and $^2B_2$, in order of increasing ionization potential.

Methanol

In the photoelectron spectrum of methanol shown in *Figure 1.11*, there is little resolved vibrational structure, and analysis of the spectrum depends mainly on comparison with the photoelectron spectrum of water. The molecule has at the most a plane of symmetry, so the symmetry labels of the different molecular orbitals are not very informative. It is more useful to describe the

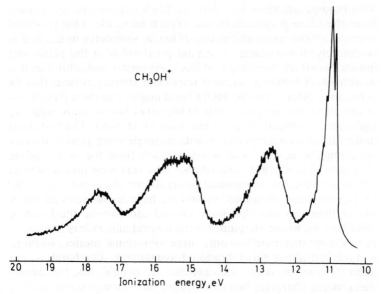

Figure 1.11   Photoelectron spectrum of methanol. (By courtesy of Professor W.C. Price)

orbitals approximately in terms of their atomic orbital parentage and bonding character, which can be derived either by calculation or from empirical considerations. The occupied orbitals of the valence shell are:

3a′	O 2s	Weakly bonding
4a′	C 2s	Weakly bonding
5a′	O 2p + C 2p + H 1s	HOC bonding
1a″ ⎫ 6a′ ⎬	C 2p + H 1s	CH_3 bonding
7a′	O 2p	HOC angle-determining
2a″	O 2p	Out-of-plane, non-bonding

Of these seven orbitals, the 3a′ oxygen 2s orbital and the 4a′ carbon 2s orbital have too high a binding energy to be observed with He I excitation, so five bands are to be expected. The fact that only four distinct bands appear shows that two must be overlapping, and the most likely pair is 1a″ and 6a′. If the OH group of methanol lay along the axis of the CH_3 group, 1a″ and 6a′ would be degenerate and form an e orbital responsible for $C–H_3$ bonding, and the splitting between the two orbitals in methanol is therefore probably small. Only the third band in the spectrum is intense enough to represent ionization from two occupied orbitals, so it can be tentatively assigned to $1a''$ and $6a'$ together. This assignment is supported by the fact that similar bands of double intensity and attributed to the CH_3 e orbitals are found at the same ionization potential in the spectra of CH_3I, CH_3CN and CH_3SH. The three bands that remain unassigned are the first, third and fourth, and the orbitals whose ionization they must represent, $2a''$, $7a'$ and $5a'$, are all based on oxygen 2p orbitals and correspond to the three occupied orbitals of water. The first band of methanol is identified by its narrow contour and vibrational structure as the $2a''^{-1}$ ionization, the second band must be ionization from the angle-determining $7a'$ orbital and the fourth band is probably $5a'^{-1}$ ionization from the main H–O–C bonding orbital. This analysis of the spectrum is consistent with all the evidence from the spectrum itself and from the spectra of related compounds, but because of the lack of vibrational structure in the spectrum it is not completely certain. Additional support for it comes from *ab initio* SCF–MO calculations, which, with Koopmans' theorem, predict exactly the same order [13].

1.4.2 External evidence for band assignments

The comparison of photoelectron spectra with detailed molecular orbital calculations like those mentioned above is an important tool in their analysis. This topic will be described separately in Chapter 4, while here the experimental evidence relevant to the analysis of photoelectron spectra is considered. The most useful evidence is spectroscopic, and a distinction can be made between information about the molecular ground states and information about the ionic states themselves.

Most molecules have singlet ground states in which the electronic wave-function is totally symmetric, but this is seldom true of atoms, and there are also many molecules that have open shells, particularly among transition metal compounds. Molecular oxygen is the most familiar example, and if its ground state were $^1\Delta_g$ instead of $^3\Sigma_g^-$, its photoelectron spectrum would be very different. If a molecule has an open shell, the species of the ground state may be determined by optical spectroscopy or electron spin resonance spectroscopy or from magnetic susceptibility measurements. Evidence from electron spin resonance spectroscopy, for instance, has been used in the analysis of the spectra of transition metal π-arene complexes[14]. If the ground state of an atom or molecule happens to be a spin doublet, its species identifies the outermost orbital directly. Nitric oxide has a $^2\Pi$ ground state, so the outermost occupied orbital is a π orbital and the first band in the photoelectron spectrum represents a π^{-1} ionization. The ground states of NF_2 and ClO_2 both have the species $^2B_1$, and the first bands in their spectra are therefore attributed to b_1^{-1} ionizations[15,16].

The electronic excited states of molecules that are studied in optical spectroscopy are reached by the transfer of one electron from an occupied to an unoccupied orbital. Two types of transitions are distinguished, *intervalence* or *sub-Rydberg* transitions and *Rydberg* transitions. In intervalence transitions, the electron is promoted to an orbital made up from atomic orbitals with the same principal quantum number as those which make up the valence shell. The excited states produced are the lowest-lying excited states of the molecule, and are seen as absorption or emission bands in the visible and ultraviolet regions of the spectrum. The characteristics of the absorption bands can sometimes show which orbital of the molecule is outermost, but deductions about the molecular orbital diagram are difficult to make because two orbitals of unknown energy are involved in every transition. Furthermore the energy of a visible or ultraviolet absorption is *not* equal to a difference in orbital energies, even in the simplest quantitative molecular orbital model. In Rydberg transitions, the excited state has one electron in an orbital with a principal quantum number greater, and often much greater, than the number characteristic of the valence shell. The excited electron is in a Rydberg orbital, which typically has a large radius and approaches a hydrogenic atomic orbital in form. The electron moves in a field defined by the positively charged core, which is the molecular ion in a particular electronic state. Rydberg states with successively higher principal quantum number form a series in the spectrum that converges on the ionization limit at which the excited electron is free, and the molecular ion which formed the core remains. The frequencies at which absorption to Rydberg states occurs can be expressed by the equation

$$\nu = \nu_\infty - \frac{R}{(n - \delta)^2} \tag{1.8}$$

where ν_∞ is the ionization limit, R the Rydberg constant, n the principal quantum number and δ the quantum defect or Rydberg correction. This equation is exactly the same as that for atomic

Rydberg lines. For molecules, the Rydberg bands have vibrational and rotational structure, but as the outer electron is so far away it has little influence on the bonding in the core, and the vibrational structures are very similar to the vibrational structures seen in the photoelectron spectrum. This fact can be used to help in the analysis of the Rydberg bands; each member of a series has nearly the same vibrational structure, and it is the same as the structure of the photoelectron band at the ionization potential on which the series converges.

If a Rydberg band converging on a particular limit has been rotationally analysed, the symmetry species of the ionic core, and therefore of the ion state at the limit, will have been determined or confirmed. This has been done, for instance, for a Rydberg state ($\tilde{C}$) converging on the ground state $^2B_1$ of H_2O^+. If the photoelectron spectrum of a molecule contains only continuous bands, there may be no resolved Rydberg bands and analysis is impossible. Even when the bands are well resolved, the spectrum of Rydberg states is often very complex because there are usually several series converging on each ionization limit. The Rydberg bands are found in the far ultraviolet and vacuum ultraviolet regions of the spectrum, where the experimental difficulties of optical spectroscopy are severe, but the new experimental technique of electron energy loss spectroscopy (Chapter 3, Section 3.5.3) makes it much easier to observe them. They are generally found within an energy range of about 2 eV from the ionization limit on which their series converges.

While the absorption and emission spectra of neutral molecules are universally available, but only indirectly relevant to the analysis of photoelectron spectra, the optical spectra of the positive ions themselves are directly relevant but more rarely known. About 100 molecular ions have been found (up to 1982) to give emission spectra[17], containing information on the electronic separations and the vibrational–rotational structure of ionic states seen in photoelectron spectroscopy. Because of the high resolution possible in optical spectroscopy the ionization potential differences, vibration frequencies and bond lengths derived from such emission spectra are much more precise than those determined from photoelectron spectra. In some cases the optical spectra yield unambiguous state assignments unobtainable from photoelectron spectra alone, but in the majority of cases the optical analysis has been based on, and confirms the results of, photoelectron spectroscopy.

1.5 The literature of photoelectron spectroscopy

An enormous number of publications have been devoted to photoelectron spectroscopy during the last decade, and the spectra of a great many compounds have been put on record. There are two periodical journals with specialist interest in this subject, namely the *Journal of Electron Spectroscopy and Related Phenomena* and the *International Journal of Mass Spectrometry and Ion Physics*, but articles appear throughout the chemical literature. The journals which most regularly contain articles of importance on photoelectron spectroscopy are the *Journal of Chemical Physics*, the *Journal of the Chemical Society: Faraday Transactions II*, and the *Journal of Physics B: Atomic and Molecular Physics*. Other journals which are regularly patronized by certain active research groups are the *Proceedings of the Royal Society of London A*, *Helvetica Chimica Acta*, and *Physica Scripta*. Some workers, when they feel they have made dramatic or fundamental advances, like to chronicle the fact in *Physical Review Letters*, and *Chemical Physics Letters* also gets a share.

In addition to research papers a number of books and many reviews have appeared, and several compilations of spectra have been published. No attempt is made in this book to present or refer to a multitude of spectra, but a 'compilation of compilations' is offered as a supplementary bibliography to this chapter. In the great majority of cases where a new spectrum is to be analysed, spectra of related compounds are already available and can be located with the aid of one or other of the works cited. The assignments provided with compiled spectra should not be accepted unquestioningly, however, as many have been made tentatively, or perhaps on the basis of unreliable molecular orbital calculations. A few of the spectra themselves are also found to be corrupted by unrecognized impurities in the sample or lamp light, but such cases are fortunately rare.

1.5.1 General bibliography

Books

1. *Photoelectron Spectroscopy, Chemical and Analytical Aspects*, by A.D. Baker and D. Betteridge, Pergamon Press, Oxford (1972)
2. *Photoabsorption, Photoionization and Photoelectron Spectroscopy*, by J. Berkowitz, Academic Press, New York (1979)
3. *Handbook of X-ray and Ultraviolet Photoelectron Spectroscopy*, edited by D. Briggs, Heyden, London (1977)
4. *Electron Spectroscopy: Theory, Techniques and Applications*, edited by C.R.

Brundle and A.D. Baker, Academic Press; Vol I (1977), Vol II (1978), Vol III (1979)
5. *Photoelectron and Auger Spectroscopy*, by T.A. Carlson, Plenum Press, New York (1975)
6. *Principles of Ultraviolet Photoelectron Spectroscopy*, by J.W. Rabalais, Wiley-Interscience, New York (1977)
7. *Photoelectron Spectroscopy and Molecular Orbital Theory*, by R.E. Ballard, Adam Hilger, Bristol (1978)

Compilations of ultraviolet photoelectron spectra

1. *Molecular Photoelectron Spectroscopy*, by D.W. Turner, A.D. Baker, C. Baker and C.R. Brundle, Wiley, London (1970). This, the first book in the field, presents about 180 spectra of simple compounds, with partial assignments.
2. *CRC Handbook of Spectroscopy*, Vol I, edited by J.W. Robinson, CRC Press, Boca Raton (1974). This compilation lists about 900 spectra, some duplicated, giving ionization potentials and some assignments, covering the literature to 1974. There are no pictures of spectra.
3. *Handbook of He I Photoelectron Spectra of Fundamental Organic Molecules*, by K. Kimura, S. Katsumata, Y. Achiba, T. Yamazaki and S. Iwata, Japan Scientific Societies Press, Tokyo (1981). This presents 220 spectra of small inorganic and organic molecules measured under comparable conditions, with assignments. It also lists results of SCF–MO calculations, and gives references to other spectra of the same molecules up to 1980.
4. *Data Bank of He II Photoelectron Spectra*, published in the Journal of Electron Spectroscopy and Related Phenomena:

Part I, Hydrocarbons (C,H), *J. Electron Spectrosc. Rel. Phen.*, **10**, 149 (1980)
Part II, Aza-compounds (C,H,N), *ibid*, **21**, 93 (1980)
Part III, Oxo-compounds (C,H,O), *ibid*, **21**, 175 (1980)
Part IV, Fluoro-compounds (C,H,F), *ibid*, **23**, 281 (1981)
Part V, Hetero-compounds containing first-row elements (C,H,B,N,O,F), *ibid*, **24**, 293 (1981)
Part VI, Halogen compounds (C,H,X; X = Cl,Br,I)
Part VII, Miscellaneous compounds, *ibid*, **27**, 129 (1982)

These contributions to the Data Bank, by G. Bieri, L. Asbrink and W. von Niessen cover complete valence shells, and include detailed comparisons with the best available theoretical calculations.

References

1. AL-JOBOURY, M.I. and TURNER, D.W., *J. Chem. Soc.*, 5141 (1963)
2. AL-JOBOURY, M.I. and TURNER, D.W., *J. Chem. Phys.*, **37**, 3007 (1962)
3. VILESOV, F.I., KURBATOV, B.L. and TERENIN, A.N., *Dokl. Akad. Nauk SSSR*, **138**, 1329 (1961) [in Russian; English translation in *Sov. Phys. Dokl.*, **6**, 490 (1961)

4. SIEGBAHN, K., NORDLING, C., FAHLMAN, A., NORDBERG, R., HAMRINN, K., HEDMAN, J., JOHANSSON, G., BERGMARK, T., KARLSSON, S.E., LINDGREN, I. and LINDBERG, B., *Nova Acta Regiae Soc. Sci. Upsal., Ser. IV*, **20** (1967)
5. KOOPMANS, T., *Physica*, **1**, 104 (1933)
6. EDQVIST, O., LINDHOLM, E., SELIN, L.E. and ASBRINK, L., *Physica Scripta*, **1**, 25 (1970)
7. EDQVIST, O., LINDHOLM, E., SELIN, L.E., SJOGREN, H. and ASBRINK, L., *Ark. Fysik*, **40**, 439 (1970)
8. BRINK, D.M. and SATCHER, G.R. *Angular Momentum*, Oxford University Press, London (1968)
9. COX, P.A. and ORCHARD, F.A., *Chem. Phys. Lett.*, **7**, 273 (1970)
10. COX, P.A., EVANS, S. and ORCHARD, F.A., *Chem. Phys. Lett.*, **13**, 386 (1972)
11. PRICE, W.C., POTTS, A.E. and STREETS, D.G., in Shirley, D.A. (Editor) *Electron Spectroscopy*, North Holland, Amsterdam, 187 (1972)
12. HERZBERG, G. and LEW, H., *Astronom. Astrophys.*, **31**, 123 (1974); LEW, H., *Canad. J. Phys.*, **54**, 2028 (1976)
13. ROBIN, M.B. and KUEBLER, N.A., *J. Electron Spectrosc. Rel. Phen.*, **1**, 13 (1972)
14. EVANS, S., GREEN, J.C. and JACKSON, S.E., *J. Chem. Soc., Faraday Trans. II*, **68**, 249 (1972)
15. FROST, D.C. and MCDOWELL, C.A., *J. Chem. Phys.*, **54**, 1872 (1971)
16. CORNFORD, A.B., FROST, D.C., HERRING, F.G. and MCDOWELL, C.A., *Chem. Phys. Lett.*, **10**, 345 (1971)
17. MAIER, J.P., *Chimia*, **34**, 219 (1980)

2

Experimental methods

2.1 Introduction

The essential components of a photoelectron spectrometer are a lamp that produces suitable radiation, an ionization chamber in which molecules can be ionized at a defined electrical potential, an electron energy analyser, an electron detector and a recorder. These components are shown schematically in *Figure 2.1* and are

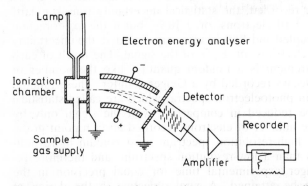

Figure 2.1 Essentials of a photoelectron spectrometer. All the electron optics must be within a vessel evacuated to 10^{-5} mmHg or less

discussed sequentially in the next section. A photoelectron spectrum is measured by varying the energy of the photoelectrons allowed to reach the detector and recording the rate at which electrons of each energy arrive. An ideal photoelectron spectrometer should give a complete and accurate record of the energy distribution of the electrons that are actually emitted from the sample molecules, but no practical instrument does this. The performance of real instruments can be discussed in terms of the accuracy with which the energies and relative intensities characteristic of the true distribution can be measured.

An important factor that affects the accuracy of energy measurements is the resolution of a photoelectron spectrometer, the smallest energy difference between two groups of electrons that will result in separate photoelectron peaks being registered. The best resolution so far achieved is 4–5 meV, which corresponds to 32–42 cm^{-1}, so photoelectron spectroscopy still has some way to go before it can compete in resolution with optical spectroscopy, where a resolution of 0.1 cm^{-1} is normal. Accurate energy measurements also depend on the proper calibration of the instrumental energy scale, which is more difficult than in optical spectroscopy because of the susceptibility of electrons to stray electric and magnetic fields.

The precision of intensity measurements in photoelectron spectroscopy is largely a matter of the time allowed for the experiments. Each point in a photoelectron spectrum represents the detection of a definite number of electrons, the product of the electron arrival rate and the experimental time, and the intensity has an uncertainty equal to the square root of this number. If 100 electrons are recorded, the statistical uncertainty (one standard deviation) is ± 10 electrons, or $\pm 10 \%$, but if the experimental time is quadrupled and 400 electrons are recorded, the uncertainty is only ± 20 electrons, or $\pm 5\%$ of the signal. The result of each single measurement is a random quantity, like the number of radioactive decays recorded by a Geiger counter. These random fluctuations in photoelectron spectra, which are called statistical noise, can be reduced in comparison with the signal only by increasing the number of electrons recorded at each point in the spectrum. A high-resolution spectrum must contain more individual points than a low-resolution spectrum, and therefore requires a longer experimental time for equal precision in the intensities to be attained. A vital objective in the design of photoelectron spectrometers is to ensure that the arrival rates of electrons are high enough to make the measurement of complete spectra possible in a reasonable time.

2.2   Light sources

The most desirable properties of a light source for photoelectron spectroscopy are narrowness of the principal ionizing line, the absence of any other lines, and high intensity. Much development effort has been concentrated on light sources because deficiencies there are hard to compensate for in the remainder of the instrument, whereas a high intensity of the light source can permit the use of high resolution without making the measurement of a spectrum unduly lengthy.

2.2.1   Discharges in helium and other gases

The most useful and widely used light source in photoelectron spectroscopy is a discharge in pure helium, which gives the He I resonance line at 584 Å, equivalent to a photon energy of 21.22 eV, as its main output. This light is energetic enough to cause ionization of the majority of valence electrons, and is almost pure, the only very intense impurity line being H Ly α at 10.20 eV. The development of the He I resonance lamp as a source of ionizing radiation was a major factor in the early success of photoelectron spectroscopy[1]. In different forms of the lamp, radiation is excited by a high-voltage direct-current discharge in a capillary, by microwave discharge or by a high-current arc discharge using a heated cathode as electron source. Some designs of these three types of lamp are shown in *Figure 2.2*. The transition responsible for producing the 584 Å line is from He 1s2p... ^{1}P to the ground state 1s ^{2}... ^{1}S; higher members of this series, that is, 1s np... ^{1}P to the ground state, are also present in the output of the lamps, but their intensity is not more than a few per cent of that of the 584 Å line. The lines of this series, starting from the 584 Å line, are called He Iα, He Iβ, etc., and are listed in *Table 2.1*; when the higher

Table 2.1   Lines from helium discharge lamps

Line	Wavelength, Å	Energy, eV	Intensity
He Iα	584.334 0	21.218 2	100
He Iβ	537.029 6	23.084 8	2
He Iγ	522.212 8	23.742 3	0.5
He IIα	303.781	40.814 0	<1
He IIβ	256.317	48.371 8	
He IIγ	243.027	51.017 0	
He IIδ	237.331	52.241 5	
H Lyα	1 215.67	10.198 9	
N I	1 134.414 7	10.929 4	
Ne Iα	735.895	16.848 2	

The relative intensities given are typical for a capillary discharge under normal conditions for He Iα output. The relative abundance of the lines of higher energy can be increased at low pressures, as explained in the text. The last three lines mentioned arise from common impurities either in the helium supply or de-gassed from the lamp structure.

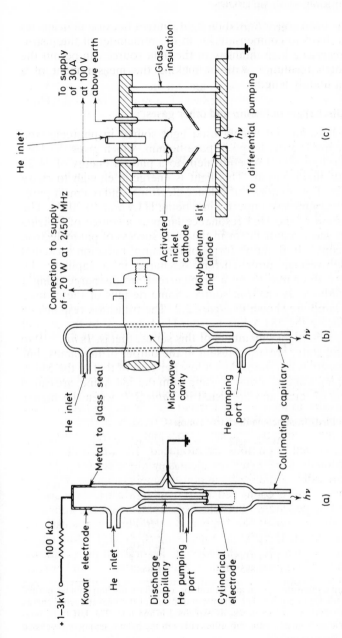

Figure 2.2   Three types of gas discharge lamp used in photoelectron spectroscopy: (a) a simple all-glass capillary discharge; (b) microwave discharge; (c) high-current arc discharge. The working helium pressure is 0.1–1 mmHg in all instances

lines are not referred to specifically, the Greek letters can be omitted and the designation He I alone in this book and elsewhere always refers to the 584 Å line.

All the transitions of the He I series are fully allowed in absorption as well as emission, and for this reason the 584 Å and other lines are always self-reversed. The hot gas in the discharge emits lines that are broadened by the Doppler effect of the velocities of the emitting atoms, but it passes through cold gas outside the discharge region, which absorbs the centres of the lines completely, so that the effective widths of the lines are then much greater than their intrinsic widths. Samson[2] has examined the sharpness and intensities of the He I lines produced by some practical photoelectron spectrometer lamps and found that their energy widths were of the order of a few millielectronvolts and therefore small enough not to degrade spectrometer resolutions. Nevertheless, it is important to minimize the amount of cold helium gas through which the light has to pass if this small width is to be attained, and also to avoid loss of intensity. The wavelengths and energies of the He I lines are given in *Table 2.1*, which also shows the commonest impurity lines found in the output of helium discharge lamps.

Discharges in helium can also generate a series of lines from ionized helium, He II, with the main line at 303 Å, equivalent to 40.81 eV. This line is of great interest for photoelectron spectroscopy as it makes complete valence shells accessible. In order to produce substantial amounts of He II light from a discharge lamp, it is necessary to increase the current density and to decrease the helium gas pressure. When this is first tried in a He I lamp the result is that either the discharge goes out, or large numbers of electrons as well as photons are produced. The first problem can be overcome to some extent by increasing the area of the cathode and by providing a high-voltage power supply (about 10 kV), and the second can be countered by providing electric or magnetic deflection of the charged particles before they reach the ionization source. The output of the lamp may then contain a substantial proportion of He II light, perhaps as much as He I, although its total intensity will be much reduced. Several lamps specifically designed for He II production have been described[3-7], and provide more reliable sources of this radiation. One type[4] involves large electrodes and a short discharge path in a ceramic capillary. Another uses a shaped electric field between two wires and a concentric cylinder, causing electron oscillations and a very long electron pathlength[5,6]. All such lamps still emit He I and impurity lines (chiefly H Ly α), as well as He II, and if pure He II is required either a monochromator (below) or a filter must be used. Very pure He II can be obtained, for instance, by use of a filter[8] consisting of a thin carbon foil (5 μg cm^{-2}) to remove He I, covered with a layer of aluminium (8 μg cm^{-2}) to remove H Ly α.

The gas discharge lamps can be run on gases other than helium or on gases mixed with helium to produce ionizing lines of lower energy. The most intense is hydrogen Lyman α, the most useful

Table 2.2 Lines from discharges in gases other than helium

Gas	Line	Energy, eV	Intensity
Neon	Ne Iα	16.6709	15
		16.8482	100
	Ne Iβ	19.6883	<1
		19.7799	<1
	Ne II	26.8141	(100)
		26.9110	(100)
	Ne II	27.6867	(20)
		27.7625	(20)
		27.7836	(20)
		27.8599	(20)
	Ne II	30.4530	(20)
		30.5493	(20)
Argon	Ar Iα	11.6237	100
		11.8282	50
	Ar II	13.3024	30
		13.4799	15
Hydrogen	Lyman α	10.1989	100
	Lyman β	12.0876	10
	Lyman γ	12.7486	1

The relative intensities given are a rough guide for capillary discharge lamps. The intensities of the Ne II lines given in parentheses are from J.A.R. Samson, *Techniques of Vacuum Ultraviolet Spectroscopy*, John Wiley, New York (1967), and refer to a duoplasmatron light source.

the pair of neon resonance lines. All of these sources contain ionizing radiation of several frequencies and different intensities, which complicate the interpretation of the observed spectra. Details of the energies of the useful lines, together with some very approximate relative intensities, are given in *Table 2.2*.

2.2.2   Continuum sources: synchrotron radiation

The isolation of individual lines from the discharge lamps described above requires only very low resolution monochromators. These can be of the concave reflection grating type[9], or they can use the new vuv transmission gratings, which permit extremely simple arrangements[10]. But there are also powerful laboratory light sources that emit continua over a wide energy range, such as the Hopfield continuum of helium[11], the low-pressure capillary spark discharge in hydrogen[12], and the BRV lamp[13]. High-resolution monochromators are required to isolate narrow enough wavelength bands from such sources to be useful in photoelectron spectroscopy, and normal incidence concave reflection grating monochromators of 1 M to 3 M radius are frequently used. In the energy region above 12 eV, no window material exists that will both transmit light and tolerate the working conditions of the lamps, so the vacuum monochromator and lamp must be differentially pumped.

The most useful continuum source for photoelectron spectroscopy is synchrotron radiation emitted by accelerated electrons or positrons in storage rings, which is, indeed, the only effective source in the energy range 40–1000 eV. Unfortunately, it is not a 'laboratory' source; rather, a photoelectron spectrometer is likely to be a small, often parasitic appendage to a huge national accelerator/storage ring operation. In a storage ring, electrons of energy 100 MeV to 10 GeV are confined to circular orbits by strong magnetic fields. Synchrotron radiation is emitted whenever the electron path is curved, in each bending magnet, and emission is predominantly forward at a tangent to the path. The considerable amount of energy lost by the electrons in producing the radiation is made up on every circuit by acceleration in an RF cavity. The intensity of the light depends on the electron energy and radius of curvature as E^4/R, and directly on the circulating current. There is a continual slow loss of electrons from the beam by collisions with residual gas molecules, even under the ultra-high vacuum conditions used ($\sim 10^{-11}$ torr), and this loss limits the life time of the beam to between four and twenty-four hours, after which recharging is necessary. The need to maintain and protect the ultra-high vacuum dictates stringent requirements of differential pumping for gas phase experiments like photoelectron spectroscopy, greatly magnifying the complexity and cost of the experiments.

The characteristics of synchrotron radiation from a storage ring are that its spectrum is an absolutely smooth continuum, the light is almost 100% polarized in the plane of the ring, and it comes in ~1 ns pulses spaced 30 to 1000 ns apart, according to the size of the ring[14]. For photoelectron spectroscopy it must be monochromatized; for energies above 30 eV grazing incidence grating monochromators are used because no material is normally reflective at the corresponding wavelengths. The intensity of the analysed radiation can easily be 10^{11} photons per second per Ångstrom, with the result that photoelectron spectra of low or medium resolution can be obtained at any photon energy up to 200 eV without much difficulty. Special devices to enhance synchrotron radiation emission, such as wigglers, undulators and free electron lasers, promise to increase the available fluxes manyfold.

2.2.3 Lasers

In many branches of spectroscopy, lasers have supplanted traditional light sources, and it is an obvious possibility that they may eventually replace both line sources and synchrotron radiation in photoelectron spectroscopy. Laser action has been achieved at many vuv wavelengths[15], and the short wavelength limit of convenient 'off-the-shelf' devices has been pushed deep into the 'quartz' uv by excimer lasers (ArF, 1730 Å). Tunable coherent vuv radiation can be generated by harmonic generation in metal vapours and in rare gases[16,17]. The vuv lasers which have been demonstrated so far (1982) are all pulsed devices with rather low repetition rates, however, and would not be convenient as sources in photoelectron spectroscopy.

An alternative approach of great interest is to use lasers producing visible or near-ultraviolet light to bring about or assist in *multi-photon* ionization[18,19]. There are a whole family of multi-photon ionization processes, all more complex than single photon ionization, some of which have begun to be studied by analysis of the photoelectrons produced. It is already clear that these new techniques offer some very special advantages over the traditional single photon ionization.

Because most ionization potentials are 10 eV or higher, while visible wavelengths where lasers operate well are equivalent to 2 or 3 eV, multi-photon ionization (MPI) normally calls for participation of at least three or four photons. In one generally applicable process, all the photons are involved simultaneously, and pumping goes entirely via *virtual* states of the molecule. As explained further in Chapter 3, the probability of such processes depends on the nth power of light intensity, where n photons are required. High laser powers are indispensable, and can be supplied only by pulsed lasers, such as dye lasers pumped by nitrogen lasers, excimer lasers or frequency doubled neodymium YAG solid state lasers.

When absorption of any intermediate number of photons can populate a real excited state of the neutral molecule, the probability of ionization is very greatly increased. This resonance enhanced multi-photon ionization (REMPI) requires somewhat lower laser power, which can be supplied by smaller nitrogen-pumped dye lasers, by flash-pumped dye lasers or even (exceptionally) by cw lasers. It is a great advantage in this technique to have two or three independently tunable lasers available, so that each step up the ladder towards ionization can be separately tuned to a resonance; the lasers can be fired simultaneously or with small delays.

An obvious advantage of using visible laser light for photo-ionization is that ordinary quartz or glass windows can be used and differential pumping is not needed. Several other advantages accrue from the very narrow bandwidths (to $0.005\,\mathrm{cm}^{-1}$) easily achieved in laser tuning. The efficiency of the final non-resonant ionization step into the continuum can be examined at very high resolution, so details of autoionizing resonance structures can be studied. More important, the intermediate neutral resonances are normally selected with rotational resolution, so that only a single J level is populated in the neutral state from which ionization eventually takes place. If the photoelectrons are analysed, this means that photoelectron spectra can be taken of molecules in *single selected rotational levels*. This completely eliminates the line broadening due to rotational envelopes, and makes possible direct experimental study of rotational selection rules and rotational effects on angular distributions. For purposes of photoelectron spectroscopy it may be most effective to use visible lasers for the resonant steps exciting the neutral molecule to a level near the first ionization limit, then ionize from there into the continuum with a vuv light source, laser or non-laser. A wavelength just too long to ionize directly by the normal one-photon process would allow the widest possible range of ionic states to be studied in the photoelectron spectrum of the electronically excited species. Besides single rotational levels, the selection of single vibrational levels could be very useful in simplifying vibrational structure in photoelectron spectra of large molecules, where hot bands often blur the structure. The Frank–Condon factors will, of course, be different in ionization from different vibration levels, and from electronic states other than the ground state.

Selection of single rotational and vibrational levels *within* electronic ground states may also be possible using infrared lasers. The laser would be used to modulate selected level populations, and synchronous detection could, in principle, extract the modulated photoelectron spectrum. This technique will probably prove more difficult than the use of visible laser light. Infrared lasers can also give high enough powers to bring about ionization by ten or more photons. The mechanism of this process is of great interest, but it is unlikely to be a useful source for general work in photoelectron spectroscopy.

2.3 Electron energy analysers

The electron energy analyser is the heart of any spectrometer, as it is here that the photoelectrons are separated according to their kinetic energies. The aim of electron analyser design is to provide high resolution and high sensitivity simultaneously, requirements which naturally conflict. The theoretical resolution of any analyser can be increased by placing restrictions on the paths that electrons must follow in order to enter the analyser, but the gain in resolution achieved in this way results in a large decrease in intensity. Practical analysers must be designed with focusing properties such that they can accept as large a fraction as possible of the electrons produced in a properly matched source, while still giving the desired resolution.

The two major classes of analyser are those in which retarding fields are used to produce integral photoelectron spectra such as that in *Figure 1.1*, and those in which deflecting fields separate the electrons of different energies and give differential spectra.

2.3.1 Retarding-field analysers

Retarding-field analysers operate on the principle of permitting only those electrons which have energies higher than a retarding potential to reach the detector. Spectra are produced by recording the photoelectron current as the retarding potential is varied, and should contain a step in the current for each group of photoelectrons of discrete energy. The steps for low-energy electrons are superimposed on the electron current of all electrons of higher energy, and as the statistical noise in the spectrum is proportional to the total electron current, the examination of low-energy electrons is sometimes difficult. However, these analysers have the important advantages of being almost equally sensitive to electrons of all energies, with perhaps a slight bias in favour of low-energy electrons, and of being able to accept electrons in a large solid angle or from extended sources. They are generally more sensitive than deflection analysers in terms of the collection

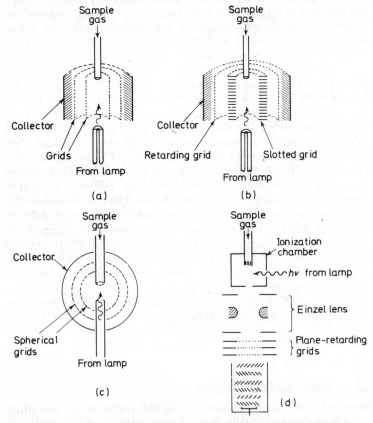

Figure 2.3   Retarding-field electron energy analysers: (a) cylindrical grid; (b) slotted grid; (c) spherical; (d) Einzel lenses. All the analysers are rotationally symmetrical about a vertical axis

efficiency for electrons, and this advantage is especially important at low energies, where differential analysers are usually least sensitive. *Figure 2.3* shows the designs of a number of different retarding-field analysers.

The cylindrical grid analyser (*Figure 2.3a*) is now of mainly historical interest, being the analyser used in the earliest work in molecular photoelectron spectroscopy[1]. It has the grave defect that electrons which are emitted at an angle to the electric field, that is, in a direction which is not perpendicular to the grids, are detected at too low an apparent energy, so that the steps produced in the spectrum are not sharp. In later retarding-field analysers, this defect is overcome in various ways. In the slotted grid analyser (*Figure 2.3b*), the cylindrical form is retained, allowing a long ionization region and a high photoelectron current. One grid is replaced by a pile of spaced discs[20], which transmits electrons only in a small range of angles about the normal to the photon beam. In the spherical retarding-field analyser[21] (*Figure 2.3c*), the grids and collector are spherical and the ionization region is point-like, so that electrons ejected at all angles are collected and all of them automatically travel in the direction of the retarding field. The minimum number of electrodes in all of these retarding-field analysers is two, one to define the electrical potential at which electrons are formed and a second, which can also be the collector, to define a retarding potential. In most designs, a separate electrode for the retarding potential is provided, but some workers have reported that the highest resolution is attained with the minimum number of electrodes. The resolution depends on the uniformity of the fields and potentials and on the relative radii of the ionization volume and the surface defining the retarding potential. Electrons formed at points off the optic axis or centre can traverse the retarding field at an angle, and so appear to have a lower energy than they actually possess. The simplest approximation for the theoretical resolution is

$$\frac{\Delta V}{V} = \left(\frac{r}{R} \right)^2 \tag{2.1}$$

where ΔV is the smallest resolvable energy difference at electron energy V, r is the radius of the ionization region and R that of the retarding electrode. Any lack of concentricity of the ionization source and retarding field contributes to r, so precise alignment is essential. More detailed theory on the resolution of spherical retarding-grid analysers has been given by Huchital and Rigden[22].

The most successful retarding-field analysers in terms of resolution are those based on the electron lens principle[23], as illustrated in *Figure 2.3d*. Ionization occurs at a point-like source, which may be defined by the intersection of the light beam with a beam of target gas, and the paths of electrons ejected into a certain solid angle defined by apertures are made parallel by an electron lens before the electrons impinge on a system of plane retarding grids. The electrons transmitted through the retarding field can conveniently be detected by using an electron multiplier. The resolution of this type of analyser depends on the excellence of the lens system and on the accuracy with which a retarding potential is defined by the grids; several grids are often provided in order to eliminate the effects of field penetration. A resolution of 5 meV has sometimes been attained but, as with all retarding-field analysers, it is extremely difficult to maintain high resolution in the presence of reactive target gases. Adsorption of gases on the grids causes local changes of contact potential, which are immediately and directly reflected in loss of resolution, because the electrons inevitably travel very close to the surfaces of the grid wires.

2.3.2   Deflection analysers

In deflection analysers, electric or magnetic fields are used in order to make electrons of different energies follow different paths, and so to separate them. Magnetic analysers are not very suitable for low-energy electrons, because weak magnetic fields are needed and it is difficult to shield the analyser from stray fields present in the laboratory while applying a controlled field. Electrostatic analysers have come to predominate in photoelectron spectroscopy for this reason. There are many different types, each of which offers particular advantages and disadvantages, and most require a substantial mathematical treatment in order to describe their theoretical properties. Only the simplest, the 45 degree parallel-plate analyser, will be described in detail, and then the important properties of the different analysers will be mentioned.

Figure 2.4 shows a parallel-plate analyser schematically. A uniform electric field, E, is established between two parallel plates a distance d apart. Electrons of energy eV_0 and mass m_e enter the field at an angle θ by passing through a slit in the plate. The initial electron velocity, v_0, is given by

$$v_0 = (2\,eV_0/m_e)^{1/2} \tag{2.2}$$

and its components in the two directions x and y perpendicular and parallel to the field, respectively, are

$$v_{0x} = v_0 \cos \theta \tag{2.3}$$

$$v_{0y} = v_0 \sin \theta \tag{2.4}$$

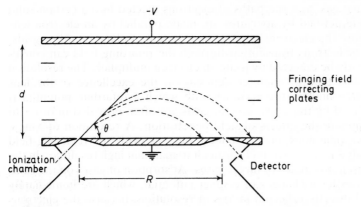

Figure 2.4   Parallel-plate electrostatic analyser in the 45 degree configuration

The field is of such a polarity as to decelerate the electrons in the y direction, while it has no effect on their motion in the x direction. The equations of motion are therefore

$$\frac{\mathrm{d}v_y}{\mathrm{d}t} = -\frac{eE}{m_e} \tag{2.5}$$

$$v_y = v_0 \sin \theta - \frac{eE}{m_e} t \tag{2.6}$$

$$y = v_0 t \sin \theta - \frac{eE}{2m_e} t^2 \tag{2.7}$$

$$x = v_0 t \cos \theta \tag{2.8}$$

The electrons follow parabolic trajectories, reaching a maximum height above the lower plate when $\mathrm{d}y/\mathrm{d}t = 0$, that is, when

$$t = \frac{mv_0}{eE} \sin \theta \tag{2.9}$$

The second half of the trajectory is the mirror image of the first, so that the total time until the electrons return to the lower plate is just twice this value. The distance they have then travelled in the x direction, the range, is

$$R = 2v_0 \cos \theta \, \frac{mv_0}{eE} \, \sin \theta \tag{2.10}$$

$$R = \frac{2eV_0}{eE} \, \sin 2\theta \tag{2.11}$$

The condition for focusing is that the range should be independent of θ, that is, $dR/d\theta = 0$. This is fulfilled at $\theta = 45$ degrees, where $\sin 2\theta = 1$.

In a practical analyser, the range, R, is fixed by the positions of the inlet and entrance slits, and different electrons are brought into focus on the exit slit by varying the electric field. If a potential, V, is applied to the plates, the field is V/d, so that the operating condition of the analyser is

$$\frac{V}{V_0} = \frac{2d}{R} \tag{2.12}$$

Hence, if the distance between the plates is exactly half the distance between the inlet and exit slits, the potential that must be applied to the plates to focus an electron is numerically equal to the energy of that electron in electronvolts.

A real analyser will have inlet and exit slits of finite widths S_1 and S_2 respectively, and the electrons will not all enter at exactly 45 degrees but in a range of angles near this value. The sensitivity of the analyser depends on the width of the slits and the range of angles that can be accepted, but the energy resolution also depends on these quantities. In practice, the resolution of photo-electron spectrometers is usually quoted in millielectronvolts as the width at half-height of the $^2P_{3/2}$ line of argon, near $5.5 \, eV$ electron energy. Theoretically, the energy width, ΔV, at an energy V is proportional to V for all deflection analysers, so a numerical resolution $V/\Delta V$ can be defined. For the 45 degree parallel-plate analyser, the resolution is given by an equation of the form

$$\frac{\Delta V}{V} = \frac{S_1 + S_2}{R} + A\alpha^2 + \text{higher terms} \tag{2.13}$$

where A is a constant and α is the fractional deviation of the electron entry angle from 45 degrees, when the angle is expressed as $45 \, (1 + \alpha)$ degrees. Because the term in α vanishes, while that in α^2 is not zero, the 45 degree parallel-plate analyser is said to have first-order focusing. Equation 2.13 or a related equation applies to all deflection analysers, and in some instances the terms in α^2 also vanish, giving second-order focusing. The 45 degree analyser focuses electrons in only one plane (the plane of the paper in *Figure 2.4*) and this is called single focusing; other types of analyser focus in two planes simultaneously and are said to have double-focusing properties. An analyser with just first-order, single focusing can accept electrons only in a rather small solid angle while maintaining a given resolution. The actual angular deviation that is acceptable for a given resolution depends on the numerical value of the constant A, which for the 45 degree parallel-plate analyser is relatively large; it has weak first-order focusing.

A number of figures of merit for electron analysers have been proposed, such as the *luminosity*[24], *étendue*[25] or simply *transmission*. These all purport to be proportional to the signal strength that can be achieved for a given resolution and absolute source intensity, but are not, in fact, very helpful. Analysers are needed for different purposes, even within photoelectron spectroscopy, where each has its own special advantages. Furthermore, the energy range can always be scanned either by varying the field within the analyser, or by varying a pre-acceleration or deceleration of the electrons so as to bring them to a single fixed energy. Pre-acceleration can be a very simple procedure or involve subtle lenses with quadrupole or hexapole optics that match the characteristics of the electron source to the entrance aperture. These external arrangements or operating conditions have at least as strong an effect on the final performance of a spectrometer as the choice of analyser type. The forms of ionization region to which the different types of analyser can most advantageously be matched without lens systems are among their characteristics, which are discussed briefly in the following paragraphs.

45 degree parallel-plate analyser

The weak first-order single focusing of this analyser means that electrons can be accepted only within a small range of angles (± 3 degrees) for useful resolution[26]. The analyser can be matched to a line source of electrons, such as the pencil light beam from a capillary discharge lamp ionizing gas in a target chamber, but because of its poor collection efficiency it is not a good choice for normal photoelectron spectroscopy. In experiments where the angular deviation of the electrons must in any event be limited, as in studies of angular distributions, it is no worse than other analysers, and its advantages then come into play. These are its ease of construction and the fact that its inlet and exit slits are in an equipotential plane, which eliminates problems of fringing fields.

30 degree parallel-plate analyser

If the inlet and exit slits of a parallel-plate analyser are moved a calculated distance away from the positive plate and the electrons travel in a field-free space before entering the field at 30 degrees, an analyser with good second-order single focusing is obtained[27] (*Figure 2.5*). A further improvement can be made by placing the

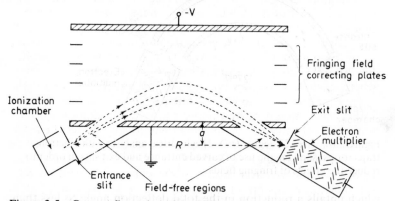

Figure 2.5   One configuration of the 30 degree parallel-plate electron energy analyser. When the exit and entrance slits are equidistant from the base plate of the analyser, the condition for second-order focusing is $R/a = 6/\sqrt{3}$

exit slit not at the position of second-order focus but at that of the minimum trace width* for a given angular deviation[28], and with this modification the 30 degree analyser is theoretically very attractive. It retains the advantages mentioned above for the 45 degree parallel-plate, but has the disadvantage that the large holes necessary in the first analyser plate must be covered with mesh for the sake of field uniformity. The mesh will cause a slight loss in transmission and introduces risks of contact potential effects.

---

*The position of minimum trace width is that where the bundle of trajectories for electrons of a single energy but different initial angles is narrowest in a real analyser. It does not normally coincide with the position of the second-order focus.

127 degree cylindrical analyser

The 127 degree cylindrical analyser[29,30] is the one most commonly used in photoelectron spectrometry. It has strong first-order focusing in one direction, and is suited to a line source of electrons. One problem is that the inlet and exit slits are not in an equipotential plane, and so precautions must be taken in order to prevent the presence of the slits from disturbing the field. Two solutions to this problem are to have specially shaped slit jaws, as shown in *Figure 2.6*, or to use a fringing field corrector element[31],

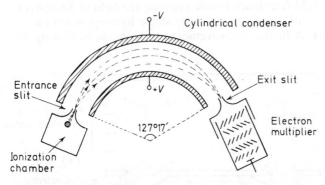

Figure 2.6 The 127 degree ($\pi/\sqrt{2}$) cylindrical analyser with electron trajectories, showing the use of curved entrance and exit slits in order to reduce the effects of fringing fields

which entails a reduction in the total deflection angle to less than 127 degrees. An attractive alternative form of correcting plate, which requires no change in deflection angle in this or the following (spherical) analyser, has been described by Jost[32].

Hemispherical analyser

The 180 degree hemispherical condenser analyser[33] (*Figure 2.7*) has first-order double focusing and matches a point source of electrons particularly well. The object and image points are again not in equipotential planes, so that a problem arises in the provision of slits. Kuyatt and Simpson[33] have provided a most elegant solution to this problem by having no real slits at the analyser entrance or exit points, but lens systems which produce there the images of the real, physically distant slits. The theoretical performance of the hemispherical analyser with pre-acceleration

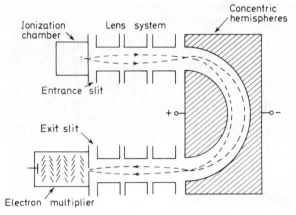

Figure 2.7   Hemispherical electrostatic energy analyser using virtual slits

of the electrons in the lens system is very good, and it is often used in photoelectron spectrometers[34].

Cylindrical mirror analyser

The system of coaxial cylinders as an energy analyser[35,36] can have second-order focusing for angular deviations in the planes of the electron trajectories and perfect focusing, because of its geometry, for variations of the radial angle. This is theoretically the best

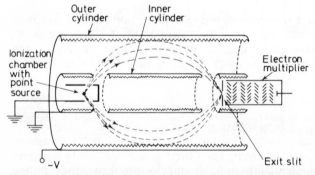

Figure 2.8   Cylindrical mirror electron energy analyser. The apertures in the inner cylinder must be interrupted for mechanical support, and covered with mesh for the sake of field uniformity. Fringing-field corrector plates must also be provided between the ends of the inner and outer cylinders as in parallel-plate analysers, but are omitted from the drawing for the sake of clarity

analyser available for electrons from a point source, apart from the impractical 30 degree parallel-plate fountain. The focusing in the cylindrical mirror is good over a wide range of angles, and the 'magic' angle of 54 degrees 44 minutes, at which variations of angular distribution of electrons have no effect on intensities, can conveniently be used. Apart from its excellent focusing properties, the cylindrical mirror analyser (*Figure 2.8*) has the advantage that the entry and exit slits are at earth potential and field free. One disadvantage is that the object point, where the ionization region must be located, is rather deeply buried and inaccessible within the analyser construction. There is another version of the cylindrical mirror analyser, not illustrated here, in which the inlet and exit slits are at the surface of the inner cylinder; the theory of both types has been thoroughly developed[37].

The Bessel box analyser

This analyser (also known as the pill-box) combines an exceptionally simple mechanical design (*Figure 2.9*) with good resolution and sensitivity[38]. Its design was perfected in an unusual way,

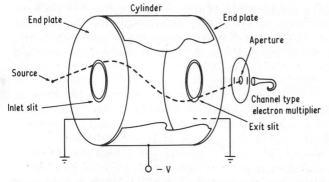

Figure 2.9   The Bessel box analyser, which has advantages of mechanical simplicity, high sensitivity and resolution, and source and detector in field-free regions

by numerical calculations of fields and electron trajectories, rather than by analytical solution of the equations of motion. Like all high resolution deflection analysers, this one is very sensitive to the presence of stray magnetic fields. The circular form of its entrance slit means that it is best matched to a point source of electrons, and again allows one to choose the magic angle of 54

degrees 44 minutes between the photon beam and ejected electrons. It has been used in very high resolution photoelectron
spectroscopy[39], and in photoelectron–photoion coincidence
spectroscopy[40].

Other deflection analysers

Both the 45 and 30 degree parallel-plate analysers can be imagined
in 'fountain' geometry, with rotational symmetry about a point
source of electrons. Electron trajectories would begin below a
lower circular plate, pass through a ring-shaped slit and spread like
water from a fountain until they pass through a second ring slit to
the detector. Such analysers could have good collection efficiency
and resolution[28], but are probably impractical because of the
inconvenient shape of the electron collector required. Several
other types of electron energy analysers have been described but
none, apart from minor variations of the types discussed before,
has found widespread use in photoelectron spectroscopy.

2.3.3 Hybrid analysers

By combining the principles of retarding fields and deflection it is
possible to design analysers with exceptional electron collection
efficiencies combined with differential operation and good resolv-
ing power. Differential operation can be achieved, for instance, by
arranging a chromatic electron lens to selectively focus onto the
detector only those electrons that have been retarded to zero
energy. Electrons of lower energy fail to pass, while those of
higher energy are not focused. A very good analyser using this
principle has been designed by Lindau *et al.*[41] and used successfully in photoelectron spectroscopy by Hotop and Hübler[42].

A retarding field acts, in general, as a high-pass filter, so
differential operation or band pass can be achieved by adding a
low-pass filter element in series. The chromatic lens carries out
this function in the Lindau analyser, but it can also be performed
by an *electron mirror*. This is a field by which electrons are
reflected, unless they have enough energy to pass right through the
field. If the reflected electrons impinge on a retarding field, set to
transmit those that have only just been reflected, a differential
analyser results. A remarkably effective analyser of this type has
been used for photoelectron spectroscopy using very faint
monochromatized synchrotron radiation from a synchrotron[43] (not
a storage ring). The analyser depicted in *Figure 2.10* has an

ellipsoidal electron mirror, with the ionization region at one focus. The other focus, on which electrons converge after reflection, is surrounded by spherical retarding grids. The collection efficiency of this analyser for electrons from a point source is some 16%— several hundred times that of any normal deflection analyser involving slits.

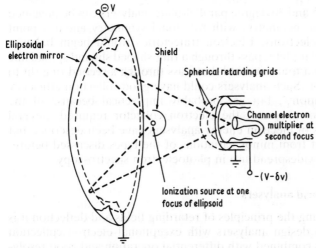

Figure 2.10   The ellipsoidal mirror-retarding field analyser[57]. The figure must be viewed as having cylindrical symmetry about the horizontal axis, the mirror being a segment of an ellipsoid of revolution. This analyser offers extreme sensitivity, with differential (low-pass + high-pass) operation

Very high collection efficiency is also achieved in hybrid analysers which use inhomogeneous magnetic fields to 'parallelize' the electrons emerging from a point source. One analyser of this kind has been developed to make use of the imaging properties of the diverging magnetic field[44]. Another, which has been very fully studied and described[45] is optimized for extremely efficient spectroscopy of photoelectrons from pulsed laser multiphoton ionization, using time-of-flight (next section) as the analysis method. The principle of these instruments is that the Lorenz force makes all electrons spiral around magnetic field lines, initially in a source region of high uniform magnetic field. The field has a smooth (adiabatic) transition to a low field region where the field lines are again parallel, and where the electrons would normally follow spirals of much greater pitch. Because angular momentum along the field lines must be conserved, however, the transition from high to low field produces a transformation of velocities which are transverse to the high field into velocities along the low field lines, thus making the electron trajectories nearly parallel. The parallelized electron can be energy analysed by time-of-flight, as in Kruit and Read's analyser[45], or by retardation methods. Electrons can be gathered from the whole (4π) or half (2π) of the solid angle into which they are emitted.

2.4   Electron detectors and recording systems

The electron currents encountered in photoelectron spectroscopy range from about 10 electrons per second (10^{-18} A) in differential spectrometers operated at the highest resolution, to 10^8 electrons per second (10^{-11} A) in the most efficient retarding-field spectrometers. For currents higher than 10^{-14} A, simple electron collectors (Faraday cups) can be used with electrometer amplifiers. In an electrometer, the electron current develops a voltage across a very high resistor and this voltage is then amplified by special methods for display and recording. A good electrometer approaches closely the fundamental limit of sensitivity, which is set by the random thermal motions of electrons in the input resistor, called Johnson noise. This Johnson noise is additional to the statistical fluctuations that arise from collecting finite numbers of electrons, and limits the minimum currents that can be measured with any electrometer to about 10^{-16} A.

For the majority of photoelectron spectrometers, it is much more satisfactory to detect the photoelectrons singly by using an electron multiplier, which can be either a traditional type with 10 to 20 discrete electrodes (dynodes) or a member of the 'channeltron' family, with sensitive material in the form of a continuous film. When a single electron strikes the first dynode of a multiplier with an energy of a few hundred electronvolts, it causes the emission of two or three secondary electrons, which are attracted to the second dynode. More secondary electrons are produced at the second dynode and after the same process has been repeated 10–20 times there are enough electrons to produce an easily measurable pulse in an external electrical circuit. The same process occurs in a channeltron, each collision taking place a little further down the curved electrode channel. Either the pulses can be counted and their number recorded or the rate in pulses per second can be converted into analogue form in a ratemeter for display or recording.

The simplest way to record and display a photoelectron spectrum is to use an X–Y plotter in which the vertical position of the pen is controlled by the count-rate and the horizontal position by the scanning voltage. The speed of the scan and the electrical time constant of the recording circuit must be carefully chosen according to the resolution and the signal to statistical noise ratio desired, so that an appropriate number of electrons are detected at each point in the spectrum.

In a second system of recording, the spectrum is scanned rapidly many times, and the count of electrons detected at each energy is accumulated digitally in a multi-channel analyser. The contents of the multi-channel analyser memory can later be processed mathematically or read out on to an X–Y recorder. The advantages of this second method are that relative band intensities in the measured spectrum are not affected by slow changes of sensitivity, caused, for instance, by changes in the pressure of the sample gas, and that the problem of choosing the correct electrical time constant for a given scan speed is eliminated. The independence of the spectrum from sample pressure effects is important when only small amounts of sample are available, as it greatly increases the effective sensitivity. A disadvantage is that if variations of contact potentials change the effective energy scale during a measurement, the effect on the spectrum will be a reduction in the resolution. In the direct recording method, these very common energy scale drifts do not cause a loss in resolution but instead shift the peaks relative to one another and cause errors in the energy calibration.

2.4.1 Electron time-of-flight analysis

Since the velocity of a particle is proportional to the square root of its energy, the time-of-flight of a photoelectron from formation to detection is clearly a measure of that energy. The application of this principle to electron energy analysis has been delayed, until recently, by the need for very good time resolution in both light source and detector if useful energy resolution is to be achieved. The light source problem has been solved by the advent of synchrotron radiation and pulsed lasers, which readily provide light in 1 ns or shorter packets. Electron multipliers and channeltrons provide a detector resolution of about 10 ns, while specially designed multipliers and channel plates approach 100 ps. The advantages of using the time-of-flight method of energy analysis are that the device is mechanically extremely simple—a shielded tube and detector—and that electrons of all energies can be looked for after every light pulse. This contrasts with normal deflection analysers using slits, where electrons of only one single energy can be searched for at a time. The time-of-flight analyser is thus a *multiplex* device, since all its channels are open simultaneously, and it can theoretically be hundreds of times more sensitive than non-multiplex analysers. The *disadvantages* of the simple time-of-flight analyser, even apart from possible non-availability of a suitable light source in the laboratory, is that resolution is poor for electron energies greater than about 2 eV. For a typical path length of 10 cm and an optimistic time resolution of 1 ns, energy resolution would be 12 meV at 1 eV, 22 meV at 2 eV, but 132 meV at 5 eV and 370 meV at 10 eV. The loss of resolution can be reduced by judicious use of retarding fields, preferably with electron lenses or magnetic fields to 'parallelize' the electrons and with extensive computer 'massaging' of the raw data, but the attractive simplicity of the device is then lost. A most important use of electron time-of-flight analysis is the study of low energy electrons, which are most poorly seen by traditional deflection analysers. The development of threshold photoelectron spectroscopy (TPES) and related techniques using synchrotron radiation has relied heavily on the time-of-flight method, which has been thoroughly analysed[46] in this application. The time-of-flight technique is actually the only one which allows recording of *complete* photoelectron spectra including the threshold electrons, with accurately calculable collection efficiencies, and for this reason it is a powerful tool in the measurement of partial cross-sections. It has also provided the first complete measurements of electron spectra from multiphoton ionization[47], which are crucial for understanding the mechanism of this process.

2.4.2   Position-sensitive detectors

Multiplex operation of deflection analysers, with a consequent enormous increase in sensitivity, is made possible by position-sensitive detectors, which are used instead of an exit slit. They not only signal the arrival of charged particles but also tell the position at which each particle impinges on the sensitive surface, which in a deflection analyser indicates the original energy.

For single electron detection, as required in photoelectron spectroscopy, the first element is usually a tandem channel-plate electron multiplier, which turns a single electron arrival into a cascade of some 10^6–10^8 electrons. The position of the cascade at the exit of the channel plate, which faithfully reproduces the position of the incident electron, can be determined by accelerating the electron into a phosphor (as on a television screen), and viewing the resulting flash of light using a television camera. Alternatively, the electron cascade can be located by collecting it on a resistive strip; the position along the strip is determined from the fraction of the total charge deposited at each end, where separate charge-sensitive pre-amplifiers are connected. Systems of this sort have been well studied[48], and it has been shown that a spatial resolution of ~50µ for single electrons is possible.

To use a position sensitive detector in a photoelectron spectrometer it is necessary to couple it with an electron energy analyser which has an accessible image plane. The most popular analyser for this purpose is the hemispherical condenser, whose double focusing gives it excellent imaging properties. Because sensitivity may not be completely uniform over the whole detector it is advantageous to scan the spectrum over each detector channel in turn by changing the deflecting field, and to accumulate the spectrum using an on-line computer[49,50]. This technique smooths out any sensitivity variations, but retains the full multiplex advantage of detection in many channels at once. The increased sensitivity offers the opportunity for very high resolution or high signal-to-noise ratio, and makes it possible to use very low density gas targets, such as molecular beams[50].

The superiority of photoelectron spectrometers using multiplex detection is amply demonstrated by excellent spectra emerging from the few current (1982) instruments of this type, and their use is bound to expand. Time-of-flight analysis of electrons is also a multiplex technique, but has hitherto been limited by technical electronics problems to low count rates, making it less attractive. The disadvantage of low resolution for high energy electrons can be removed by progressive retardation if the electrons have once been parallelized, as in Kruit and Read's analyser, so the obstacles to widespread use of this technique are also disappearing. Both methods rely heavily on the on-line computer, which is becoming an indispensable element of most laboratory instrumentation.

2.5 The operation of photoelectron spectrometers

There are several precautions to be observed in measuring photoelectron spectra which require mention, although they are trivial in principle. The samples must be proved to be pure by techniques other than photoelectron spectroscopy, such as mass spectrometry, because the photoelectron spectrum itself is a poor indicator of the presence of impurities. Furthermore, certain compounds can decompose within the target chamber, and many polar molecules may be partly dimeric under the flow conditions that exist there, even if they ought to be monomeric at equilibrium. Problems of dimer and oligomer formation are especially severe in supersonic jets and seeded beam targets, so it is good practice to monitor the target gas by observing the mass spectra of the ions as well as the photoelectron spectra.

Even when the sample itself is pure, monomeric and undecomposed, the photoelectron spectrum does not necessarily represent the pure compound alone. A background spectrum is produced by scattered electrons and by foreign gases present in the source, the latter produced mainly by desorption from the walls. The usual causes are water, giving its characteristic peak at 12.6 eV ionization energy, or a previous sample being displaced by the new sample. Polar compounds are particularly strongly adsorbed, and the most peculiar spectra are sometimes seen when one compound displaces another from the surfaces of the inlet system and target chamber. It is good practice to allow a sample to flow through the spectrometer continuously for up to an hour before taking a spectrum, both to reduce these effects and to allow contact potentials to become stabilized. The background spectrum is definitely not independent of the presence of sample, so there is little point in measuring a background spectrum without the sample and subtracting it from the final observed spectrum.

The resolution of photoelectron spectrometers and the accuracy of energy and intensity measurements are partly a matter of spectrometer design, as described earlier in this chapter, but are also determined by the conditions under which the spectrometer operates. These topics are discussed in more detail in the following sections.

2.5.1   High resolution

The theoretical resolution of any differential energy analyser can be made arbitrarily high by narrowing the slits and restricting the angular deviations of the electrons that enter the analyser. When this procedure is attempted, however, the experimental resolution is very seldom as good as the theoretical resolution, particularly at low electron energies. As the numerical resolution, $\Delta V/V$, should be constant, the instrumental peak width, ΔV, ought to be proportional to the electron energy, and this is usually found to be true for energies above about 5 eV. At lower energies, the peak width often tends to a constant value, and the numerical resolution becomes progressively lower as the electron energy decreases. The cause of this behaviour is probably not simple, but it is frequently attributed to local variations in surface potential and, hence, of the real potential difference between the target chamber and analyser. Surface conditions have a very strong effect on measured electron energies; variation of the pressure of even a rare gas can cause peak shifts of up to 0.5 eV. The only way to prevent such effects from decreasing the resolution is to make all critical surfaces of the target chamber and analyser as electrically uniform as possible, which can be achieved either by covering all surfaces with a film of noble metal, usually gold, and then keeping them scrupulously clean, or by covering them with a layer of colloidal graphite. Apart from providing uniform electrical potentials, the graphited surfaces have the advantage of lower reflection coefficients than those of bare metals for low-energy electrons and thereby reduce the background signal of scattered electrons.

Two other risks to satisfactory resolution are the presence in the spectrometer of unwanted magnetic and electromagnetic fields. Low-energy electrons are remarkably sensitive to the presence of magnetic fields, and the longer the electron path length in the analyser the more serious the problem becomes. Both continuous and fluctuating magnetic fields must be eliminated, and this elimination can be attempted either by screening with high-permeability material (Mumetal) or by cancellation of the fields by using large and stable coil systems in which the currents are controlled by feed-back from sensitive magnetometers. For high resolution work, all magnetic fields must be reduced to less than a few thousandths of the earth's field, and field gradients must also be made very small. Electromagnetic radiation, whether broadcast intentionally or unintentionally, can not only affect the electron trajectories directly but can also induce pick-up on any unscreened electrical leads, which act as antennae. In order to minimize such effects, the whole spectrometer and its electronic equipment must be earthed effectively, preferably at a single point, and all electrical connections to the spectrometer should be provided with low impedance pathways to earth (decoupling).

The experimental or technical problems mentioned above are far more likely to limit resolution in practice than any fundamental physical effects. The few groups of workers who have achieved resolutions much better than 13 meV have done so by paying painstaking attention to all these practical factors[51]. There is, however, one physical effect that limits resolution significantly, often called a Doppler effect. The target molecules before ionization have random thermal motions, and the components of their velocities in the direction of the spectrometer entrance slit are added to the electron velocities. The narrowest lines in a photoelectron spectrum have a width and shape characteristic of the molecular thermal velocity distribution, which can be derived from the kinetic theory of gases. With a differential electron energy analyser, which accepts electrons in a single direction only, the one-dimensional velocity distribution is relevant and the observable line width, ΔV, in millielectronvolts is given by

$$\Delta V = 0.75 \left(\frac{VT}{M} \right)^{1/2} \tag{2.14}$$

where V is the electron energy in electronvolts, T the absolute temperature and M the mass in atomic mass units. The same equation is valid, with slightly different numerical factors[52], for analysers that accept electrons over wider angular ranges. For 10 eV electrons ejected from a molecule of mass 100 at room temperature, the energy spread, ΔV, is only 4 meV, which is well below normal analyser resolutions. It is for light molecules and high electron energies or gas temperatures that this Doppler effect becomes important, and the extreme case is hydrogen. Ionization of H_2 with He I light gives peaks 22 meV wide, and in ionization with He II light their width is 46 meV. The argon $^2P_{3/2}$ peak, which is often used as a standard test of resolution, has a Doppler width of 5 meV when ionization is by He I and 10 meV under He II ionization, all calculated at 300 °K.

It is clear that for work at very high resolution, or even at high resolution when high temperatures or He II light are used, some effort must be made to reduce the Doppler widths. Early very high resolution measurements were all made by reducing the electron energy as far as possible by using light of the longest usable wavelength, because the $V^{1/2}$ term in equation 2.14 can thereby be reduced by a large factor. Cooling the bulk gas much below room temperature is impracticable for most substances, and can in any event have little effect until temperatures below that of liquid nitrogen are reached. A more generally attractive solution is to provide a target gas in the form of a molecular beam or a supersonic jet, in which the effective transverse kinetic temperatures in equation 2.14 can easily be reduced to below 10 °K. The supersonic jet or seeded beam has the very important additional advantage that in the nozzle expansion, molecular rotation and vibration are also cooled. This can so sharpen the fine structure in the spectrum of a complex molecule that entirely new vibrational structure is seen. Furthermore, the weakly bound molecular clusters and van der Waals complexes which are formed in such beams can also be studied by photoelectron spectroscopy. The costs of these advantages are a high throughput of gas, which demands very fast, large and expensive pumping systems, and a relatively low density of target molecules. The need for high pumping speed can be avoided, however, by use of a pulsed molecular beam[53], and low target density can be compensated by use of an efficient analyser or multiplex system[50].

2.5.2   Calibration and energy measurements

The energy scale of a photoelectron spectrum can be scanned either by varying the potentials in the electron energy analyser or by varying a potential difference between the target chamber and analyser entrance slit. The second method has the advantages that the analyser is set to transmit electrons of a fixed energy for which its resolution and transmission can be optimized, and that the resolution of the resulting spectrum is independent of electron energy. Neither method, however, permits an absolute calibration of the energy scale from instrumental parameters alone, and calibration is always made by reference to the known ionization potentials of some standard compounds. Contact potential effects vary from compound to compound and shift the effective energy scales as a function of pressure, so that it is essential to take the spectrum of a mixture of sample and calibrant. When this is impossible, for instance, because the gases react chemically, spectra of sample and calibrant have to be taken alternately, as rapidly as possible, several times.

The gases used for calibration are chosen so as to give sharp peaks in the spectrum at precisely known ionization potentials; the most useful for the ionization energy range below 15 eV are argon, xenon and methyl iodide. Some other gases and different ionizing radiations from discharge lamps can be used in order to extend the range to higher and lower ionization energies, and the most useful are given in *Table 2.3*. Once the spectrum of sample with calibrant has been obtained, the usual method of fixing the energy scale and determining ionization potentials is to make a linear interpolation between calibrant lines, based on the potential which is scanned

Table 2.3   Useful calibration lines

Substance	Ionic state	Ionizing line	Electron energy eV	Apparent* ionization potential, eV
Ne	$^2P_{3/2}$	He IIα	19.249	1.968
Ne	$^2P_{1/2}$	He IIα	19.346	2.065
He	^2S	He IIα	16.227	4.991
MeI	$^2E_{1/2}$	He Iβ	12.922	8.296
MeI	$^2E_{3/2}$	He Iα	11.680	9.538
MeI	$^2E_{1/2}$	He Iα	11.053	10.164
Xe	$^2P_{3/2}$	He Iα	9.088	12.130
Xe	$^2P_{1/2}$	He Iα	7.782	13.436
Kr	$^2P_{3/2}$	He Iα	7.219	13.999
Kr	$^2P_{1/2}$	He Iα	6.553	14.665
Hg	$^2D_{5/2}$	He Iα	6.378	14.840
Ar	$^2P_{3/2}$	He Iα	5.459	15.759
Ar	$^2P_{1/2}$	He Iα	5.281	15.937
Hg	$^2D_{3/2}$	He Iα	4.514	16.704
N₂	$^2\Sigma_u^+$	He Iα	2.467	18.751
Ne	$^2P_{3/2}$	He Iβ	1.522	19.695
Ne	$^2P_{1/2}$	He Iβ	1.425	19.792
MeI	$^2E_{3/2}$	H Ly α	0.661	20.557

*As if the ionization were by He Iα radiation in all instances.

experimentally. Lloyd[54] has shown, however, that in his spectrometer (127 degree analyser), exact linearity between analyser potential and electron energy cannot be relied upon in the region of electron energy below 5 eV. Deviations from exact linearity are probably more common than is often assumed, and for this reason the calibrant lines should always be as near as possible in energy to an ionization peak whose position is to be determined.

2.5.3   Intensity measurements

In differential photoelectron spectra, the relative heights of two bands that have intrinsically different widths, such as the first two bands in the spectrum of methanol (*Figure 1.11*), vary with the resolution of the analyser. As the resolution improves, the height of sharp peaks apparently increases while the height of broad bands is reduced. For a truly narrow peak, all the electrons can be transmitted through the analyser at a single setting, because their energies are all within the energy width, ΔV, which defines the resolution; if the true energies cover a range broader than ΔV, the fraction of them that can pass through the analyser is proportional to ΔV itself. Peak heights are therefore not an appropriate measure of intensity, and it can easily be shown that areas rather than heights should always be used. With photoelectron spectra from retarding-field analysers, this problem does not arise as the measured step heights in integral spectra correspond exactly to areas in differential spectra.

A more serious difficulty arises from variations of analyser sensitivity with energy, generally called energy discriminations, which distort the spectra and must be allowed for. All photoelectron spectrometers have some energy discriminations; simple deflection instruments are more sensitive to high-energy than low-energy electrons and retarding-field instruments often favour electrons of the lowest energy. In order to correct raw spectra one can either measure the energy discriminations experimentally using the methods outlined below or one can accept the theoretical variations of sensitivity with energy for each type of analyser, and to use them to correct measured spectra. For deflection analysers without pre-acceleration of the electrons, the resolution, ΔV, and thus the energy bandwidth within which electrons are transmitted, is proportional to the electron energy, V. The areas of both sharp peaks and broad bands are proportional to ΔV, so that their measured intensities can be corrected by dividing them by the electron energy. Retarding-field analysers and deflection analysers in which pre-acceleration is used for scanning are assumed to have no energy discrimination, but in both instances with the constraint that at the low electron energy end of the scale the measured intensities are probably inaccurate. Deflection analysers with pre-acceleration are free from discrimination only if the solid angle within which electrons from the ionization region are collected is geometrically fixed before pre-acceleration; otherwise, this solid angle, and therefore the intensity, depend on the accelerating field.

The most troublesome problem in converting measured photoelectron spectra into true photoelectron energy distributions is that the electrons are not ejected in equal numbers in all directions and their angular distributions vary from one band to another. The angular distributions are described in detail in Chapter 3; from their form it transpires that there are three ways of allowing for, or eliminating, their effect on a spectrum.

(1) All electrons can be collected and measured, as in the spherical retarding-field analyser or the magnetic parallelizers.

(2) Electrons can be collected in a small solid angle centred at 54 degrees 44 minutes from the propagation direction of an unpolarized light beam, at which 'magic' angle the angular effects vanish.

(3)   If the parameter β, which describes the angular distributions, is known at every electron energy or, at least, for every band, the spectrum can be corrected whatever the spectrometer geometry.

Experimental methods of measuring spectrometer energy discrimination obviously require means of dealing with the angular effects, and use of the 'magic' angle is the most convenient. The best technique also calls for a tunable light source, either a continuum, or a many-line lamp with a monochromator, and for a way of measuring the light intensity independent of its wavelength. Count rates per unit incident light intensity are then determined for rare gas targets at different wavelengths, and are compared with the known photoionization cross-sections of these atoms. Extrapolation to zero pressure is needed to eliminate electron scattering effects.

A less accurate but more convenient way of determining a spectrometer sensitivity function is to measure photoelectron spectra of a number of standard substances and compare them with published 'corrected' spectra (and angular distribution parameters). The comparison must clearly be based on peak areas and again pressure effects need to be eliminated, and angular distributions allowed for.

Table 2.4   Spectra for intensity calibration

Substance	Ionic state	Electron energy, eV	β	σ_{tot}	$\sigma\perp$
N_2	$X^2\Sigma_g^+$	5.6	0.7	67	71 ± 2
	$A^2\Pi_u$	4.3	0.4	100	100
	$B^2\Sigma_u^+$	2.5	1.25	20	24 ± 3
O_2	$X^2\Pi_g$	8.9	−0.3	100	100
	$a^4\Pi_u + A^2\Pi_u$		0.35	113	133 ± 5
	$b^4\Sigma_g^-$	3.05	0.6	70	87 ± 5
	$B^2\Sigma_g^-$	0.92	1.0	33	45 ± 15
CO_2	$\tilde{X}^2\Pi_g$	7.4	−0.15	70	79 ± 5
	$\tilde{A}^2\Pi_u$	3.6	0.8	63	89 ± 2
	$\tilde{B}^2\Sigma_u^+$	3.2	−0.6	100	100
	$\tilde{C}^2\Sigma_g^+$	1.9	1.2	15	23 ± 7

The β parameters for this table have been collated from several sources, culminating with the work of J. Kreile and A. Schweig, *J. Electron Spectrosc. Rel. Phen.*, **20**, 191 (1980). The relative partial cross-sections also come from several sources, particularly the work of K. Kimura, Y. Achiba, M. Morishita and T. Yamazaki, *J. Electron Spectrosc. Rel. Phen.*, **15**, 269 (1979) and of J.L. Gardner and J.A.R. Samson, *J. Electron Spectrosc. Rel. Phen.*, **8**, 469 (1976), who also give relative intensities of the vibrational lines in each band.

Published 'corrected' spectra do not agree at all well on band intensities; *Table 2.4* offers collated spectra of a few compounds, thought to be fairly reliably known. Since only relative sensitivities at discrete band energies are determined by this method, it gives fragmentary coverage, and is perhaps best used to confirm or confound the applicability of a theoretical sensitivity curve to a particular analyser.

2.6 Sample preparation

Because photoionization cross-sections are relatively small (10–150 $\times$ 10^{-18} cm^2), even the high intensity of the resonance lamps is not sufficient to make photoelectron spectrometry a very sensitive technique. The pressure in the target chamber needed to measure a useful spectrum is 10^{-3}–10^{-1} torr, and the amount of sample required is correspondingly of the order of milligrams rather than micrograms. This limits the substances that can be examined without heated inlet systems to those with rather high vapour pressures at room temperature, and for compounds less volatile than, say, naphthalene, some form of heating is required. Manufacturers of commercial photoelectron spectrometers generally provide a heated inlet system in which the inlet system and the target chamber alone are heated, and vapour is allowed to escape into the body of the cold spectrometer by passing it through the exit slit of the target chamber. The pressure in the target chamber is 10–100 times higher than that in the analyser because of differential pumping, so that condensation on the spectrometer surfaces need not be a problem. When very involatile substances are examined in this way, however, condensation is bound to occur and the analyser must be cleaned periodically. Care must be taken that the multiplier does not become contaminated, because the dynodes are very sensitive and multipliers are expensive. Many involatile compounds have been examined using both commercial and home-built heated inlet systems that operate on this principle. If the vapours to be studied are brought into the spectrometer from the exterior, much can be gained by making the pipes that carry them as short, wide and direct as possible. The sample is continually being pumped away through the exit slit of the ionization chamber, and the throttling effect of a long connecting tube can reduce the pressure in the target chamber much below the vapour pressure of the sample at a given temperature.

An alternative and superior method is to supply target gas in the form of a jet or beam from an oven ('Knudsen cell'), crossed with the photon beam in a well pumped target chamber and later condensed on a designated, preferably cooled, surface. This method offers the widest range of temperature and volatility and is unquestionably the best way of examining high-temperature vapours. It has the advantage that the ordering of molecular motions in the jet or beam can reduce the Doppler broadening of photoelectron peaks, which might otherwise be severe at high temperatures. Involatile compounds examined in this way include all the alkali halides, silver, indium, thallium, tin and lead halides. Temperatures above 2000°C can be reached by both radiative[55] and inductive[56] heating, so that all but the most refractory substances are now liable to be subject to photoelectron spectroscopic scrutiny.

2.7   Vacuum requirements

Under normal working conditions, when involatile substances are not involved, the pressure in the vacuum vessel of a photoelectron spectrometer may easily reach 3×10^{-4} torr. The normal working conditions often approach closely the point at which the electron signal is no longer proportional to the pressure and where peaks are broadened because electron scattering processes become significant. This high-pressure region must, of course, be avoided in accurate work, but the range of pressure involved is sufficient to show that the most stringent conditions of high-vacuum technology need not be used in photoelectron spectroscopy. Oil diffusion pumps without cold traps are normally satisfactory, and brass, aluminium, rubber gaskets and other poor high-vacuum materials can be used without adverse effects, so long as the critical surfaces are given new coatings of graphite from time-to-time. An alternative policy is to use no graphite or gold coatings, but maintain very clean metal surfaces, often of molybdenum or stainless steel. This approach requires the use of much better vacuum conditions, cold traps and mercury diffusion pumps or, for preference, modern turbomolecular pumps, and the very careful examination of every material to be used within the vacuum system. This policy is essential if surface effects are to be examined, but is not generally necessary when only gaseous samples are studied.

References

1. AL-JOBOURY, M.I. and TURNER, D.W., *J. Chem. Soc.*, 5141 (1963)
2. SAMSON, J.A.R., *Rev. Sci. Instrum.*, **40**, 1174 (1969)
3. POTTS, A.W., WILLIAMS, T.A. and PRICE,W.C., *Discuss. Faraday Soc.*, **54**, 104 (1973)
4. KATSUMATA, K., NOMOTO, K., OHMORI, K., KIRIHATA, Y., YAMAZAKI, T., ACHIBA, Y. and KIMURA, K., *J. Electron Spectrosc. Rel. Phen.*, **16**, 485 (1979)
5. BURGER, F. and MAIER, J.P., *J. Electron Spectrosc. Rel. Phen.*, **16**, 471 (1979)
6. COATSWORTH, L.L., BANCROFT, G.M., CREBER, D.K., LAZIER, R.J.D. and JACOBS, P.W.M., *J. Electron Spectrosc. Rel. Phen.*, **13**, 395 (1978)
7. PELLACH, E. and SAR-EL, H.Z., *J. Electron Spectrosc. Rel. Phen.*, **14**, 259 (1978)
8. TSAI, B.P. and ELAND, J.H.D., *J. Mass Spectrom. Ion Phys.*, **36**, 143 (1980)
9. SHEVCHIK, N.J., *Rev. Sci. Instrum.*, **47**, 1028 (1976)
10. FLODSTROM, S.A. and BACHRACH, R.Z., *Rev. Sci. Instrum.*, **47**, 1464 (1976)
11. HUFFMAN, R.E., TANAKA, Y. and LARRABEE, J.C., *Bull. Amer. Phys. Soc. II*, **7**, 457 (1962)
12. WEISSLER, G.L., *Handbuch der Physik*, Vol. XXI, Springer Verlag, Berlin (1956)
13. LUCATORTO, T.B., McILRATH, T.J. and MEHLMAN, G., *Appl. Optics*, **18**, 2916 (1979)
14. LINDAU, I. and WINICH, H., *Comm. Mod. Phys.*, **D6**, 133 (1976)
15. BLOOM, D.M., in Jacobs, St.F., Scully, M.O. and Sargent, M. (Editors) *'Physics of Quantum Electronics'* Vol 3, Addison-Wesley, London (1976)
16. SOROKIN, P.P., ARMSTRONG, J.A., DREYFUS, R.W., HODGSON, R.T., LANKARD, J.R., MARGANARO, L.H. and WYNNE, J.J., in *Laser Spectroscopy*, Vol 43 of *Lecture Notes in Physics*, Springer, Berlin (1975)
17. HILBIG, R. and WALLENSTEIN, R., *IEEE J. Quantum Electr.*, **E17**, 1566 (1981)
18. PARKER, D.H., BERG, J.O. and EL-SAYED, M.A., in Zewail, A.H. (Editor) *Advances in Laser Chemistry*, Berlin (1978)
19. MILLER, J. and COMPTON, R., *J. Chem. Phys.*, **75**, 22 (1981)
20. PRICE, W.C., in Hepple, P. (Editor) *Molecular Spectroscopy*, Institute of Petroleum, London, 221 (1968)
21. FROST, D.C., McDOWELL, C.A. and VROOM, D.A., *Proc. R. Soc., Lond.*, **A296**, 566 (1967)
22. HUCHITAL, D.A. and RIGDEN, J.D., in Shirley, D.A. (Editor) *Electron Spectroscopy*, North Holland, Amsterdam, 79 (1972)
23. SPOHR, R. and VON PUTTKAMER, E., *Z. Naturforsch.*, **22a**, 409 (1967)
24. AKSELA, S., KARRAS, M., PESSA, M. and SUONINEN, E., *Rev. Sci. Instrum.*, **41**, 351 (1970)
25. HEDDLE, D.W.O., *J. Phys. E, Sci. Instrum.*, **4**, 589 (1971)
26. HARROWER, G.H., *Rev. Sci. Instrum.*, **26**, 850 (1955)
27. GREEN, T.S. and PROCA, G.A., *Rev. Sci. Instrum.*, **41**, 1409 (1970)
28. SCHMITZ, W. and MELHORN, W., *J. Phys. E, Sci. Instrum.*, **5**, 64 (1972)
29. HUGHES, A.L. and ROJANSKY, V., *Phys. Rev.*, **34**, 284 (1929)
30. ROY, D., DELAGE, A. and CARETTE, J.D., *J. Phys. E, Sci. Instrum.*, **8**, 109 (1975)

31. HERZOG, R., *Z. Physik*, **97**, 586 (1935)
32. JOST, K., *J. Phys., E, Sci. Instrum.*, **12**, 1001 (1979)
33. KUYATT, C.E. and SIMPSON, J.A., *Rev. Sci. Instrum.*, **38**, 103 (1967)
34. NEDDERMEYER, H., HEINMANN, P. and ROLOFF, H.F., *J. Phys., E, Sci. Instrum.*, **9**, 756 (1976)
35. ZASHKVARA, V.V., KORUNSKII, M.I. and KOSMACHEV, O., *Sov. Phys.-Tech. Phys.* [English translation], **11**, 96 (1966)
36. AKSELA, S., *Rev. Sci. Instrum.*, **42**, 810 (1971)
37. ROY, D. and CARETTE, J.D. in Ibach, H. (Editor) *Topics in Current Physics*, Vol 4, Springer, Berlin (1977)
38. ALLEN, J.D., DURHAM, J.D., SCHWEITZER, G.K. and DEEDS, W.E., *J. Electron Spectrosc. Rel. Phen.*, **8**, 395 (1976)
39. ALLEN, J.D. and GRIMM, F.A., *Chem. Phys. Lett.*, **66**, 72 (1979)
40. POWIS, I., *Chemical Physics*, **68**, 251 (1982)
41. LINDAU, I., HELMER, J.C. and UEBBING, J., *Rev. Sci. Instrum.*, **44**, 265 (1973)
42. HOTOP, H. and HÜBLER, G., *J. Electron Spectrosc.*, **11**, 101 (1977)
43. UNWIN, R., KHAN, I., RICHARDSON, N.V., BRADSHAW, A.M., CEDERBAUM, L.S. and DOMKE, W., *Chem. Phys. Lett.*, **77**, 242 (1981)
44. BEAMSON, G., PORTER, H.Q. and TURNER, D.W., *Nature*, **290**, 556 (1981)
45. KRUIT, P. and READ, F.H., *J. Phys. E, Sci. Instrum.*, **16**, 313 (1983)
46. MORIN, P., NENNER, I., GUYON, P.M., DUTUIT, O. and ITO, K., *J. chim. Phys-biol*, **77**, 605 (1980)
47. KIMMAN, J., KRUIT, P. and van der WIEL, M.J., *Chem. Phys. Lett.*, **88**, 576 (1982)
48. PARKES, W., EVANS, K.D. and MATHIESON, E., *Nucl. Instrum. Methods*, **121**, 151 (1974)
49. KARLSSON, L., MATTSSON, L., JADRNY, R., BERGMARK, T. and SIEGBAHN, K., *Physica Scripta*, **14**, 230 (1976)
50. POLLARD, J.E., TREVOR, D.J., LEE, Y.T. and SHIRLEY, D.A., *Rev. Sci. Instrum.*, **52**, 1837 (1981)
51. ÅSBRINK, L. and RABALAIS, J.W., *Chem. Phys. Lett.*, **12**, 182 (1971)
52. TURNER, D.W., *Phil. Trans. R. Soc. Lond.*, **A268**, 7 (1970)
53. ADAMS, T.E., ROCKNEY, B.H., MORRISON, R.J.S. and GRANT, E.R., *Rev. Sci. Inst.*, **52**, 1469 (1981)
54. LLOYD, D.R., *J. Phys. E, Sci. Instrum.*, **3**, 629 (1970)
55. BERKOWITZ, J., BATSON, C.H. and GOODMAN, G.L., *J. Chem. Phys.*, **71**, 2624 (1979)
56. BULGIN, D., DYKE, J., GOODFELLOW, F., JONATHAN, N., LEE, E. and MORRIS, A., *J. Electron Spectrosc.*, **12**, 67 (1977)
57. EASTMAN, D.E., DONELON, J.J., HIEN, N.C. and HIMPSEL, F.J. *Nuclear Instrum. Methods*, **172**, 327 (1980)

3
Ionization

3.1 Introduction

A more detailed examination of photoelectron spectroscopy must begin with the process of photoionization itself. Most photoelectron spectra can be interpreted in terms of the simplest process, in which one photon interacts with one electron in a single step or, in other words, following a single channel between the initial and final state. This is not the whole story, however, as becomes very apparent when spectra are measured using light of different wavelengths. Even to understand the finer details of He I spectra we must sometimes consider processes that involve more than one channel or more than one electron, and must turn to other techniques of molecular ion physics for elucidation. A photoelectron spectroscopist should therefore have some familiarity with other techniques of ion physics and chemistry, and some of them are introduced briefly in this chapter.

3.2 Photoionization

In the study of electronic absorption and emission spectra of atoms and molecules, much importance is attached to the selection rules that indicate which transitions are allowed and which are forbidden in terms of various quantum numbers. These selection rules are mnemonic devices to aid the use of conservation laws (symmetry) and the strengths of different interactions to judge the intensity of a given transition. Although photoionization is an electronic transition and is an interaction with electric dipole radiation, there is no need to remember a large number of selection rules that describe it. For all common photoionization processes, one rule suffices, namely that they are *one-electron transitions*. Normal photoionization is the removal of a single electron from the neutral species without changing the quantum number of any other electrons, and this is allowed whatever orbital the electron is in. For an atom or linear molecule, if the angular momentum of the original electron is l then, considering the change between the neutral molecule and the ion, the angular momentum change, ΔL, is given by

$$\Delta L = \pm l \tag{3.1}$$

As one electron with spin $\pm \frac{1}{2}$ is removed, the rule for the change in multiplicity is automatically

$$\Delta S = \pm 1 \tag{3.2}$$

Equations 3.1 and 3.2 are not rules that somehow restrict the possibilities of photoionization, but are simply a description of the difference between the molecule and the ion formed from it by removal of one electron without disturbing the others. This catholicity of photoionization is due to the fact that the final state of the system is the molecular ion plus a free electron. The change in the whole system between molecule plus photon and ion plus electron is restricted by the usual dipole selection rules, but the free electron can leave the ion carrying whatever angular momentum and parity is needed to satisfy the conservation laws. The motion of the free electron is described by a wave-function, and it can be an s, p, d or f wave, carrying zero, one, two or three units of angular momentum, respectively. Conservation requires that the electron must carry an angular momentum of $l \pm 1$ and when two different angular momenta of the electron are possible by this rule both may be utilized, giving an outgoing wave of mixed character. If the original electron is in a molecule with low symmetry where angular momentum is not defined, the outgoing electron wave-function is a mixture of s, p, d or f waves. The angular distribution of photoelectrons is determined by the l character of the outgoing wave, as discussed below.

The only forbidden processes of importance in photoelectron spectroscopy are two-electron processes, such as the ionization of one electron and simultaneous excitation of another, or the ejection of two electrons from a molecule by a single photon. The forbidden nature of these processes arises in a different way from the usual selection rules, which are based on symmetry; it is derived from the fact that the electronic structure of most molecules or atoms is well described by the familiar one-electron orbital model. If the motions of electrons are independent of one another, which is the fundamental assumption of the molecular orbital model, a transition induced by radiation that changes the quantum numbers of one electron must leave the quantum numbers of all other electrons unchanged[1]. Two-electron transitions occur because the motions of electrons are not completely independent but are correlated, and the intensity of two-electron transitions is a measure of this electron correlation. An example of a two-electron transition is the very weak band found in the spectrum of atomic mercury for the process[2]

$$Hg(5d^{10}\,6s^2\ldots{}^1S) + h\nu \rightarrow Hg^+\,(5d^{10}\,6p\ldots{}^2P) + e \qquad (3.3)$$

Another two-electron excitation occurs in the photoelectron spectrum of hydrogen ionized by 247 Å light[3]:

$$H_2(1s\sigma^2\ldots{}^1\Sigma_g^+) + h\nu \rightarrow H_2^+(2s\sigma_u\ldots{}^2\Sigma_u^+) + e \qquad (3.4)$$

Within the energy range of the first few ionization potentials of a molecule (the outer valence region), processes like these are rare, or weak. They are called satellite bands, because their formation can be described as the ionization of one valence electron with simultaneous excitation of another. Accordingly, they are most likely to be found in photoelectron spectra of molecules which are easy to excite—coloured compounds, or those with relatively long wavelength absorptions. Two examples are found in the spectrum of CS_2 (*Figure 3.1*), where there are six bands but only four orbitals to ionize. Satellite bands would probably be seen quite

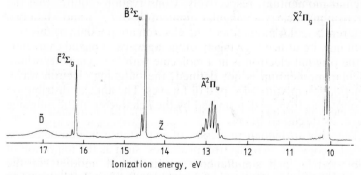

Figure 3.1   Photoelectron spectrum of CS_2, showing the two satellite bands $\tilde{Z}$ and $\tilde{D}$, which arise from simultaneous ionization from π_u and excitation of a π_g electron. The spin–orbit splitting has been resolved in $\tilde{A}$ $^2\Pi_u$ as well as in $\tilde{X}$ $^2\Pi_g$, but cannot be reproduced at this scale. (Spectrum by courtesy of M.J. Hubin-Franksin and J. Delwiche)

often in the spectra of organic compounds but for their low intensity and concealment by the overlapping of broad simple ionization bands. In the *inner valence* region, on the other hand, the energy range of about 20–40 eV, where 2s electrons of carbon or 3s electrons of second row atoms would be ionized, multiple excitations are very common—in fact they dominate the photo-electron spectra of most molecules. As a result, the one-to-one correspondence of molecular orbitals and photoelectron bands breaks down in this region, the spectra containing many more bands than there are orbitals.

The spectrum of N_2 at 50 eV photon energy[4] is an example (*Figure 3.2*); here the inner valence region contains at least five

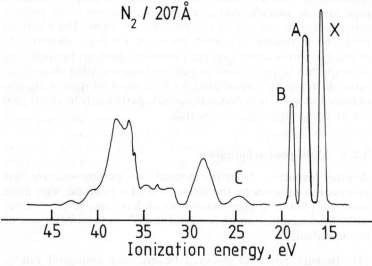

Figure 3.2   Photoelectron spectrum of N_2 at 59.9 eV photon energy, after Krummacher, Schmidt and Wuilleumier[4]. The X, A, B and C states actually have vibrational fine structure, which is seen in higher resolution photoelectron spectra (compare with *Figure 1.4*). The other bands represent states of N_2^+ with no agreed names or attributions, mostly arising from $2s\sigma_g^{-1}$ ionization

bands, where the single $2\sigma_g^{-1}$ ionization would be expected according to the orbital model. The main reason for this behaviour is strong electron correlation in the ionic state. At energies near that of the (imaginary) pure $2\sigma_g^{-1}$ ionization there are many doubly excited states of the same symmetry, which mix with the $2\sigma_g$ hole state. All the ionic states have mixed configurations containing either some $2\sigma_g^{-1}$ character or some outer valence ionization character, from which they 'borrow' intensity. We cannot point to any single band and identify it as the prototype $2\sigma_g^{-1}$ ionization—in fact the orbital model is not an appropriate description of these inner ionic states. The same situation arises in the inner valence regions of the photoelectron spectra of most molecules, as measurements[5] and calculations[6] confirm.

At photon energies of 25 eV and above the ejection of two electrons by a single photon becomes possible for most molecules. This process also depends on electron correlation for its occurrence, which is quite general. Measurements of photoionization mass spectra, showing both singly and doubly charged ions, demonstrate that as much as 30% of total ionization by He IIα light may be two-electron ejection[7], the fraction being roughly proportional to the size of the molecule or atom. The electrons produced in double ionization have not yet been identified in molecular photoelectron spectra, however, perhaps because they are expected to have more or less continuous rather than structured distributions[8]. Structured double ionization spectra are also expected to arise from Auger processes, particularly in atoms, and are an interesting topic of research.

3.2.1 Multi-photon ionization

Another departure from the normal one photon–one electron process is ionization by the interaction of a molecule with more than one photon, a phenomenon which has come to prominence with the dissemination of powerful lasers[9]. Several cases can be distinguished.

(1) In very powerful, focused beams field ionization can be brought about by the intense electric field arising from the coherent superposition of many photons. The primary electrons are accelerated and may cause further ionization by collision, leading to plasma breakdown. Electrons produced by this process have a wide range of energies.

(2) One or more photons may be absorbed and populate a real excited state of the neutral molecule, from which photo-ionization follows by subsequent absorption of another photon. This very interesting technique, resonance enhanced multi-photon ionization (REMPI), yields a structured photo-electron spectrum[10], which may contain bands for ionic states in which one electron is in a normally unoccupied orbital. If

the ionizing photon is of low energy the previously excited electron will normally be the one to be ionized, however, leaving the molecular ion in its ground electronic state. Its vibrational energy distribution, the band structure, will be different from that seen in the one-photon photoelectron spectrum, since the Franck–Condon factors from the excited state to the ion will not be the same as those from molecular ground state to ion. Furthermore, excellent energy resolution may be possible because the intermediate resonant absorption can select single rotational levels, eliminating rotational line widths. This technique therefore offers the opportunity to glean new information on both electronic states of the ion and on their vibrational structure. The intensity of multiple photon ionization can be greatly enhanced if the ionizing photon energy is chosen to match an autoionizing resonance (*see below*) and this fact has been utilized in some schemes for laser isotope separation.

(3)   Two or more photons may be absorbed simultaneously in a single ionization step, which can be modelled as climbing a ladder of virtual states. The probability of multi-photon ionization should depend on the light intensity raised to the nth power, where n photons are involved. The photoelectron spectrum is likely to show the ground ionic state band, with overtone bands at electron energies $h\nu$, $2h\nu$, $3h\nu$ ... or higher, as has been observed in multi-photon ionization of atoms[11] by high-power lasers.

3.3   Ionization at different wavelengths

Because all one-electron photoionizations are allowed, the partial photoionization cross-sections, or the probabilities of ionization to particular states of ions, are all of the same order of magnitude. There are variations within a factor of two or three between one doubly occupied orbital and another, as already mentioned in Chapter 1, and there are also variations with the wavelength of the ionizing radiation. Photoionization is not a resonance process, and once the threshold for a given ionization has been passed, light of all shorter wavelengths can cause the same process, the excess energy appearing as kinetic energy of the electrons. The cross-section is usually highest near the threshold, after which it decreases with increasing photon energy. When the photon energy is very high compared with the threshold energy, the cross-section should be proportional to v^{-3}, but this does not apply in the energy region used in ultraviolet photoelectron spectroscopy.

3.3.1 Direct photoionization

In the photon energy region 10–50 eV the partial photoionization cross-sections may rise, fall or remain almost constant, depending on the nature of the orbitals involved. As mentioned in Chapter 1 (Section 1.3.2) gross differences in the molecular partial cross-section variations can be traced back to atomic orbital ionization cross-sections, and different molecular orbitals made by combining the same atomic orbitals will have the same large-scale photon energy variation. The cross-section variations of individual atomic orbitals have to be mapped out by experiment[12], but there are some useful general rules relevant to photoelectron spectra.

(1) Orbitals with at least one *radial node* (2s, 3p, 4d ...) have deep minima in the cross-section (Cooper minima) at energies between 2 and 5 times the threshold energy. The minima may be pictured as due to interference between partial waves arising from the inner and outer parts of the orbital. They can be very useful in suppressing unwanted spectral features—photoelectrons from surface metal atoms, for instance, where adsorbate levels are to be studied. Note that orbitals without radial nodes (1s, 2p, 3d ...) have no such minima in the cross-sections.

(2) In the region where cross-sections fall off with increasing energy the fall is most rapid for extended orbitals (the outermost ones) and for higher *l* values. For instance, s-orbitals have better staying power than p- or d-orbitals, and become more prominent in spectra taken with high energy photons.

(3) Orbitals of high *l*, that is d or f orbitals, often have maxima in their cross-sections at energies of the order of tens of eV above threshold: these are related to the centrifugal barrier that high *l* electrons must surmount in order to escape. The maxima produce an initial rise in cross-section from threshold, making d-electron ionizations in group IIB metal compounds, for instance, much more prominent with He II ionization than with He I.

Many atomic cross-sections have been studied as functions of wavelength, and a useful compilation is available[12]. In laboratory ultraviolet photoelectron spectroscopy utilizing He I and He II light only, effects of the cross-section variations are undramatic for C, H, O and N compounds, but become noticeable when heavier atoms are involved.

3.3.2   Fine structure in photoionization cross-sections

When molecular or atomic partial photoionization cross-sections are examined in detail as functions of wavelength they are found to contain a wealth of structure, particularly in the photon energy range below 20 eV. This structure immensely complicates the interpretation of photoionization yield curves, and is the main reason why molecular inner ionization potentials were not well known before the advent of photoelectron spectroscopy. Two types of features in cross-sections are distinguished, *shape resonances* which are generally broad, and *autoionization* which may produce broad or sharp features. It is a great advantage of photoelectron spectroscopy that unless the wavelength used, He I say, happens to coincide with a shape resonance or autoionizing resonance, all such complications are avoided. If there is a coincidence, even a partial overlap, on the other hand, the photoelectron spectrum may be distorted from its normal form.

Shape resonances are best envisaged in terms of the encounter between an electron and a molecular ion in a particular electronic state. The potential energy curve for ion–electron interaction will be attractive at large distances, but for d,f ... electrons of large l it will contain a centrifugal barrier at intermediate distance, just outside the valence orbital radii. The exact shape of the potential well engendered by the combination of long-range attraction and shorter range repulsion depends critically on the electronic configuration and internuclear distance(s) in the molecular ion. If the well is deep enough to support a (quasi-) bound energy level of the electron, there will be a strong enhancement of the scattering cross-section at the corresponding energy. Because the initial state of the scattering process and the final state of photoionization are identical, the enhancement also appears in the photoionization cross-section, but *only* for processes that yield an electron of the correct symmetry (l in atoms) and of the correct kinetic energy. Shape resonances are thus highly specific, appearing only in the partial ionization cross-sections that provide electrons of the correct symmetry. Evidently a photoelectron spectrum taken at the wavelength matching such a resonance will emphasize particular ionic states; furthermore, because the potential well's shape depends on the ion geometry, the vibrational intensities will be very different from those seen in direct photoionization. It may be that the coupling of nuclear positions and electronic energy in the shape resonance is so strong that a breakdown of the Born–Oppenheimer approximation results, and description in terms of a potential energy curve is no longer appropriate[13]. *Figure 3.3* illustrates the effects of a shape resonance upon the cross-sections and photoelectron spectrum of N_2.

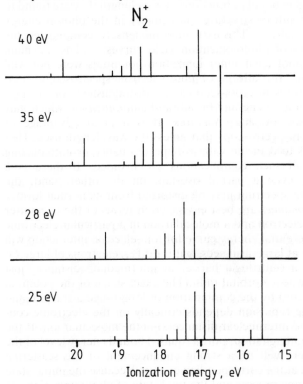

Figure 3.3 Simulated photoelectron spectra of N_2 at the photon energies shown on the left, covering the position of a shape resonance of σ_u symmetry in the $^2\Sigma_g$ ionization channel. The peak intensity of resonance is at about 28 eV, and its vibrational effects give a minimum $v = 1$ intensity at 25 eV, followed by a maximum at 35 eV. The spectra show true relative intensities for equal light flux at the four photon energies, and are drawn on displaced energy scales for clarity

The specificity of shape resonances can be utilized in photoelectron spectroscopy with tunable light sources in order to intensify particular features of a spectrum (e.g. an adsorbed molecule band) and also to aid in the assignment of complex spectra[14].

Autoionization is a more widespread phenomenon than shape resonance ionization, occurring prominently in all photoionization spectra. In addition to the direct ionization process we have been considering so far, there is the possibility of an indirect process:

$$M + h\nu \rightarrow M^* \rightarrow M^+ + e \qquad (3.5)$$

Here M^*, the autoionizing state, is formed as an intermediate, and since its formation is a normal absorption, it is subject to the condition $h\nu = E^* - E$. Each quantum state of the intermediate M^* can be populated by light of the correct resonant wavelength only, and the transition is subject to normal electric dipole selection rules. The vast majority of super excited states of M^* seen in the photoionization are Rydberg states of series converging on inner ionization potentials–such states are available below every ionization threshold, and production of at least some of them is as allowed as the ionization itself. Autoionizing Rydberg states are very clearly seen in the photoionization spectrum of CS_2 (*Figure 3.4*); compare the complexity of this spectrum with the simplicity of its photoelectron spectrum (*Figure 3.1*). Because the Rydberg series converge on inner ionization potentials, and cover ranges of about 3 eV below the limits on which they converge, the sharp autoionizing resonances are most numerous in the region of the allowed one-electron outer valence ionizations below 20 eV. At higher energies one-electron allowed bands (carrying the intensity) are sparse, and the bands which do appear (often two-electron bands) tend to be broad. The nature of Rydberg states is to have a molecular ion core in the ionic state to be reached at convergence, with an electron orbiting at a distance. The ionic core is so similar to the molecular ion that the Franck–Condon factors for formation of Rydberg states are essentially the same as those for producing the ions; hence, series converging on states giving sharp resolved photoelectron bands, are sharp, while broad Rydberg bands converge on broad photoelectron bands. In the high energy region, particularly the inner valence region, the overlapping of broad Rydberg bands may look very much like a continuum, and the contribution of autoionization cannot be judged reliably. At the lower energies, however, autoionization will affect photoelectron spectra directly only if the

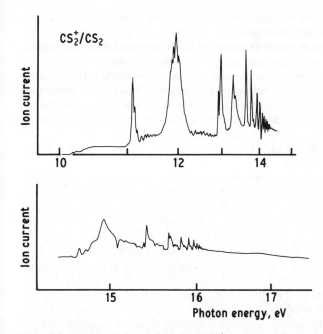

Figure 3.4 Photoionization yield of CS_2^+ ions from CS_2 in the wavelength range from the first ionization potential to beyond the highest state seen in the He I photoelectron spectrum (*Figure 3.1*). The prominent structures are Rydberg series converging on the $\bar{B}$ and $\bar{C}$ states of CS_2^+

wavelength used happens to hit a resonance feature. If this does happen profound changes of the photoelectron spectrum are seen.

The superexcited Rydberg state M* involved in autoionization is excited to a level above one or more ionization limits. It may decay in several ways:

(1) By dissociating into neutral fragments. In this case no electrons are produced. Fluorescence of superexcited states is similarly unproductive, but has been detected only in H_2.

(2) By converting excess *vibrational* energy of its ionized core into electronic energy, ejecting the Rydberg electron. This is *vibrational autoionization*; it produces electrons of very low energy, and has little effect on normal photoelectron spectra. Theory[15] and experiment[15,16] show that in general the vibrational quantum number may change by any integer. The smallest change, $\Delta v = -1$, is favoured in special cases where

the resonance interacts equally with the ionization and dissociation continua.

(3)   By converting excess electronic excitation energy into kinetic energy of one electron, which is ejected. This is a concerted two-electron process; one electron falls back into an inner orbital hole, while another electron leaves the molecule. Electronic autoionization, as this is called, can have substantial effects on photoelectron spectra, because the autoionization step may populate the accessible ionic states in quite different proportions from those observed in direct photoionization[16].

For a given super-excited Rydberg state these three decay channels may all be possible and all may compete. The extent of dissociation into neutrals is determined by comparing the ionization cross-section with the total absorption cross-section; the ratio of these quantities is called the ionization efficiency, or quantum yield of ionization. At 58.4 nm and shorter wavelengths in the vuv region ionization efficiencies are almost always unity, but they may be less at longer wavelengths. For large organic molecules the quantum yields of ionization are often quite small at the first ionization threshold (⅓ or less) and rise steadily as the valence ionization region is transversed to shorter wavelengths. In small molecules, on the other hand, the quantum yield of ionization is liable to vary widely from one wavelength to another as sharp resonances are encountered, but values lower than one half are uncommon.

When a superexcited state does decay by autoionization, it may distort the photoelectron spectrum in two ways:

(1)   Changes in the vibrational structure of electronic bands. Both the formation of the autoionizing state and its ionization are separately governed by the Franck–Condon principle, so the shape of the vibrational structure in the photoelectron spectrum depends on the equilibrium internuclear distances in the autoionizing state, as well as in the ground-state molecule and the final ionic state. A possible situation is illustrated in *Figure 3.5*, which shows how vibrationally excited states of a molecular ion that cannot be reached in direct ionization can be populated by the indirect process. The best example of this is the dramatic change in the photoelectron spectrum of oxygen between He I and Ne I

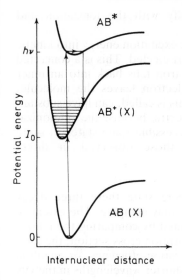

Figure 3.5 Potential energy diagram to illustrate how electronic autoionization can populate highly excited vibrational levels of an ionic state

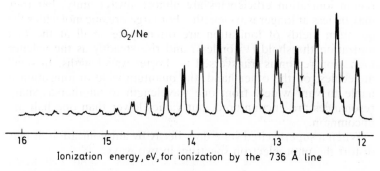

Ionization energy, eV, for ionization by the 736 Å line

Figure 3.6 $^2\Pi_g$ band in the photoelectron spectrum of oxygen excited by neon resonance radiation, to be compared with *Figure 1.6*. The extensive vibrational structure is due to autoionization caused by the strong neon line at 736 Å. The weaker line at 744 Å gives only normal direct ionization, producing the peaks marked with arrows. The doublet structure of the peaks is due to spin–orbit coupling. (By courtesy of Professor W.C. Price)

radiation, shown by *Figure 3.6*. The photoelectron spectra of many molecules excited by Ne I or Ar I radiation show similar, though less marked, distortions[17]. A systematic examination of these vibrational effects of autoionization has been made in a few small molecules by scanning over resonances using tunable light sources, and measuring photoelectron spectra at each point[18,19]. The results are explained in terms of a well-developed but rather poorly tested[18] theory[20], according to which the probability of exciting a given vibrational level (α) in the photoelectron spectrum at a particular wavelength near resonance (ν), is a sum of three terms[20]. First there is the normal Franck–Condon factor (F^2) for direct ionization to the level concerned; second, there is the product of Franck–Condon factors for production of the resonance state and for its 'subsequent' autoionization, and third, there is a term representing quantum-mechanical interference between these two distinct pathways. The theoretical expression is

$$\sigma_{\alpha/\sigma_a} = F_{i\alpha}^2 + F_{i\nu}^2 F_{\nu\alpha}^2 C - 2F_{i\alpha} F_{i\nu} F_{\nu\alpha} C' \tag{3.6}$$

where i denotes the initial state of the molecule, and C and C' are wavelength dependent factors, representing how far off resonance the measurement is made. The interference term produces asymmetrical line shapes (Fano profiles), but these are only seen in the cross-sections as functions of wavelength, and not in the photoelectron spectra themselves. It is possible that spectra taken at 584 Å contain more examples of this type of distortion than is usually assumed, because it is impossible to detect unless a spectrum taken at a different wavelength is available for comparison.

(2)   Changes in relative band intensities. If the autoionizing state has a higher energy than those of several ionic states, the branching ratios to the different states may not be the same as in direct ionization. The selection rules do not help in the estimation of the branching ratios, because any state reached in direct ionization by an allowed one-electron transition can also be reached by autoionization from neutral states populated by an allowed absorption. Some ionic states could be produced in autoionization even though their formation is not allowed (one-electron rule) in direct ionization. This is most likely to happen with photons of high energy, in the inner valence region, where Rydberg states of 'mixed configuration' converge on the configurationally mixed excited states. Because of intensity problems it is very difficult in experimental studies of electronic autoionization to preserve at the same time a sufficient photon energy resolution to cleanly separate individual resonances, and sufficient

electron energy resolution to characterize the ionic states being populated. Nevertheless, a number of experiments on these lines[21,22] have clearly demonstrated that electronic autoionization can be highly specific in populating certain ionic states exclusively, or in excluding the population of certain states. Some resonances, on the other hand, exhibit the same branching to final ionic states as the nearby continuum does. Experimentally, the best photon energy resolution has not been achieved in photoelectron spectroscopy experiments, but in techniques which recognize the final ionic state populations by their decay characteristics, through fluorescence[23] or ionic dissociation[24]. The underlying reasons for these differences in behaviour are not at all clear, but a few tentative generalizations can be made from experimental results[16]. First, specific branching in autoionization is most likely to occur from Rydberg states converging on inner valence shell or high-energy outer valence shell ionization limits. Second, a degree of forbidden character in the absorption, evidenced by low intensity or asymmetric line shape, is often associated with the greatest specificity.

When differences in relative band intensities are found between photoelectron spectra taken at two photon energies, it is sometimes possible to conclude that different branching ratios in electronic autoionization are their cause. A striking change occurs in the photoelectron spectrum of sulphur hexafluoride between excitation by He I and He II light, and is illustrated in *Figure 3.7*. The changes in relative intensity are so strong, and the intensities at 584 Å deviate so much from the predictions of the limiting rules

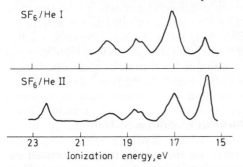

Figure 3.7   Photoelectron spectra of sulphur hexafluoride excited by He I and He II light. (From Price, W.C., Potts, A.W. and Streets, D.G., in Shirley, D.A. (Editor) *Electron Spectroscopy*, North Holland, Amsterdam (1972))

for intensities (Chapter 1, Section 1.3), that in this instance electronic autoionization at 584 Å seems a likely cause. There is another ionization limit at 22.5 eV, and Rydberg series that converge on this limit might well include a line at 584 Å. It is an open question how many other photoelectron spectra taken at 584 Å are similarly distorted, but probably the answer will be that very few are. Changes in experimental relative band intensities with wavelength are also caused by variations in the direct photoionization cross-sections and in the angular distributions of the photoelectrons, and such changes are more common than those caused by electronic autoionization.

In addition to normal autoionization, a more complex auto-ionization process that involves fluorescence emission was at one time proposed[25] to explain the appearance of certain photoelectron bands which did not correlate with known ionic states. It was suggested that superexcited states might emit fluorescence radiation, but still retain enough energy to autoionize:

$$M + h\nu \rightarrow M^{**} \rightarrow M^* + h\nu_{fluor} \tag{3.7}$$

$$M^* \rightarrow M^+ + e \tag{3.8}$$

This suggestion was quite reasonable, especially as the existence of this process has since been demonstrated[26] in atomic Cs. More recent work has proved, however, that this 'fluorescent autoionization' does not occur in one of the molecular cases where it had been proposed[21]. The most probable explanation of the original observations seems to be that scattered light, which is frequently present in vuv instruments, allowed the strongest autoionizing resonances with their huge absorption cross-sections to continue to be populated even when the monochromators used were set to other wavelengths. This produced photoelectron bands of fixed energy, independent of the light's apparent wavelength, the energies being exactly equal to the difference between those of the strongest resonances and the nearby accessible ionic states.

3.4 Angular distributions of photoelectrons

In photoionization, the photoelectrons are not emitted equally in all directions, nor are their angular distributions the same when different ionic states are produced. Band areas in experimental photoelectron spectra therefore depend on the angle with respect to the light beam at which electrons are accepted by the energy analyser. A deflection analyser that accepts electrons only at right angles to the photon beam gives a spectrum with different relative band areas from that given by a spherical retarding-field analyser, which accepts almost all the electrons. For the interpretation of spectra by using relative band intensities, the intensity must be integrated over all angles, so while results from spherical retarding-field analysers can be used directly, those from most differential analysers must first be corrected. It will be seen that the corrections are fortunately small in most instances, but on the other hand the measured angular distributions contain important information about the photoionization processes that can also be of help in the analysis of photoelectron spectra.

3.4.1 Form of the angular distribution

The motion of the electrons ejected in photoionization can be described by wave-functions according to the angular momentum that the electrons must carry in order to satisfy the dipole selection rules. The angular distribution of the photoelectrons is determined by the s, p, d or f character of those outgoing spherical waves. The full form of the distributions will not be derived here, but can perhaps be made plausible by comparison with hydrogenic wave-functions. In ionization of an s electron from an atom, the electron wave must be a p wave, just as electric dipole-allowed transitions from S states lead only to P states in atomic spectroscopy. As the s electron wave-function has no defined orientation, the axis of the p wave-function is the direction defined by the dipole interaction, which is the direction of the electric vector of the electromagnetic wave. For plane-polarized light, the electric vector lies in the plane of polarization at right angles to the direction of propagation, so the electron signal can be measured as a function of the angle from the electric vector. The angular part of the electron wave-function is the same as that of an atomic p_z electron, where the electric vector of the light defines the z axis. The angular part of the p_z wave-function is the spherical harmonic Y_{10}, and the probability of observing an electron is proportional to its square. Hence, for the angular distribution $I(\theta)$:

$$I(\theta) \propto Y_{10}^2 = \left(\frac{3}{2\sqrt{\pi}} \cos \theta \right)^2 = \frac{3}{4\pi} \cos^2 \theta \qquad (3.9)$$

In ionization of an atomic s orbital, the electrons therefore have a $\cos^2 \theta$ distribution about the direction of the electric vector. When ionization is from a p orbital, on the other hand, s and d outgoing waves are allowed and usually both types of wave are involved. The s waves, like s atomic orbitals, are spherically symmetrical and correspond to isotropic angular distributions, while d wave distributions are peaked along the electric vector, but not so sharply as the p wave distributions.

Whatever the mixture of s, p, d or higher partial waves involved, the photoelectron angular distributions can be expressed by a single equation. If the angle of observation is measured from the direction of the electric vector of a plane-polarized light beam, the equation is

$$I(\theta) = \frac{\sigma}{4\pi} \left[1 + \frac{\beta}{2} \left(3 \cos^2 \theta - 1 \right) \right] \tag{3.10}$$

where σ is the total cross-section integrated over all angles and β, called the anisotropy parameter, is the single parameter needed to characterize the photoelectron angular distribution. For a pure p wave, β has the value $+ 2$, and equation 3.10 reduces to equation 3.9 apart from the inclusion of σ. In most photoelectron spectrometers the light is unpolarized, and the intensity must be measured as a function of the angle θ' away from the direction of the light beam. The distribution of intensity is then

$$I(\theta') = \frac{\sigma}{4\pi} \left[1 + \frac{\beta}{2} \left(\frac{3}{2} \sin^2 \theta' - 1 \right) \right] = \frac{\sigma}{4\pi} \left\{ 1 - \frac{\beta}{4} \left(3\cos^2 - 1 \right) \right\} \tag{3.11}$$

where β is the same parameter as in equation 3.10. The possible range of β values is from $- 1$ to $+ 2$, and the value of β completely determines the angular distributions in the ionization of both atoms and molecules.

Equation 3.10 can actually be derived in a very general way from the nature of dipole radiation and the symmetry constraints of the experiment[26], and is valid for photodissociation, for instance, as well as photoionization. Relationships between β and theoretical quantities that describe the ionization process have been derived for atoms[27] and diatomic molecules[28]; they are complicated and involve several unknowns. The formula for β in atomic ionization illustrates the factors involved:

$$\beta = \frac{l(l-1)\sigma_{l-1}^2 + (l+1)(l+2)\sigma_{l+1}^2 - 6l(l+1)\sigma_{l+1}\sigma_{l-1} \cos(\delta_{l+1} - \delta_{l-1})}{(2l+1)(l\sigma_{l-1}^2 + (l+1)\sigma_{l+1}^2)} \tag{3.12}$$

Here l is the angular momentum of the electron in the atom before ionization, where Russell–Saunders coupling is assumed, σ_{l-1} and σ_{l+1} are the partial cross-sections for production of the $l - 1$ and $l + 1$ waves, and $(\delta_{l+1} - \delta_{l-1})$ is the phase difference between the two waves. The value of β depends not only on the strengths of the two partial waves but also on their phases, which control the interference between them. Negative β values can arise only when the interference term in equation 3.12 is large. Both the partial cross-sections and the phases depend on the electron energy, so β values are energy dependent. The theory of photoelectron angular distribution has recently been reviewed in detail by Berkowitz[12].

Because of the mathematical difficulties, calculations of β directly from molecular wave-functions have been made only for a few atoms and very simple molecules[29,30]. Some general characteristics of β values have, however, emerged from the theory, and also from experimental results[31–33].

(1)   The β values vary quite rapidly with the energy of the ejected electrons in the range covered by ultraviolet photoelectron spectroscopy, but approach constancy when the electrons have energies of fifty to several hundred eV. The variations are especially rapid for electron energies of less than $5\,\mathrm{eV}$, and also in regions where the photon energy matches shape resonances, autoionizing resonances or Cooper minima. The reason is that in equations such as (3.12) both the partial cross-sections and phase shifts are energy- and path-dependent[34].

(2)   Within the vibrational structure of a single band β is constant, apart from the effects of electron energy variation. When two or more photoelectron bands arise from ionization out of a single orbital, their β values are also likely to be similar because β depends mainly on the electronic character of the orbital, rather than on the nature of the ionic state.

(3)   Just as ionization out of a pure s orbital of an atom gives $\beta = 2$, so ionization from molecular orbitals built up mainly from atomic s orbitals is likely to give relatively high β values. In $1s\sigma_g^{-1}$ ionization of hydrogen, for instance, $\beta = 1.8$ and in $2s\sigma_u^{-1}$ ionization of nitrogen, $\beta = 1.2$. It is found that in the ionization of atoms out of orbitals with l greater than one, high l values are associated with low β values, and the higher is l the lower is β. This relationship can be generalized to molecular ionizations if a theoretical means is found of estimating l in molecular orbitals, where it is not a good quantum number.

(4) If the photon energy happens to match that of a sharp (long lifetime) autoionizing resonance, the resulting β values are likely to be low. Rotation of a superexcited molecule after absorption but before autoionization will partially destroy the orientations induced by the photon absorption; if a value β characterizes an original orientation, it will be only $\beta/4$ after a few rotation periods. Even if the intermediate state is not long·lived, angular distributions of electrons from auto-ionization or shape resonances will not generally be the same as those characteristic of direct ionization. Bands in photo-electron spectra to which these processes contribute may have anomalous β values, and as the vibrational structure is also different in autoionization, β may vary within a band. The clearest example of this effect is the autoionization of oxygen at 736 Å (*Figure 3.6*); the first few peaks in the $^2\Pi_g$ band, to which the contribution from direct ionization is large, have $\beta \approx -0.5$, whereas the later peaks up to $v' = 12$ caused by autoionization alone have $\beta \approx 0.0$.

3.4.2 Experimental methods and examples

The original experimental method of investigating angular dis-tributions of photoelectrons was to bring about photoionization in

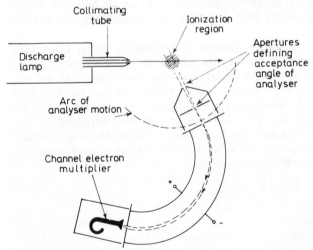

Figure 3.8 Schematic diagram of an apparatus for measuring the angular distribution of photoelectrons

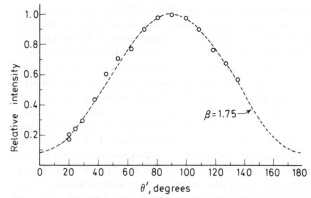

Figure 3.9   Experimental angular distribution of photoelectrons (corrected by multiplication by sin θ') from ionization of hydrogen by He I light to the state $X\,^2\Sigma_g^+$, $v' = 2$ of H_2^+. (From Carlson, T.A. and Jonas, A.E., *J. Chem. Phys.*, **55**, 4913 (1971), by courtesy of the American Institute of Physics)

a small defined volume and to measure the electron signals at different angles by moving either the analyser or the light beam. There are many variants of this method, which has been used to establish the validity of equations 3.10 and 3.11 experimentally, and to measure the most accurate β values. A schematic diagram of one form of suitable apparatus is shown in *Figure 3.8*, and *Figure 3.9* illustrates the form of the experimental angular distributions.

When the ionization volume is defined by the position of a narrow light beam passing through a diffuse gas, the effective volume from which photoelectrons can enter the analyser is a function of the angle of measurement. The raw experimental data must usually be multiplied by sin θ' in order to correct for this volume effect and obtain the true angular distribution. The anisotropy parameter can be evaluated from the experimental angular distribution, $I(θ')$, by making a least-squares fit to the theoretical distribution in the form

$$I(θ') = 1 + B \sin^2 θ' \tag{3.13}$$

where

$$B = \frac{3β}{4 - 2β} \tag{3.14}$$

Because of the simple form of the angular distributions, the value of β can be found by measuring the intensity at just two angles. The angle 54 degrees 44 minutes [54.736 degrees or $\cos^{-1}$ $(1/\sqrt{3})$], the so-called 'magic' angle, is particularly useful, because at this angle the intensity is completely independent of β whether the light is polarized or not. It is very convenient to choose this angle as one of those at which photoelectron spectra are determined, as relative intensities in the spectrum are here undistorted by variations in angular distributions. Measurements at just two angles suffice in any event to determine β, and ingenious devices have been proposed in order to accomplish this determination without physical motions in simple photoelectron spectrometers. These devices, however, have not generally proved to give accurate values, perhaps because the actual distributions were distorted by uncompensated magnetic fields in the apparatus. This difficulty is completely overcome by the newest and most promising technique, which is to leave the electron analyser fixed and vary the polarization direction of the ionizing radiation[35]. Several rotatable polarizers of the reflection type have been designed for use in photoelectron spectroscopy[36]; they generally give more than 80% polarization, with about 10% transmission at 584 Å.

The anisotropy parameters for some important photoelectron bands are given in *Table 3.1* in order to illustrate the range of values encountered. One example of the variation of β within a single band is included, namely the $2p\sigma_g^{-1}$ ionization of nitrogen by He I light to give N_2^+ ($X\,^2\Sigma_g^+$) ions. The marked deviation of the β value for $\upsilon' = 1$ from the values for $\upsilon' = 0$ and $\upsilon' = 2$ has not been satisfactorily explained, despite having been known for more than a decade. One possibility is that the shape resonance in N_2 at 28 eV, which is so broad that some intensity in its wings may remain at 584 Å, is implicated. Theory shows, in fact, that the disturbing effects of such resonances on vibrational intensities and angular distributions can extend beyond the range of the peak in ionization cross-section. Measurements of vibrational intensities and angular distributions at wavelengths within the resonance show marked deviations from the normal direct ionization behaviour, and it has been suggested that vibrational–electronic interaction is so strong in the resonance that the Born–Oppenheimer approximation breaks down. It is important to notice that this proposed breakdown is in a (resonant) state *from which ionization occurs*, not in the ionic state. If vibronic interactions in ionic states affected ionization one would expect variations in β values in ionization processes where there is definitely an interaction of nuclear and electronic motion, as for instance in

Table 3.1   Anisotropy parameters

Substance	Ionic state	Photon energy, eV	β
Ar	$^2P_{3/2}$, $^2P_{1/2}$	21.22	0.9
Kr	$^2P_{3/2}$, $^2P_{1/2}$	21.22	1.3
Xe	$^2P_{3/2}$	21.22	1.7
	$^2P_{1/2}$	21.22	1.6
	$^2P_{3/2}$	16.85	1.3
	$^2P_{1/2}$	16.85	1.1
H_2	$X\ ^2\Sigma_g^+$	21.22	1.8
N_2	$X\ ^2\Sigma_g^+$ $(v' = 0)$	21.22	0.65
	$X\ ^2\Sigma_g^+$ $(v' = 1)$	21.22	1.5
	$X\ ^2\Sigma_g^+$ $(v' = 2)$	21.22	0.6
	$A\ ^2\Pi_u$	21.22	0.4
O_2	$X\ ^2\Pi_g$	21.22	−0.3
	$X\ ^2\Pi_g$ $(v' = 1)$	16.85	−0.5
CO_2	$X\ ^2\Pi_g$	21.22	−0.2
	$A\ ^2\Sigma_u$	21.22	0.7
	$B\ ^2\Sigma_u^+$	21.22	0.6
	$C\ ^2\Sigma_g^+$ $(v' = 0)$	21.22	1.1
H_2O	$^2B_1$	21.22	1.0
	$^2A_1$	21.22	0.3
	$^2B_2$	21.22	−0.1
CH_3I	$^2E_{3/2}$, $^2E_{1/2}$	21.22	1.5
	$^2A_1$	21.22	0.6
	^2E	21.22	0.9

Data in this table are taken from the work of several groups. No error limits are given, but the results of different workers agree to within about ±0.1 in β.

ionization to states that undergo a Jahn–Teller effect. Although bands that correspond to such states have been examined (e.g., the first band in the spectrum of methane), no variation of β within them has been found. Other cases of anomalous β variations within resolved vibrational structure have been found[31] in the $X\ ^2\Sigma^+$ band of CO^+ and in the fourth bands in the spectra of the triatomic molecules CO_2 and COS; an explanation in terms of vibronic interaction between ionic states has been proposed[37] in the case of the $\tilde{C}$ state of CO_2^+.

The β values given in *Table 3.1* for ionizations by He I light are all (except the $1s\sigma^{-1}$ ionization of H_2) within the range from −0.5 to +1.5, and this range is typical of the anisotropies that have been measured. In a photoelectron spectrometer that accepts photoelectrons in a narrow angle around 90 degrees to the photon beam, this range corresponds to a maximum variation in relative band intensities by a factor of 1.6 due to variations in angular distribution alone. This factor is small enough not to affect seriously the application of the limiting rules for band intensities given in Chapter 1, Section 1.3. Within the photoelectron spectrum of a single compound, the range of variation of β values is usually even smaller than this, especially if bands at very low electron energy are excluded from consideration.

3.4.3 Molecular rotation

Since molecular rotation is a form of quantized angular momentum whose change on ionization must be coupled with annihilation of the photon angular momentum and production of angular momentum of the photoelectron, we ought to expect different angular distributions for different rotational transitions. Photoelectron peaks are usually unresolved blends of transitions from many rotational levels of the neutral molecule (rotational quantum numbers N'') to many levels of the ion (quantum numbers N') involving several *branches* characterized by

$$\Delta N = N' - N'' = 0, \pm 1, \pm 2 \ldots$$

In order to model molecular angular distributions we need to know the intensities of the different branches, the initial population of different N'' levels, and how β varies with ΔN and with N''. The populations of initial N'' levels can be calculated from the Boltzmann distribution and present no difficulty, but both of the other questions are very hard to answer. A qualitative idea of the relative intensities of different branches can be gained from the 'rotational Franck–Condon principle' of Jungen* which is in effect the rotational selection rule in photoionization. The principle states:

$$\Delta N = 0, \pm 1, \ldots \pm l$$

where l is the effective orbital angular momentum of the electron in the neutral united atom. In other words, considering the molecule condensed into a single atom, one must deduce from the orbital symmetry (particularly the number and location of nodes) the type of central atomic orbital to which the molecular orbital corresponds. The *maximum* $|\Delta N|$, which is just equal to the deduced atomic orbital l value will normally give rise to the most intense transitions; a different lower $|\Delta N|$ cannot be assumed to be

---

*Jungen demurs that the rotational Franck–Condon principle is implicit in work such as ref. 28. The clarity of expression and apt name are, however, his (ref. 38).

equally probable—more complex calculations are needed to determine quantitative relative intensities. Consider, for example, the photoelectron spectrum of N_2. The first ionization band is $2p\sigma_g^{-1}$ ionization; this orbital is an s-orbital in the united atom, so we expect $\Delta N = 0$ (Q branch) only. In agreement with this, the photoelectron peak at very high resolution[39] is a narrow, single spike. The third ionization band is σ_u^{-1} ionization, the orbital being p in the united atom, so that $N = 0, \pm1$ is predicted. Because $^{14}N_2$ is homonuclear, it has *ortho* and *para* states, in which the nuclear spins are parallel and antiparallel, respectively. *Ortho* states exist only on *even* rotational levels in the $X^1\Sigma_g^+$ ground state of N_2, but only on *odd* rotational levels in the $B^2\Sigma_u^+$ state of N_2^+ (the converse holds for *para* levels). Therefore, the nuclear spin statistics, and the fact that nuclear spins are not affected by ionization, enforce a *strict* selection rule, $\Delta N = $ odd. Thus, $\Delta N = \pm1$ is the only possibility, and the third photoelectron band of N_2 has, indeed, a double-peaked profile, showing P and R branches, like a classic parallel band[39].

The same line of argument can be applied to H_2 ionization, the only case in which rotational branches have been properly resolved[40]. Here the nuclear spin statistics enforce the strict rule $\Delta N = $ even, while the s atomic orbital character of the $1s\sigma_g$ molecular orbital predicts $\Delta N = 0$. Examination of the photoelectron spectrum of H_2 at very high resolution shows that $\Delta N = 0$ does predominate, but some $\Delta N = \pm2$ transitions can also be detected. Their intensity is a measure of how far the $1s\sigma_g$ orbital deviates from spherical symmetry.

To understand the angular distributions in these different cases we must turn now to the most difficult question; how does β depend upon ΔN and upon N? A formal theory encompassing the answer was developed by Buckingham, Orr and Sichel[28] in 1970, but unfortunately it can be applied only by actual numerical calculation involving the wave-functions. The case of H_2 is especially simple, since for $\Delta N = 0$ (the Q band), which predominates, the angular distribution has $\beta_Q \simeq 2$, corresponding to a pure p wave. Values of β in the $\Delta N = 2$ S-branch transitions have been measured using both He I and Ne I light[40,41], and are found to be substantially smaller than two. The most recent results[40] are β_s (736 Å) = 0.08, β_s (584 Å) = 0.87. Now in the case of $\Delta N = 0$ the observed distribution coincides with expectation for ionization from an s orbital giving a pure p wave; according to the rotational 'selection rule', $\Delta N = \pm2$ first arises for d-orbital ionization; in other words the intensity of the $\Delta N = 2$ transitions represents a d-like contribution to the description of H_2 $1s\sigma_g$ electrons in terms of centrosymmetric atomic orbitals. Now from the formula (3.12) we can calculate that, for ionization from a d-orbital giving a p-wave, the asymptotic values of β would be 0.2, whereas for a d orbital giving a pure f-wave, β would be 0.80. The most satisfactory theory[42] indicates that a p-wave final state is most important, but that f-waves make an increasing contribution at higher electron energies.

To summarize this section, the effective atomic l value of a molecular orbital determines both the 'electronic' angular distribution (for nominal $\Delta N = 0$) and the intensities of different rotation branches. Branches of different ΔN evidently have different β values, so calculations of the electronic part alone (the majority of extant β calculations) are unlikely to be reliable where several branches are present.

3.4.4   Orientated molecules

If molecules were held rigidly fixed in space during ionization, the angular distribution of the photoelectrons would be very complex, and could be no more symmetrical than the molecules themselves. The very simple form of the usual angular distributions (equations 3.10 and 3.11) arises from the presence of an isotropic target, in which the molecular structure is washed out by averaging over all possible orientations. Angular distributions from orientated molecules would be much richer in form, reflecting the molecular structure directly. Because the photoelectron de Broglie wavelengths are comparable with molecular dimensions, a departing electron is diffracted by the molecule itself, and the angular distribution may contain a simple signature of the internuclear distances—particularly with the more energetic electrons ejected by He II light or soft X-rays.

The first gas-phase measurement of angular distributions from orientated ions was made by detecting photoelectrons in coincidence with ionic dissociation products[43]. If a diatomic ion dissociates very rapidly (before it has time to rotate) the fragments fly apart along the line of the atoms at the instant of ionization. The electron angular distribution can therefore be measured with respect to this line, which is fixed in the molecule. Such distributions are indeed more complex than the normal ones, in the expected way; unfortunately, the technique is limited to ionic states which dissociate rapidly. In theory, photoelectron angular distribution measurements could be made on orientated molecular beams, but this has not yet been tried.

Much more important in potential application are electron angular distribution from molecules orientated by absorption onto surfaces. Study of these angular distributions has been proposed as a method of determining adsorbate orientations[44], but this requires (theoretical) knowledge of the distribution for different molecular orientations, to be compared with experiment. The theory involves some uncertainty, with the result that the method has not achieved wide currency. A promising variant is to use a tunable vuv source for ionization (e.g. synchrotron radiation) and to examine the adsorbate photoelectron angular distributions at a shape resonance wavelength, where strong orientational effects on the angular distribution are predicted[45]. Unfortunately the effects of the adjacent metal surface are not yet fully understood.

3.4.5 Photoelectron spin polarization

When an isotropic molecular target is ionized by unpolarized or linearly polarized photons the starting conditions contain no helicity, so any spin polarization of the electrons in the final state must be compensated by an opposite polarization of the molecular ion. Such electron polarization, which is observed only when spin–orbit splitting in the ion is resolved, has been detected and measured[46]. If the ionizing light is circularly polarized a helicity transfer can take place so the photoelectrons may be spin polarized even if all electrons are collected, irrespective of their angles of emission; this strong effect, the Fano effect, was at one time proposed as a source of spin-polarized electrons for high energy physics experiments. It has been clearly shown both theoretically[47] and experimentally[46,48] that spin polarization of photoelectrons is actually the rule, rather than an exception, and that complete characterization of the ionization of atoms and molecules requires measurements of this spin polarization as well as the normal angular distribution. The spin-polarization measurements are particularly important as tests of the most advanced theories of molecular electronic structure, since they arise from effects (mainly relativistic) which are entirely neglected in naive models.

One interesting possibility, which has not yet been examined, would be to provide initial helicity in the form of optically active molecules as targets. These should have different cross-sections for ionization by right and left circularly polarized light, and the experiment might even point the way to a new method for configuration determination.

3.5 Related techniques

The study of positive molecular ions by techniques other than photoelectron spectroscopy has a long history, and in its early stages the development of photoelectron spectroscopy was greatly assisted by the knowledge of ionic states that was already available. Reliable first ionization potentials of atoms and molecules were obtained by the study of Rydberg series in absorption spectra, and also by the conventional technique of photoionization. Some excited ionic states had been discovered as limits of Rydberg series, and others were known from the emission spectra of the ionized species. All of these techniques have taken on a new lease of life in recent years, partly as a result of the stimulus of photoelectron spectroscopy, and new techniques have been added to them.

3.5.1 Ion emission spectra

Excited states of positive ions can be created not only by photo-ionization but also by impact with electrons, ions or even neutral species. The excited ions can emit light in reverting to a lower ionic state, and so produce emission spectra. Because these fluorescence transitions occur between two bound states of the ion, they are governed by the selection rules for dipole radiation. Details of the emission spectra of small molecules, especially the rotational fine structure, can indicate the electronic species of the two states involved and also the molecular geometry of the ions in those states. The origin of an emission band gives the energy difference between two ionic states very precisely, and the vibrational structure gives precise information on vibrational intervals in both ground and excited states. This information about ions from emission spectra is usually much more detailed than that which can be obtained from a photoelectron spectrum, but unfortunately it is very rarely available. Whereas the emission spectra of atomic ions are commonplace and many diatomic ions also emit, intensive search has uncovered only a hundred or so polyatomic ions that emit at all, and many of these are closely related compounds[49]. One reason for this is that many molecular ions in excited states dissociate before they can emit light; another more important reason is that most molecular ions in their first electronic excited states undergo internal conversion to high vibrational levels of the ground state, instead of emitting radiation. The common occurrence of this process in ions is a simple consequence of the small energy gaps between ground state and first excited state in ions (average first gaps: 4.9 eV in molecules, 1.3 eV in radical cations) and the energy gap law of radiationless transitions[50] (see Chapter 7).

3.5.2 Ion absorption spectra

The lack of ion emission spectra could be made up if ion absorption spectra were measurable, but unfortunately this is an even more difficult task. Only a few very stable ions can be prepared in sufficient concentration (10^9 ions per cm^3) in the gas phase to give detectable absorption, though microwave absorption spectra of the triatomic ions HCO^+, HN_2^+ of some diatomic molecules have been recorded[51]. A recent triumph has been the measurement of the infrared vibration–rotation spectrum of H_3^+ by a laser technique[52]. One very sensitive indirect technique for measuring ion absorption, ion photodissociation spectroscopy, is discussed in Chapter 7.

Although few gas phase absorption spectra of ions are known, there are many absorption spectra of radical cations in solution and in solid matrices[53]. The naphthalene cation $C_{10}H_8^+$ has been well studied in argon matrices, and its absorption spectrum[54] can be directly related to its photoelectron spectrum. In comparing photoelectron spectra with absorption spectra of the cations we must be aware, however, that the final electronic states reached in the two processes are *not necessarily the same*. Photoionization populates ionic states which have a single hole (electron vacancy) in one orbital, whereas ion absorption can also produce states in which one electron is excited to a normally unoccupied orbital. Such states would require a two-electron jump for their production in photoionization, and are therefore very weak or absent in normal photoelectron spectra. An extensive study of ion absorption spectra in glassy media shows that the absorption spectra of most ions in the visible/near uv region match the photoelectron spectra, so that 'new' states lie at a higher energy than the first few simple hole states. In compounds whose HOMO–LUMO gap is small, however, the 'new' excitation bands may be prominent, and several have been identified[55].

The most promising technique for measurement of gas-phase ion absorption spectra is laser-induced fluorescence excitation spectroscopy. In this technique, ions are produced as abundantly as possible in their ground state by electron bombardment or Penning ionization (see below), and are irradiated by an intense laser beam. Absorption is monitored by detecting the undispersed fluorescence of excited ionic states; this sensitive, high resolution technique is unfortunately limited, of course, to ions that fluoresce, of which several have been studied[51,56].

3.5.3   Photoionization techniques

In photoionization mass spectrometry, yields of molecular ions and fragment ions, sorted according to charge and mass, are measured as functions of the ionizing wavelength. The need for a continuously tunable source of vuv radiation makes this a much more demanding experimental method than photoelectron spectroscopy, and it has been pursued by fewer research groups. Its advantages are that the energy calibration (wavelength) is precise, and that the resolution, not limited by problems of electron optics, can be high; 1 meV is easily attained. As explained earlier in this chapter, the main disadvantages in terms of the characterization of ion states are the integral form of the spectra, and the ubiquitous

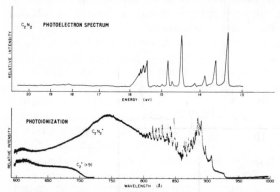

Figure 3.10   Photoelectron and photoionization spectra of cyanogen, drawn on a common horizontal scale. The photoelectron spectrum shows distinct ionic states with vibrational structure, while in photoionization the information is concealed by the complex structure of autoionizing Rydberg series

intervention of autoionization. *Figure 3.10* shows another photoionization spectrum for comparison with the photoelectron spectrum. An important advantage of photoionization mass spectrometry is that fragment ions, and therefore photodissociation processes, can be studied in addition to parent molecular ion formation; this point is taken up again in Chapter 7.

Where a tunable vuv source is available, it can be used to excite photoelectron spectra at any desired wavelength; special interest has been attached to photoelectron spectra at shape resonances[19,22] and autoionizing resonances[21]. Alternatively, new forms of spectra can be produced by recording the yield of electrons at a *fixed energy*, while scanning the ionizing wavelength.

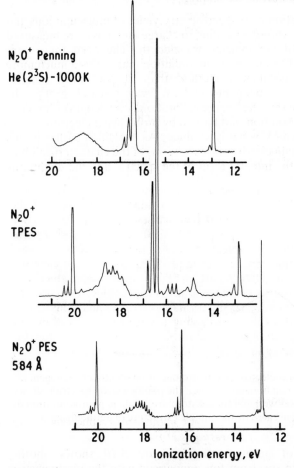

Figure 3.11   Comparison between photoelectron (PES), threshold photoelectron (TPES) and Penning ionization spectra of N_2O. The great differences in relative intensities of different electronic states in the three ion spectroscopies are apparent, as are the 'interloper' peaks from threshold autoionization

The fundamental energy balance is:

$$KE = h\nu - I_j \tag{1.3}$$

from which it follows that fixing the KE of the electron and scanning $h\nu$ is equivalent to fixing $h\nu$ and scanning KE. In practice, although it has been shown that advantages accrue from fixing the electron KE at a non-zero value[57], it is usually the condition $KE = 0$ which is chosen. This choice is made because zero-energy electrons can be collected with 100% efficiency by application of small electric fields, making the technique known as *threshold* photoelectron spectroscopy (TPES) very sensitive[58]. The threshold photoelectron spectrum and the regular fixed wavelength photoelectron spectrum (PES) of the same compound are similar, but also exhibit striking differences. The same one-electron ion states appear in both, though not generally with the same relative intensities. Not only are there differences arising from the wavelength dependence of the ionization cross-sections, but also, as in all variable wavelength techniques, from autoionization. Wherever it happens that an autoionizing resonance coincides in energy with a Franck–Condon-allowed vibrational level of an ionic state, there is likely to be a huge enhancement of the threshold photoelectron signal. This causes violent local distortion of the intensities within bands in TPES, compared with normal PES. Second, threshold electron spectra contain additional broad bands or a baseline strongly rising toward higher photon energies, features having no counterpart in PES or in the ionic state term schemes. The origin of these extra zero-energy electrons is not yet clear, but they may signal the formation of molecular ions in very high vibrational levels, by coupling between the ionization continua and dissociation continua of the neutral molecules. Most of these features are illustrated in the PES–TPES comparison shown in *Figure 3.11*.

3.5.4   Penning ionization

Penning ionization[59,60] is brought about not by photons but by metastable atoms, usually rare gas atoms:

$$A + B^* \rightarrow A^+ + B + e \tag{3.15}$$

The process resembles photoionization in that only one electron is involved, and because of its low mass this electron carries away most of the excess energy of the process. The spectrum of Penning electrons resembles a photoelectron spectrum, as illustrated in

Figure 3.11, but also differs in the following important respects. The available energy is the excitation energy of B^* plus a contribution from the relative kinetic energies of A and B^*, and this energy provides for ionization and excitation of A^+, as in photoelectron spectroscopy. Part of the excess energy after the collision goes into relative translation of A^+ and B, although most appears as electron energy. This complication of the energy balance has the effect that peaks in Penning electron spectra are broader than those in photoelectron spectra, even when the original particles have only thermal kinetic energies. The peaks are also shifted by the heavy-particle kinetic energy effects, so that the precise energies of the ionic states of A^+ produced cannot be determined. The exact energies of the ionic states are usually taken from photoelectron spectroscopy, whereupon the measured shifts give information about the details of the Penning ionization process itself[61].

The transition probabilities for producing different electronic states of A^+ are different in Penning ionization and photoionization, and in Penning ionization they also depend on the nature of the excited atom B^* and on the relative kinetic energy of the colliding particles—that is on the temperature. There is nothing surprising about this effect as the interaction processes are different, but the differences are interesting and could be useful. One possibility is that two-electron processes may be more intense in Penning ionization than in photoionization; another is that the differences between Penning ionization and photoionization may be indicative of the nature of the orbitals from which electrons are ionized. There is some evidence that π-orbitals in aromatic hydrocarbons have larger cross-sections for Penning ionization than the σ-orbitals, for instance, and the difference has been used to help with analysis of the photoelectron spectra[62].

3.5.5 Electron energy-loss spectra

The relevance of the study of Rydberg states to the analysis of photoelectron spectra has been pointed out already in Chapter 1. Until recently, these states could be detected only by the extremely difficult technique of vacuum ultraviolet absorption spectroscopy, and because of the difficulties involved few molecules had been studied. This situation has changed with the development of the new technique of electron energy-loss spectroscopy[62,63].

An electron beam of defined energy is passed through a cell containing a gas, and the electrons that are scattered inelastically in the direction of the primary beam are examined in an electron energy analyser. The primary electrons can lose energy by exciting the gas molecules rotationally, vibrationally or electronically in the process

$$A + e \rightarrow A^* + e \qquad (3.16)$$

For the kinetic energies of the electrons before and after scattering, KE_1 and KE_2, respectively, we have

$$KE_2 = KE_1 - E^* \qquad (3.17)$$

The energy lost by the electrons, $KE_1 - KE_2$, is exactly equal to the energy gained by the molecules, and must correspond to the energy difference between the ground state and an excited state. The energy-loss spectrum therefore contains the same sort of information as an optical absorption spectrum but can cover the whole energy range from zero to hundreds of electronvolts with no special difficulty.

Another advantage of the method is its sensitivity, which can exceed that of conventional vacuum ultraviolet spectroscopy by several orders of magnitude. The resolution is not so high, however, as that which can be attained in optical spectroscopy. The selection rules for excitation by electron impact are not necessarily the same as those that govern optical transitions, and the differences are most apparent at low primary electron energies. When electrons scattered along the primary beam direction are studied, the relative band intensities are proportional to optical transition probabilities for primary electron energies of 300 eV or more. At lower electron energies and for electrons scattered through large angles, the selection rules are relaxed, and singlet–triplet transitions, for instance, may give intense energy-loss bands. Energy-loss spectroscopy therefore enables one to detect both optically allowed and optically forbidden transitions, and to distinguish between them by the energy dependence of their relative intensities or by the angular distribution of the scattered electrons. All of these characteristics can be exploited in order to study Rydberg states in conjunction with photoelectron spectra. The vibrational structure of electronic excitation bands in energy-loss spectroscopy is governed by the Franck–Condon principle in the same way as photoionization or absorption, so the Rydberg bands resemble the photoelectron bands on which they converge. An example is given in *Figure 3.12*, which shows the energy-loss spectrum of ammonia taken on a commercial spectrometer.

Electron impact can, of course, cause ionization as well as excitation. In a direct electron impact ionization process:

$$A + e \rightarrow A^+ + 2e \qquad (3.18)$$

two electrons leave the collision complex and the excess energy can be distributed between them. The electron energy distribution is therefore continuous and does not interfere with the observation of discrete energy losses in the excitation process of equation 3.16. When the energy of the primary electrons is well above the ionization limit, the electron energy distribution for ionization has

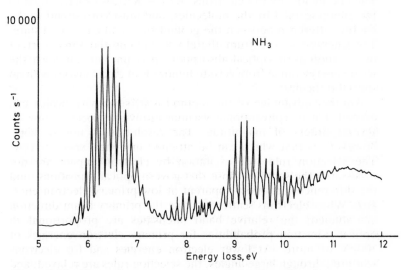

Figure 3.12   Energy-loss spectrum of ammonia. (From Rendina and Grojean[63], by courtesy of the Society for Applied Spectroscopy)

two broad peaks, one near the primary beam energy and the other nearer zero energy. One of the electrons can be thought of as a primary electron that has lost energy, and the other as a secondary electron. The energy loss of the primary electron is equivalent to the photon energy in photoelectron spectroscopy, and the secondary electron to the photoelectron. The secondary electron spectrum for a single energy loss is equivalent to a photoelectron spectrum, but as the primary energy losses are continuously distributed no structure that resembles a photoelectron spectrum is normally visible. This difficulty can be overcome in a coincidence experiment in which primary electrons that have lost energy are detected in one electron energy analyser and secondary electrons in another. By using the coincidence technique, it is possible to detect the particular secondary electrons that correspond to a chosen primary electron energy loss, using the fact that the two electrons must leave the collision simultaneously. The coincidence experiment is equivalent to photoelectron spectroscopy with a completely tunable light source, as any primary energy loss can be chosen. This experiment is technically very difficult, but considerable success has been achieved[64].

3.5.6 Electron impact ionization

The traditional method of measuring ionization potentials by electron impact is to record the molecular ion current in a mass spectrometer while increasing the energy of the thermionic electron beam used for ionization. When the electron energy is equal to the ionization potential, the cross-section for electron impact ionization is zero, and it should increase linearly with increasing energy above the threshold. Ionization potential differences between the sample and a standard are obtained by various methods of extrapolation or other treatment of the measured ion currents. In fact, the energy spread of thermionic electrons from a heated filament is so broad, and the interference of autoionization processes with the form of the cross-section behaviour so serious, that not even first ionization potentials can be measured accurately or reliably by this method. Mono-energetic electron beams can now be used instead of thermionic electrons, which makes it possible to see some structure in the cross-section functions. It is no easier to find inner ionization potentials by electron impact methods than by photoionization, however; because the cross-sections are zero at the threshold, it is even more difficult. It may nevertheless be interesting to compare electron impact ionization cross-sections with photoionization cross-sections and photoelectron spectra, as the selection rules for electron impact ionization near the threshold are different from those that govern photoionization. Ionic states that are not observed in photoelectron spectroscopy may be accessible by electron impact ionization, particularly those states which are reached by transitions with ΔS greater than unity.

References

1. CONDON, E.U. and SHORTLEY, G.H., *The Theory of Atomic Spectra*, Cambridge University Press (1935)

2. BERKOWITZ, J., DEHMER, J.L., KIM, Y-K, and DESCLAUX, J.P., *J. Chem. Phys.*, **61**, 2556 (1974)
3. SAMSON, J.A.R., *Chem. Phys. Lett.*, **12**, 625 (1972)
4. KRUMMACHER, S., SCHMIDT, V. and WUILLEUMIER, F. *J. Phys., B., Atom. Molec. Phys.*, **13**, 3993 (1980)
5. DOMCKE, W., CEDERBAUM, L.S., SCHIRMER, J., VON NIESSEN, W. and MAIER, J.P., *J. Electron Spectrosc.*, **14**, 59 (1978), and references therein
6. CEDERBAUM, L.S., SCHIRMER, J., DOMCKE, W. and VON NIESSEN, W. *Int. J. Quantum Chem.*, **14**, 593 (1978)
7. TSAI, B.P. and ELAND, J.H.D., *Int. J. Mass Spectrom. Ion Phys.*, **36**, 143 (1980)
8. CHANG, T.N., ISHIHARA, T. and POE, R.T., *Phys. Rev. Lett.*, **27**, 838 (1971)
9. PARKER, D.H., BERG, J.O. and EL-SAYED, M.A., in Zewail, A.H. (Editor) *Advances in Laser Chemistry*, Springer, Berlin (1978)
10. KIMMAN, J., KRUIT, P. and VAN DER WIEL, M.J., *Chem. Phys. Lett.*, **88**, 576 (1982); WHITE, M.G., SEAVER, M., CHUPKA, W.A. and COLSON, S.D., *Phys. Rev. Lett.*, **49**, 28 (1982)
11. KIMMAN, J., KRUIT, P. and VAN DER WIEL, M.J., *J. Phys., B, Atom Molec. Phys.*, **14**, L597 (1981)
12. BERKOWITZ, J., *Photoabsorption, Photoionization and Photoelectron Spectroscopy*, Academic Press, New York (1979)
13. DEHMER, J.L., DILL, D. and WALLACE, S., *Phys. Rev. Lett.*, **43**, 1005 (1979)
14. GUSTAVSSON, T., *Phys. Rev.*, **A18**, 1089 (1979)
15. GIUSTI-SUZOR, A. and JUNGEN, Ch., *J. Chem. Phys.*, to be published
16. ELAND, J.H.D., *J. Chim. Phys.*, **77**, 613 (1980)
17. NATALIS, P., DELWICHE, J., CAPRACE, G., COLLIN, J.E., HUBIN, M-J. and PRAET, M-Th., *J. Electron Spectrosc. Rel. Phen.*, **10**, 93 (1977); **11**, 417 (1977)
18. ELAND, J.H.D., *J. Chem. Phys.*, **72**, 6015 (1980)
19. MORIN, P., NENNER, I., ADAM, M.Y., HUBSIN-FRANKSIN, M.J., DELWICHE, J., LEFEBVRE-BRION, H. and GIUSTI-SUZOR, A., *Chem. Phys. Lett.*, to be published
20. SMITH, A.L., *J. Quart. Spectrosc. Radiat. Transfer*, **10**, 1129 (1970); *Phil. Trans. Roy. Soc. London*, **A268**, 169 (1970)
21. ELAND, J.H.D., *Mol. Phys.*, **40**, 917 (1980)
22. MORIN, P., NENNER, I., GUYON, P.M., FERREIRA, L.F.A. and ITO, K., *Chem. Phys. Lett.*, to be published
23. TABCHE-FOUHAILE, A., NENNER, I., GUYON, P.M. and DELWICHE, J., *J. Chem. Phys.*, **75**, 1129 (1981)
24. BERKOWITZ, J. and ELAND, J.H.D., *J. Chem. Phys.*, **67**, 2740 (1977)
25. BLAKE, A.J. and CARVER, J.H., *J. Quant. Spectrosc. Radiat. Trans.*, **12**, 207 (1972)
26. BREHM, B., *Z. Physik*, **242**, 195 (1971)
27. COOPER, J. and ZARE, R.N., *J. Chem. Phys.*, **48**, 942 (1968)
28. BUCKINGHAM, A.D., ORR, B.J. and SICHEL, J.M., *Phil. Trans. Roy. Soc. Lond.*, **A268**, 147 (1970)
29. ITAKAWA, Y., *Chem. Phys.*, **37**, 401 (1979)
30. RABALAIS, J.W., DEBIES, T.B., BERKOWSKY, J.L., HUANG, J.J. and ELLISON, F.O., *J. Chem. Phys.*, **61**, 529 (1974); **62**, 4588 (1975)
31. CARLSON, T.A., McGUIRE, G.E., JONAS, A.E., CHENG, K.L.,

ANDERSON, C.P., LU, C.C. and PULLEN, B.P., in Shirley, D.A. (Editor) *Electron Spectroscopy*, North Holland, Amsterdam, 207 (1972)
32. KATSUMATA, S., ACHIBA, Y. and KIMURA, K., *J. Electron Spectrosc.*, **17**, 229 (1975)
33. KREILE, J. and SCHWEIG, A., *J. Electron. Spectrosc.*, **20**, 191 (1980)
34. KENNEDY, D.J. and MANSON, S.T., *Phys. Rev.*, **A5**, 227 (1972)
35. HANCOCK, W.H. and SAMSON, J.A.R., *J. Electron Spectrosc.*, **9**, 211 (1976)
36. JACOBI, K., GENG, P. and RANKE, W., *J. Phys., E, Sci. Instrum.*, **11**, 982 (1978)
37. DOMCKE, W., *Phys. Scripta*, **19**, 11 (1979)
38. RAOULT, M. and JUNGEN, Ch., *J. Chem. Phys.*, **74**, 3388 (1981)
39. ALLEN, J.D. and GRIMM, F.A., *Chem. Phys. Lett.*, **66**, 72 (1979)
40. POLLARD, J.E., TREVOR, D.J., REUTT, J.E., LEE, Y.T. and SHIRLEY, D.A., *J. Chem. Phys.*, **77**, 34 (1982); **77**, 4818 (1982)
41. NIEHAUS, A. and RUF, M.W., *Chem. Phys. Lett.*, **11**, 55 (1971)
42. ITIKAWA, Y., *Chem. Phys.*, **37**, 401 (1979)
43. ELAND, J.H.D., *J. Chem. Phys.*, **70**, 2926 (1979)
44. SMITH, R.J., ANDERSON, J. and LAPEYRE, G.J., *Phys. Rev. Lett.*, **37**, 1081 (1976)
45. ALLYN, G.L., GUSTAFFSON, T. and PLUMMER, E.W., *Solid State Commun.*, **28**, 85 (1978)
46. HEINZMANN, U., *Applied Optics*, **19**, 4087 (1980)
47. CHEREPKOV, N.A., *J. Phys., B, Atom. Molec. Phys.*, **14**, L73 (1981), and references therein
48. HEINZMANN, U., OSTERHELD, B., SCHAFERS, F. and SCHONHENSE, G., *J. Phys., B, Atom. Molec. Phys.*, **14**, L79 (1981)
49. MAIER, J.P., *Chimia*, **34**, 219 (1980)
50. ELAND, J.H.D., in Brundle, C.R. (Editor) *Electron Spectroscopy: Theory, Techniques and Application*, Academic Press, London (1979)
51. SAYKALLY, R.J. and WOODS, R.C., *Ann. Rev. Phys. Chem.*, **32**, 403 (1981)
52. OKA, T., *Phys. Rev. Lett.*, **45**, 531 (1980)
53. HASELBACH, E., BALLY, T., GSCHWIND, R., KLEMM, U. and LANYIOVA, Z., *Chimia*, **33**, 405 (1979)
54. ANDREWS, L., KELSALL, B.J. and BLANKENSHIP, T.A., *J. Phys. Chem.*, **86**, 2916 (1982)
55. HASELBACH, E., KLEMM, U., BUSER, U., GSCHWIND, R., JUNGEN, M., KLOSTER-JENSEN, E., MAIER, J.P., MARTHALER, O., CHRISTEN, H. and BAERTSCHI, P., *Helv. Chim. Acta*, **64**, 823 (1981)
56. ENGELKING, P.C. and SMITH, A.L., *Chem. Phys. Lett.*, **36**, 21 (1975)
57. ELAND, J.H.D., *J. Chem. Phys.*, **72**, 2878 (1980)
58. GUYON, P.M., BAER, T., FERREIRA, L.F.A., NENNER, I., TABCHE-FOUHAILLE, A., BOTTER, R. and GOVERS, T., *J. Chem. Phys.*, **70**, 1585 (1979)
59. ČERMAK, V., *J. Chem. Phys.*, **44**, 3774 (1966)
60. FUCHS, V. and NIEHAUS, A., *Phys. Rev. Lett.*, **21**, 1136 (1968)
61. HOTOP, H. and NIEHAUS, A., *Z. Physik*, **228**, 68 (1969)
62. VESZPREMI, T., *Chem. Phys. Lett.*, **88**, 325 (1982)
63. RENDINA, J.F. and GROJEAN, R.E., *Appl. Spectrosc.*, **25**, 24 (1971)
64. CELOTTA, R.J. and HUEBNER, R.H., in Brundle, C.R. and Baker, A.D. (Editors) *Electron Spectroscopy: Theory, Techniques and Applications*, Vol 3, Academic Press, London (1979)

4
Electronic energies of ionic states

4.1 Introduction

Photoelectron spectra provide a wealth of information on the energies of the electronic states of positive ions, and these are closely related to the energies of molecular orbitals in neutral molecules. This is a major reason for the interest of theoreticians in photoelectron spectroscopy and has inspired many calculations of molecular electronic structures. In this chapter, we consider the relationship between experimental ionization energies, or *binding* energies, and theoretical ideas of electronic structure, including orbital energies. Electronic structure calculations are most often made as an aid to the analysis of experimental photoelectron spectra, and here they are discussed mainly from this standpoint. Experimental energy information alone can sometimes be used in a direct way to make deductions about one other aspect of molecular electronic structure, the atomic charge distribution, and this topic is examined in the final section.

4.2 Energies from photoelectron spectra

In contrast to all other methods of investigating molecular ionization, photoelectron spectroscopy often gives both *adiabatic* and *vertical* ionization potentials. An adiabatic ionization energy is unambiguously defined as the difference in energy between the neutral molecule in its electronic, vibrational and rotational ground state and the ion in the lowest vibrational and rotational level of a particular electronic state. Adiabatic transitions are often seen in photoelectron spectra as the zero vibrational levels of each electronic state, that is, as the first vibrational lines in the different bands. Since rotational structure is not resolved, the peaks of O–O vibrational lines are quoted as adiabatic ionization potentials; the corrections from the peaks to the rotational origins, which can sometimes be calculated[1], are usually small in comparison with the experimental uncertainty. The adiabatic transitions are weak, however, whenever there is a large change in equilibrium molecular geometry on ionization. Even in the spectra of triatomic molecules there are bands in which the true adiabatic ionization potentials may not yet have been found, for example, in the $^2A_1$ states of H_2O^+ and H_2S^+. In interpreting the spectra of polyatomic molecules, it is unwise to call the onset of any broad band an adiabatic ionization potential unless the shape of the band definitely indicates that the (0–0) transition has been seen. For many molecules with non-rigid skeletons, such as the aliphatic hydrocarbons, the adiabatic values are simply not known for this reason.

The vertical ionization energy is defined as the energy difference between the molecule in its ground state and the ion in a particular electronic state, but with the nuclei in the same positions as they had in the neutral molecule. The vertical transition therefore corresponds to a vertical line through the molecular ground state on a potential energy diagram, and it is usually defined experimentally as the point of maximum intensity in a photoelectron band. These definitions both lack rigour. It is not clear, for instance, whether the nuclear positions in the molecular ground state should be defined by the maximum of the vibrational wave-function, the maximum of its square or the minimum of the electronic surface. In a resolved band, the vertical transition may not exactly match a vibrational level, and then the experimental value is ambiguous. Brehm[2] has proposed that the vertical ionization potential be defined experimentally as the centre of gravity of a band. This definition has the advantage of a clear theoretical interpretation in terms of potential energy surfaces, but at the expense of simplicity. The advantage that the maximum of a band can easily be located experimentally even when bands overlap makes the vertical ionization energy defined thereby the most generally useful experimental measure of ionization energy.

Whether defined as adiabatic or vertical, the experimental ionization energies are the differences in total energy between the neutral molecule and the ion in a particular state:

$$I = E(A^{+*}) - E(A) \qquad (4.1)$$

This expression suggests that the correct way to calculate ionization energies is to determine the total energy of the ion and of the molecule separately, and then subtract the two values. When this is done, the energy of the ion is sometimes calculated at its own equilibrium geometry instead of at that of the molecule; the result must then be compared with an adiabatic ionization energy. Much more commonly, Koopmans' approximation is used and an orbital energy is available for comparison with experiment. Koopmans' theorem involves no allowance for the reorganization of the nuclei or of the electrons, and therefore it seems logical to compare orbital energies with vertical ionization energies derived from experiment.

4.3 Molecular orbitals, orbital energies and Koopmans' theorem

Koopmans' theorem defines molecular orbital energies as the difference in energy between an electron at an infinite distance from the molecular ion and the same electron in the molecule. Unfortunately, this definition is really one of the ionization energy and is valid for orbital energy only within one approximate model of molecular electronic structure, the self-consistent-field (SCF) model, and then only with special assumptions. In the SCF model and in all models that give recognizable molecular orbitals, they are *one-electron* orbitals; the electrons are taken singly and treated as moving in a field produced by the fixed nuclei and the averaged interactions with the other electrons, including exchange interactions[3]. If the interactions of the remaining electrons remain exactly the same after one of their number has been removed, then Koopmans' theorem holds for SCF orbital energies. Furthermore, although the concept of orbitals seems to be clear from long familiarity, the only unambiguous definition of orbitals and their energies is a mathematical definition based on the SCF model, namely as eigen-vectors and eigen-values of an SCF Hamiltonian. Although these definitions are precise, they do not remove all difficulties in the way of using molecular orbitals as a model for the electronic structure and hence of the photoelectron spectra of real molecules. Firstly, the motion and energy of an electron are *not* independent of the detailed positions and motions of the other electrons, particularly those in the same shell. The electrons, so far as their instantaneous positions have a meaning, tend to keep apart and so reduce their mutual repulsion energy; their motions are correlated. In other words, the orbital model is an approximation from the outset. One way to include electron correlation in calculations for many-electron systems is to use the method of configuration interaction. The calculation starts with an electron configuration with electrons in particular orbitals, corresponding to the ground state of the molecule, and then mixes in the wave-functions for excited states that have the same total symmetry but different electron configurations. The mixing coefficients are found by the variation method[3] and it can be proved that if an infinite number of excited configurations are properly mixed in, the electron correlation will be represented correctly. The result is a good total wave-function for all electrons and a good total energy, but individual molecular orbitals no longer have any meaning.

Secondly, the detailed form of the orbitals cannot be independent of the overall electronic state of the molecule, if only because the SCF procedure invokes the occupation numbers of the orbitals explicitly. Ionization is surely an extreme case, because the transition to an electrically charged state must induce changes in all orbitals to a greater extent than would promoting an electron from one orbital to another. Thus, the assumption in Koopmans' theorem of unchanged interactions is certainly not true, and if the orbital model is to be used to calculate electron binding energies the total energy difference method indicated by equation 4.1 should, logically, be employed. This method of calculation which is quite widely used, is called ΔSCF.

A third difficulty is that the orbital model is not relativistic. This means that spin–orbit effects are not included, and must be added afterwards as perturbations. Orbital energies of inner shell electrons are also likely to be grossly different from experimental binding energies, simply because the inner electrons do have notional velocities comparable with the velocity of light.

We can now consider the effects of the approximations involved in practical comparisons of ionization energies with calculated orbital energies. The approximations include the limitations of molecular orbital models in general, those of the exact model used in each instance, and of Koopmans' approximation itself[4–6]. The most important limitation of molecular orbitals is the neglect of correlation, which enters the calculation of an ionization energy as the difference in correlation energy between the neutral molecule and the ion; the neglect of correlation should, in general, make the calculated ionization energy too small. This will only be so in practice, however, if the model calculation is an SCF model carried to the Hartree–Fock limit (see Section 4.4) and made for both molecule and ion, because only with such a calculation is the neglect of correlation energy the one remaining serious approximation. In using Koopmans' theorem with a molecular orbital model, the further approximation that the electron interactions are exactly the same in the ion and molecule is introduced, which is manifestly not true. As the electrons in the ions can always attain a more stable state than the one defined by their motions in the molecule, the use of Koopmans' theorem should give an ionization energy that is too high. The difference between the ionization energy calculated by Koopmans' theorem and that obtained by calculating the total energies of the ion and molecule separately and then subtracting is called the *reorganization energy*, and both this and the correlation energy can be expected to vary from one ionic state to another. These are clearly two good reasons why even sophisticated calculations may not give correct ionization energies quantitatively; a more important question in photoelectron spectroscopy is whether the *ordering* of the ionic states can be calculated correctly. This depends on the magnitudes of deviations in the reorganization energy and the correlation energy from ionic state to state compared with the energetic separation of one state from another. It has to be investigated by comparison between theory and experiment, and this comparison is the subject of the next section. In general, it seems that the cancellation of errors in using Koopmans' theorem due to neglect of both the correlation energy and reorganization energy is only partial, as the reorganization energy is usually larger and results in calculated ionization potentials that are higher than the observed values. The variations from state to state are such that if experimental ionization potentials are separated by less than $1\,\mathrm{eV}$, even the best molecular orbital calculations cannot be relied upon for their ordering.

All of the preceding remarks apply in the first instance to the ionization of closed-shell molecules; when open-shell molecules are ionized, Koopmans' theorem in its simple form does not apply[6]. A theoretical approach to the problem has been made by Dodds and McWeeney[7], who have developed a formalism within which an analogue of Koopmans' theorem is satisfactory. The experimental fact is that in the ionization of an open-shell molecule, several ionic states are often attained by the removal of electrons from the same molecular orbital. There is no longer a one-to-one correspondence between bands in the spectrum and orbitals in the molecule, so a practical problem exists of relating the several observed ionization potentials to a single orbital energy. Evans, Green and Jackson[8] have proposed that an orbital energy can be derived by taking a weighted mean of the ionization potentials for all of the bands that correspond to a particular electron configuration. The weights are the theoretical relative cross-sections for the different ionic states, equal to their total degeneracies or fractional parentage coefficients[9]. The mean ionization energies derived in this manner are related to orbital energies by the same approximations as those for closed-shell molecules.

4.4   Molecular orbital calculations

It is usual to distinguish four types of molecular orbital calculations, and these types are listed below in order of decreasing computational difficulty.

    (1)   'Exact' Hartree–Fock calculations.
    (2)   *Ab initio* SCF calculations.
 ✱(3)   Semi-empirical calculations.
    (4)   Empirical calculations.

An 'exact' Hartree–Fock (HF) calculation means a calculation by the SCF method in which no terms are neglected and no further improvement of the total energy can be gained either by increasing the number of iterations or by expanding the basis set, the set of orbitals, atomic or otherwise, out of which molecular orbitals are built.

The advantage of the 'exact' HF method is that the meaning of the results is well defined. The calculations do not involve mathematical approximations or arbitrary parameters but only the approximations inherent in the method itself. These approximations are principally the neglect of electron correlation and of relativistic effects for inner shells. The direction in which these approximations will affect ionization energies can be clearly predicted, even though the exact magnitudes of the corrections are not known. If Koopmans' theorem is used to derive ionization energies, the reorganization energy approximation is also involved, but for HF orbitals this is of a definite direction and a magnitude that can be estimated. Ionization energies derived from HF calculations by Koopmans' theorem will definitely be too high, as neglect of reorganization energy is the dominant approximation, whereas those derived by re-calculation of the total electronic energies in the ionic states will be too low because the correlation energy is less in the ion than in the molecule. These predictions are fully borne out by the comparisons with photoelectron spectra.

Some of the advantages of the full HF calculation are shared by *ab initio* SCF calculations for larger molecules, which are generally made possible by mathematical simplification through contraction of the basis sets [10]. Although these are not true HF calculations, they do not involve any arbitrary parameters, so the effect of the approximations on the calculated energies remains reasonably well defined. As the molecules become larger, however, so the necessary approximations become more severe, and the ionization potentials predicted by using Koopmans' theorem may be either higher or lower than the experimental values. For such molecules, the use of semi-empirical SCF methods becomes necessary. The calculations here are simplified further by the neglect of certain integrals and the empirical rather than the theoretical evaluation of others. The calculations involve the use of empirical parameters that are chosen so as to give a good fit either to HF calculations or to some experimental results for a limited number of molecules. The choice of parameters makes it possible to obtain a very good fit in some instances, and the calculations are then expected to have predictive value for other and larger molecules. Semi-empirical calculations are used extensively in the interpretation of photoelectron spectra, and they have been developed over the years to such an extent that their success in predicting the ordering and energies of molecular ionizations is considerable. The problem for large molecules is certainly very difficult since, because of the high density of electronic states, a relatively small error in an orbital energy can change the order completely. In the simplest theoretical methods of all, Hückel π electron calculations for conjugated molecules, empirical parameters can be chosen specifically to give agreement with photoelectron spectroscopic data. When this is done, the predictive value of the calculations within their restricted range of application is higher than that of many of the more sophisticated calculations[11].

4.5   Orbital energies and ionization potentials

Every molecular orbital calculation produces, eventually, a list of eigenvalues or orbital energies which can be compared, invoking Koopmans, with a photoelectron spectrum. There is a great hazard in this procedure, which is to *assume* that the ordering of the calculated orbital energies and the ordering of ionic states are the same. Heilbronner has demonstrated this most graphically[12], by calculating the correlation between a photoelectron spectrum and a set of *ordered* random numbers; the correlation is excellent! The moral is that one should not assign a photoelectron spectrum on the basis of a list of orbital energies alone, unless the agreement is very good indeed. Specifically, one must either bring in other calculated characteristics, such as shapes and intensities of bands, or one must demand accurate predictions of the relative *spacings* of adjacent bands, as well as their absolute positions.

4.5.1   Hartree–Fock calculations

Experimental ionization energies of fourteen small molecules are compared in *Figure 4.1* with orbital energies[13] calculated to the HF

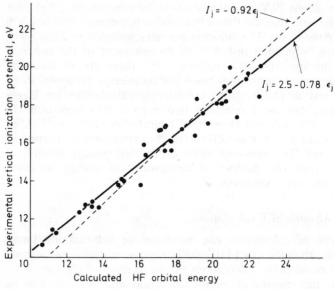

Figure 4.1   Test of Koopmans' theorem for HF orbital energies

limit. While many more molecules have been calculated since this drawing was made, the general conclusions to be drawn from the comparison are unchanged. While the correlation is clear, the points are relatively scattered about a line which does not have unit slope. The spread of the points is around ± 1 eV from the line in the middle and increases for higher ionization energies. The scatter is so large that an exact statistical treatment is not warranted; the data are best represented by a straight line of the form

$$I_{vert} = 2.5 - 0.8\,\varepsilon_j \qquad\qquad (4.2)$$

(note that the orbital energies ε_j are negative quantities).

The simpler relationship

$$I_{vert} = -0.92\,\varepsilon_j \qquad\qquad (4.3)$$

which has been used by several workers in comparing *ab initio* SCF calculations with photoelectron spectra[14], does not fit so well, but gives reasonable agreement for ionization potentials between 14 and 18 eV.

From the spread of points from the curve of *Figure 4.1*, it would seem that experimental vertical ionization energies must be separated by about 2 eV, or calculated orbital energies by 2.5 eV, for one to be sure that the theoretical and experimental ordering will agree. Among the 37 ionization energies included in *Figure 4.1*, there are only three instances of disagreement of the ordering within the spectrum of a molecule, but these are all for small molecules whose ionization bands are on average far apart, so no severe test is involved. In considering calculations on larger molecules, one must conclude that even if they approach HF accuracy, the ordering of orbitals separated in energy by 1 eV or less is as likely as not to differ from the experimental ordering of ionic states. The non-unit slope of the line results mainly, of course, from the neglect of reorganization energy in using Koopmans' approximation.

4.5.2 *Ab initio* SCF calculations

This type of calculation can be made for substantially larger molecules than the exact HF calculations; as examples to illustrate the use of *ab initio* calculations in the analysis of photoelectron spectra, the spectra of xenon difluoride and benzene can be considered.

Xenon difluoride

The photoelectron spectrum of XeF_2 has been measured by Brundle *et al.*[15] using excitation by both He I and He II radiation,

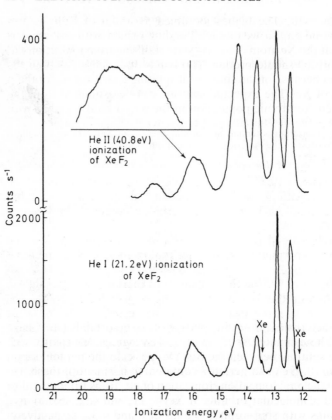

Figure 4.2   Photoelectron spectra of xenon difluoride excited by He I and He II light. (From Brundle *et al.*[15], by courtesy of the American Institute of Physics)

and the spectra are shown in *Figure 4.2*. The ionic states were identified with the help of orbital energies that were calculated by using a contracted Gaussian basis set in an all-electron SCF method. The calculated orbital energies scaled by the empirical factor of 0.92, together with the measured ionization energies, are shown in *Table 4.1*. Almost all of the experimental vertical ionization energies are separated from one another by less than 2 eV, so the use of Koopmans' theorem cannot be relied upon for the ordering of the ionic states. An assignment of the spectrum can be made, however, by taking account of the molecular orbital calculations in conjunction with the details of the photoelectron spectrum itself. The highest occupied π orbital of XeF_2 is predicted to be $5\pi_u$, a weakly antibonding orbital with the greatest density at the Xe atom. The $^2\Pi_u$ state resulting from ionization out of this orbital should produce two bands of equal intensity in the spectrum because of the spin–orbit splitting characteristic of the p orbitals of Xe. The expected splitting can be estimated from the calculated Xe atomic population in the $5\pi_u$ orbital together with

Table 4.1   Ionization potentials and orbital energies of XeF_2 (From Brundle *et al.*[15], by courtesy of the American Institute of Physics)

Orbital	Calculated orbital energies × 0.92, eV	Vertical ionization energy eV	Ionic state
$5\pi_u$	12.51	12.42	X $^2\Pi_{3/2u}$
		12.89	$^2\Pi_{1/2u}$
$10\sigma_g$	11.79	13.65	A $^2\Sigma_g$
$3\pi_g$	14.71	14.35	B $^2\Pi_g$
$4\pi_u$	15.92	15.60	C $^2\Pi_{3/2u}$
		16.00	$^2\Pi_{1/2u}$
$6\sigma_u$	16.93	17.35	D $^2\Sigma_u$
$9\sigma_g$	25.24	22.5	E $^2\Sigma_g$

the characteristic spin–orbit splitting of Xe 6p orbitals (see Chapter 6). The estimated splitting of 0.54 eV agrees sufficiently well with the splitting between the first two peaks in the photoelectron spectrum (0.45 eV) to permit a confident assignment of these two peaks to the $5\pi_u^{-1}$ ionization. Ionization of electrons from the other occupied π molecular orbitals of XeF_2, $3\pi_g$ and $4\pi_u$, should give ionic states with spin–orbit splittings of 0 and 0.37, respectively. The band near 16 eV ionization energy is split by about 0.4 eV, in agreement with the prediction for $4\pi_u^{-1}$ ionization, and the broadness of the band is in keeping with the strongly bonding character of this orbital indicated by the calculations. The $3\pi_g^{-1}$ ionization must be intermediate in energy between the two π_u^{-1} ionizations, and must give rise to one of the bands at 13.65 or 14.35 eV. The only remaining orbital whose ionization energy can lie in this region is $10\sigma_g$, which is calculated to have a lower ionization energy. As the band at 14.35 eV is approximately twice as intense as that at 13.65 eV in both the He I and He II spectra, it is assigned to ionization from the doubly degenerate $3\pi_g$ orbital, and the band at 13.65 eV must be the $10\sigma_g^{-1}$ ionization. The remaining bands in the spectrum at 16.93 and 25.24 eV can be attributed to ionization from the $6\sigma_u$ and $9\sigma_g$ orbitals, respectively, on the basis of the calculations, as these are well separated in energy and are the only remaining valence orbitals. The final assignment given in *Table 4.1* is confirmed by the changes in relative band intensities on going from He I (584 Å) to He II (304 Å) excitation. The cross-section for ionization of atomic Xe decreases very considerably between 584 and 304 Å, whereas that for Ne, which can serve as a model for the fluorine atoms, reaches a maximum near the He II wavelength. Hence ionization from orbitals with a large Xe atomic orbital contribution would be expected to have a lower relative intensity in the He II spectrum than in that excited by He I. If the π_g^{-1} band is taken as a basis, it can be seen that in fact the $5\pi_u^{-1}$, $4\pi_u^{-1}$ and $6\sigma_u^{-1}$ bands do lose intensity considerably, while the $10\sigma_g^{-1}$ band remains of almost the same intensity. This result is in exact agreement with expectation because on symmetry grounds π_g and σ_g contain no contributions from Xe 5p.

The final assignment of the photoelectron spectrum based on the preceding experimental and theoretical considerations agrees reasonably well with the SCF orbital energy scheme interpreted by Koopmans' theorem, and the theoretical and experimental orderings differ at only one point; nevertheless, it cannot be said that the SCF calculations were essential for the analysis. In fact, the photoelectron spectrum of XeF_2 was measured and analysed independently without the benefit of the SCF calculations by Brehm *et al.*[16], who reached exactly the same identification of orbitals with ionization bands. The situation with XeF_2 is typical of much work in photoelectron spectroscopy in that accurate SCF calculations are an aid to, but by no means essential for, the correct interpretation of experimental spectra in the outer valence region.

Benzene

A second example of the comparison between orbital energies calculated by the SCF method and photoelectron spectra is provided by the important case of benzene. The first assignment of the benzene spectrum was made by Jonsson and Lindholm[17], and was based on several different types of information, including SCF calculations. Since then, more experimental evidence has been accumulated, and a wider range of evidence can now be brought to bear on the photoelectron spectrum of benzene than on that of almost any other molecule. There are calculations beyond the orbital model, m.o. calculations from the simplest up to *ab initio* SCF[17-19], measurements of band intensities and the comparison of spectra excited by He I, He II and Ne I light[20], detailed analyses of the vibrational structure of resolved bands[21,22], angular distributions of the photoelectrons[23,24] and comparisons with Rydberg series and energy loss spectra[17,22].

The general appearance of the spectrum is shown in *Figure 4.3*; there are seven clearly separate bands below 30 eV ionization energy, a range which covers the whole valence electron ionization region. The number of valence orbitals, however, is 10, so

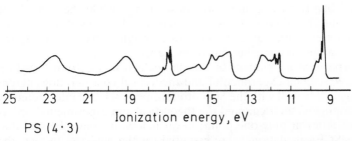

$C_6 H_6$ ionized by He II

Ionization energy, eV

PS (4·3)

Figure 4.3   Photoelectron spectrum of benzene taken using He II light and corrected for variations of analyser sensitivity with electron energy. There is another broad band near 26 eV which is not shown. (After Åsbrink *et al.*[20], by courtesy of North Holland Publishing Company)

according to the rule that ionization from each orbital gives at least one band in the spectrum, several bands must be overlapping. The overlapping bands can be identified both by the total band areas under He II excitation using the rule that the intensity per electron pair is constant, and by the variation of the angular distribution of electrons across the spectrum[23,24].

Table 4.2   Valence orbitals of benzene (After B.O. Jonsson and E. Lindholm, *Ark. Fysik*, **39**, 65 (1969))

Orbital	Type	Character
1 e_{1g}	pπ	C–C bonding
3 e_{2g}	pσ	Weakly C–H and C–C bonding
1 a_{2u}	pπ	Strongly C–C bonding
3 e_{1u}	pσ	Strongly C–H bonding
1 b_{2u}	pσ	Strongly C–C bonding
2 b_{1u}	sσ	Strongly C–H bonding and C–C antibonding
3 a_{1g}	pσ	Strongly C–H bonding, weakly C–C antibonding
2 e_{2g}	sσ	Weakly C–H bonding and C–C antibonding
2 e_{1u}	sσ	Strongly C–C bonding
2 a_{1g}	sσ	Strongly C–C bonding

Table 4.3 Analysis of the benzene spectrum

Vertical ionization energy eV	Band intensity	MO calculations	Vibrational structure	Deductions from		Final assignment
				Rydberg defect	Angular distribution	
9.3	Degen.	e_{1g}	Degen.	$1e_{1g}$		$1e_{1g}$
11.4	One degen. }	One $1a_{2u}$	Degen?			$3e_{2g}$
12.1	One single }					$1a_{2u}$
13.8	One degen. }					$3e_{1u}$
14.7	One single }				$3e_{1u}$	$1b_{2u}$
15.4	Single }	One $2b_{1u}$	$\left\{\begin{array}{l}3a_{1g}\\2b_{1u}\end{array}\right.$			$2b_{1u}$
16.9	Single }			$3a_{1g}$		$3a_{1g}$
19.2	Degen.	$2e_{2g}$				$2e_{2g}$
22.5	Degen.	$2e_{1u}$				$2e_{1u}$
25.9		$2a_{1g}$				$2a_{1g}$

From these studies, 10 distinct ionizations can be distinguished, in agreement with the number of valence orbitals. The orbitals are named and described in *Table 4.2* and the experimental ionization energies are given in the first column of *Table 4.3*. The measured band intensities also show where degenerate orbital ionizations are involved, and this information is given in the second column of *Table 4.3*.

The molecular orbital calculations can be used to identify some of the bands directly. The first ionization at 9.3 eV is identified with loss of the outermost π electron, $1e_{1g}^{-1}$, in all calculations; there is also experimental evidence for this from a study of the corresponding Rydberg series. Empirical π electron-only calculations agree with this assignment, and indicate that the second π ionization, $1a_{2u}^{-1}$, must occur at about 12 eV, and therefore corresponds to one component of the second spectral band. Next, the ionizations from orbitals based mainly on carbon 2s atomic orbitals can be recognized as they lie at higher ionization energies than those based on carbon 2p. Both the SCF calculations and empirical molecular orbital arguments indicate that the bands at 26, 22.5 and 19.5 eV correspond to $2a_{1g}$, $2e_{1u}^{-1}$ and $2e_{2g}^{-1}$ ionizations, respectively, in agreement with the degeneracies from experimental band intensities. The one remaining carbon 2s-based orbital, $2b_{1u}$, is calculated to lie near 16 eV, and must be one of the ionizations at 16.9 or 15.4 eV. These conclusions from the molecular orbital models are shown in the third column of *Table 4.3*.

Four bands in the photoelectron spectrum have resolved vibrational structure, and all have been examined at high resolution both in the spectrum of benzene and in that of hexadeuterobenzene. The vibrational structures of the bands at 15.4 and 16.9 eV contain progressions in both the C–H and C–C stretching vibrations, which shows that the orbitals concerned have C–H bonding character. The only non-degenerate orbitals with strong C–H bonding character are $2b_{1u}$, which has already been assigned to one of these two ionization bands, and $3a_{1g}$, so the two bands comprise ionization from these two orbitals; further evidence must be used to distinguish between the two bands. Firstly, the Rydberg defect of the series converging on the 16.9 eV ionization is 0.45, which is too large for d-type Rydberg orbitals, the only orbitals allowed by the selection rules if a $2b_{1u}$ s-type orbital is ionized. This shows that the 16.9 eV band must be the $3a_{1g}^{-1}$ ionization, for which the Rydberg orbitals are of p-type. Confirmation is provided by comparison with the spectrum of furan, which contains a band at 17 eV very similar to the 16.9 eV band of benzene, and for which only a p atomic orbital origin is possible. On these grounds, the band at 16.9 eV is assigned to ionization from $3a_{1g}$ and that at 15.4 eV to ionization from $2b_{1u}$.

The vibrational structure of the first band in the benzene spectrum at 9.3 eV contains progressions in a degenerate vibrational mode, ν_{18}; the excitation of such a degenerate vibration is the first sign of a Jahn–Teller effect (see Chapter 6), and is further proof that the orbital involved is degenerate. The second band also has vibrational structure similar to that of the first band, and Åsbrink et al.[21] attribute the vibration of frequency 640 cm^{-1} to the same degenerate vibration, ν_{18}. This would be proof that the orbital concerned is degenerate and cannot be $1a_{2u}$. There are also Rydberg series that converge on the first and second ionization potentials, both with quantum defects of 0.46, very close to the defect in the series that converge on $3a_{1g}^{-1}$. The Rydberg orbitals for $3a_{1g}^{-1}$ and $1e_{1g}^{-1}$ ionizations are both p-type by symmetry, and the fact that no p-type Rydberg series is allowed in $1a_{2u}^{-1}$ ionization again points to the conclusion that the second ionization cannot be $1a_{2u}^{-1}$. This conclusion is now generally accepted, though it was at one time hotly debated[22]. The second band therefore includes the $1a_{2u}^{-1}$ ionization as its second component in order of vertical ionization potentials.

The ionizations that remain unassigned are the first component of the overlapping second band and both components of the overlapping third band, at 13.8 and 14.7 eV. In both bands, one component must be degenerate and one non-degenerate according to the band areas. The analysis follows from the angular distribution measurements of Carlson and Anderson[23], because, of the three remaining orbitals, $3e_{1u}$, $3e_{2g}$ and $1b_{2u}$, only one, $3e_{1u}$, is predicted to give an angular distribution characterized by a high β value on ionization. Only the band at 13.8 eV has a high β value experimentally, and this band must be the $3e_{1u}^{-1}$ ionization; the degenerate nature of this band is confirmed by its Jahn–Teller contour, as there are two maxima within the range of the high β value. Once $3e_{1u}^{-1}$ has been assigned, the 14.7 eV ionization must be $1b_{2u}^{-1}$ and the degenerate component of the second band must be $3e_{2g}^{-1}$. The analysis is now complete, and is shown in the last column of Table 4.3.

The experimental assignment is compared in Figure 4.4 with orbital energies obtained in an ab initio SCF calculation and a semi-empirical calculation (see below), and with binding energies calculated by the Green's function method (Section 4.6). The ordering of the SCF orbital energies agrees with the order deduced

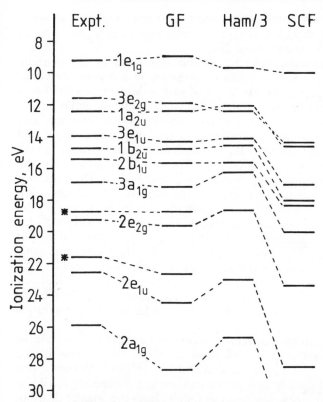

Figure 4.4   Comparison of the observed vertical ionization potentials of benzene with calculations by the Green's function method (von Niessen, W., Cederbaum, L.S. and Kraemer, W.P., *J. Chem. Phys.*, **65**, 1278 (1976), **69**, 1591 (1978)); the HAM/3 method[26] and the SCF method (Schulman, J.M. and Moskowitz, J.W., *J. Chem. Phys.*, **47**, 3491 (1967)). The two starred levels are CI bands, not shown in *Figure 4.3*, which appear weakly in the spectrum

from the photoelectron spectrum using Koopmans' theorem, while the absolute ionization energies are well reproduced by the semi-empirical calculation. The calculations going beyond the orbital model reproduce the experimental ionization potentials of benzene with great accuracy, and also get the right order. Nevertheless ionization potential calculations played only a minor role in the analysis of the spectrum. The characters of the different orbitals, on the other hand, which were obtained from the wave-functions, were essential for the assignment.

4.5.3   Semi-empirical calculations

Semi-empirical calculations involve further simplifications to the HF method, and because of the simplifications achieved they can be applied to large and complex molecules. The different methods are generally known by their acronyms such as CNDO, INDO, MINDO and SPINDO, where NDO = neglect of differential overlap, C = complete, I = intermediate, M = modified and SP = spectroscopic potentials adjusted. The semi-empirical nature of these calculations consists in the replacement of certain integrals by parameters that are chosen so that the theory agrees with experiment (or with better SCF calculations) for certain properties of a restricted range of standard molecules. It is then hoped that the calculations will have a high predictive value for these and other properties of a whole range of molecules for which they can be carried out, a hope which is sometimes fulfilled. Like the SCF calculations, they can be very useful in indicating the characters of different orbitals and hence the nature of the corresponding bands to be expected in the spectrum. Band widths, spin–orbit splittings or Jahn–Teller splittings can often be estimated more reliably than orbital energies.

Of most interest for photoelectron spectroscopy are the semi-empirical methods which have been evolved and parametrized specifically to calculate ionization energies. SPINDO was an early model of this sort[25], and HAM/3 is a worthy successor[26]. The ionization energies calculated by HAM/3, which invokes a semi-ionized transition state to overcome some of the limitations of Koopmans' approximation, are so accurate that they can be used as a tool in assigning unknown spectra, as *Figure 4.4* illustrates.

4.5.4   Empirical calculations

In empirical molecular orbital calculations, no attempt is made to mimic the HF method; the aim is rather to evolve the simplest possible theory, which can nevertheless be used to correlate a wide range of experimental results while using only a small number of arbitrary parameters. The best empirical method is Hückel molecular orbital (HMO) theory[3], which is applied to the π electron systems of conjugated and aromatic molecules, and has just two parameters. It has a most impressive record of success in correlating a wide range of physical and chemical properties of such compounds, both one-electron properties, such as the forms of the ultraviolet spectra and electron spin resonance spectra, and also properties that depend on the total π electron energy such as thermodynamic constants and many chemical reaction rates. Its success in interpreting photoelectron spectra of π electron molecules via Koopmans' theorem is no less impressive.

The simplest hydrocarbon molecules that contain π electrons are the acetylenes, in which the σ and π electron systems are completely separable because of the linear structure of the molecules. The photoelectron spectra of acetylene and diacetylene[27] are shown in *Figure 4.5*.

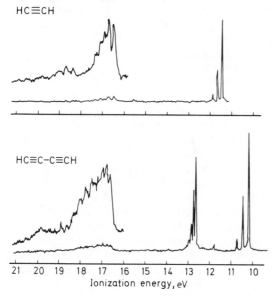

Figure 4.5   Photoelectron spectra of acetylene and diacetylene. (After Baker and Turner[27], by courtesy of the Chemical Society)

All models are in agreement that the outermost electrons in acetylene are in the degenerate π orbital, so the band with ionization potential at 11.8 eV in acetylene can confidently be attributed to the π_u^{-1} ionization. The vibrational structure excited in this ionization consists of a simple progression in 1830 cm^{-1}, which is identified as the vibration v_2. This is the symmetrical stretching of the C–C bond, exactly as expected if the effect of removing a π electron is simply to weaken this bond so that it is longer in the ion than in the molecule. When two acetylene molecules are joined together in diacetylene, two occupied π orbitals appear, one of them lower and one higher in energy than the π orbital of acetylene. The two bands in diacetylene that are placed symmetrically about the ionization potential of acetylene can confidently be attributed to ionization from these two new orbitals. The symmetrical placing of two π^{-1} ionization bands in the spectrum of diacetylene about the ionization potential of acetylene is not predicted by the simplest HMO theory, which completely omits overlap integrals and treats all bonds, whatever their length, as equivalent. If either of these two approximations is dropped, the observed pattern can be reproduced. The patterns of π molecular orbital energies for acetylene and diacetylene are, however, so simple that they could be predicted without any calculation from the empirical idea of how two new orbitals are created when two systems interact. This is no longer so for the

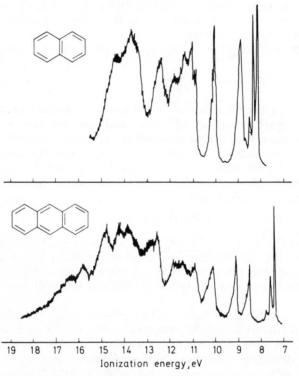

Figure 4.6 Photoelectron spectra of naphthalene and anthracene. (From Clark, Brogli and Heilbronner[30], by courtesy of the Swiss Chemical Society)

larger conjugated hydrocarbons and here HMO calculations are invaluable in interpreting the photoelectron spectra. Aromatic hydrocarbons from naphthalene[28] to ovalene[29] have been studied and their π electron ionization bands have been identified and assigned to definite ionic states by comparison with HMO calculations. The spectra of naphthalene and anthracene are shown in *Figure 4.6* as examples for this class of compound[30]. Typical features are the sharp bands at low ionization potential, all of which correspond to π electron ionizations, followed by a broad and unresolved structure at energies greater than 10 eV, corresponding to ionization from the σ orbitals. The ionization energy for the highest occupied σ orbital does not vary much from naphthalene, where it is 11 eV, to the largest molecules studied, where continuous bands begin at about 10.5 eV. The first ionization energy decreases from 9.25 eV in benzene to 8.12 eV in naphthalene and 6.74 eV in pentacene, so the outermost orbitals are predominantly of the π type.

In HMO theory, the orbital energy ε_j of the jth π orbital is given by an expression

$$\varepsilon_j = \alpha + m_j \beta \tag{4.4}$$

where m_j is the Hückel coefficient, which can easily be calculated or obtained from standard tables[31], and α and β are the only two arbitrary parameters, called the coulomb and resonance integrals. Brogli and Heilbronner[11] have compared 34 experimental ionization potentials for unsaturated and conjugated compounds ranging from ethylene to phenanthrene with the HMO orbital energies, and found the linear regression

$$I_j = 6.553 \pm 0.34 + m_j(2.734 \pm 0.333)\,\text{eV} \tag{4.5}$$

The uncertainties correspond to 90% confidence limits. Only for ethylene does the experimental ionization energy differ by more than 1 eV from the calculated value, a result which compares favourably with that obtained in HF calculations on small molecules.

The agreement between theory and experiment reached by the simplest HMO theory is already good, and enables most π electron ionization bands to be identified with reasonable certainty. Nevertheless, the deviations from exact agreement are interesting. In anthracene, it is very noticeable that whereas HMO theory predicts two pairs of degenerate orbitals, the photoelectron spectrum (*Figure 4.6*) contains only single bands (from their intensities) in the region where ionization from one of the degenerate pairs is expected. The predicted degeneracy is not a result of molecular symmetry but of the simplifying assumptions of HMO theory, particularly that all bonds are exactly equivalent. That this is not in fact true is easiest to visualize by using the valence bond model of molecular structure, because when the canonical forms for anthracene are drawn, double bonds do not occur in all possible positions with equal frequency. Compensation for the effect of this bond fixation on the ionization potentials can be made by a first-order perturbation treatment[11], which yields the equation

$$I_j = a + m_j b_1 + y_j b_2 \tag{4.6}$$

where m_j has the same meaning as in equation 4.4, y_j is a similar calculated coefficient and a, b_1 and b_2 are three empirical parameters. The fit of the measured ionization potentials to this modified HMO theory is excellent, the maximum deviation between theory and calculation for any of the sample ionization potentials being less than 0.5 eV. None of the SCF methods used on the same molecules and interpreted by Koopmans' theorem gives such a close fit, and even re-minimization of the ionic states in order to calculate first ionization potentials is not significantly better. The modified HMO model is an excellent example of an empirical theory of high predictive value for ionization potentials, and has been used in the interpretation of several photoelectron spectra.

The enormous recent increases in power and availability of computers have diminished the interest of empirical m.o. calculations, particularly those limited to π-electrons only, for the assignment of photoelectron spectra. When semi-empirical calculations for all electrons (such as HAM/3) can be carrried out easily and at little cost, the value of Hückel-type models must be mainly didactic in the insights they permit into the relationships between the orbital structures and spectra of related compounds.

4.6   Beyond orbitals and Koopmans' approximation

A straightforward way to avoid the approximations of the one-electron model and frozen orbitals would be to carry out full SCF–CI calculations on ground-state molecules and on the molecular ions in each accessible state separately. While such a procedure would undoubtedly yield excellent results it would be prohibitively costly in computer time, and it has never been done in full, not even for a single molecule. Instead, much more efficient ways of taking account of electron correlation and reorganization have been introduced. The different methods are known again by acronyms, many of which may, of course, prove to be transitory. Examples are the coupled electron pair approximation[32] (CEPA), multi-reference double excitation configuration interaction[33] (MRD–CI), frozen orbital approximation including reorganization and correlation[34] (FOA(R)), and frozen orbital configuration interaction with quadrupole correction[35] (FOCI+Q). The hitherto most successful and widely applied of these methods, however, is the Green's function approach of Cederbaum and von Niessen[36] (GF). This method takes its name from a mathematical technique widely used in physics to simplify many body problems, by transforming the representation. Its starting point is the molecular wavefunctions, usually from *ab*

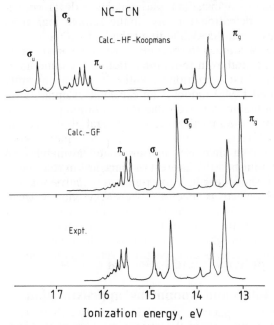

Figure 4.7   The photoelectron spectrum of cyanogen as experimentally observed (bottom), compared with an SCF calculation of full HF accuracy interpreted using Koopmans' theorem (top) and with a Green's function calculation (middle), which allows for both reorganization and correlation effects. (From Cederbaum, L.S., Domke, W. and von Niessen, W., *Chem. Phys.*, **10**, 459 (1975))

initio SCF calculations, and the final result does depend on the quality of these starting wave-functions. The improvement achieved by this method compared with HF–Koopmans' calculations is dramatically illustrated by the photoelectron spectrum of cyanogen, shown in *Figure 4.7*.

While the GF approach is at least as good as any other calculational technique for the assignment of photoelectron spectra in the normal energy range, it is in the inner valence region (usually above 18 eV) that its real power becomes apparent. As explained already, the one orbital–one band picture (indeed, the orbital model itself) fails in the inner valence region, where ionic states are not at all accurately described by the single configurations of a one-electron model. At an energy where a single ionization process might be expected, producing a hole in an inner valence orbital (C 2s, for instance), there may be many states of the same symmetry in which an outer valence orbital hole is accompanied by one or more electron excitations. If we start from the orbital model, we must conclude that correlation effects in the ion mix the single-hole state with the other states, allowing them to appear in the photoelectron spectrum. The GF technique is especially well able to cope with this situation[37], and can provide accurate predictions or explanations of complete He II photoelectron spectra, including all the 'extra' bands.

Paradoxically, the one-electron orbital model works rather better for inner shell (e.g. C 1s) ionizations than for inner valence ionizations, because the small physical extent of the inner shell holes makes the mixing with valence states negligibly weak. Thus, although satellite lines appear in X-ray photoelectron spectra, the main inner orbital ionization processes are always clearly apparent.

4.7 Ionization potentials and molecular charge distributions

In X-ray photoelectron spectroscopy, the ionization potentials of inner shell electrons are measured and are found to vary slightly with the chemical environment of the atoms in a molecule[38]. Because there are essentially no direct interactions between orbitals of the inner shells, these chemical shifts are due to changes in the electrical potential of the inner electrons caused by charges on the atoms within the molecules. Extensive comparisons of observed shift with calculated atomic charge distributions have shown that the relationship between the shift and charge is almost linear. This result agrees with an electrostatic model[39], which indicates that a charge q on a sphere of radius r produces a change of potential $\Delta U = q/r$ throughout the interior of the sphere. The chemical shift on a particular atom should be the same for all inner shells, and this is also found to be true. In a molecule, the charge removed by bond polarization from one atom is located on other atoms, so the chemical shift includes contributions from these more distant charges. The change in potential can be written as

$$\Delta U = \frac{q}{r} + \sum_i \frac{\delta q_i}{R_i} \tag{4.7}$$

where R_i is the distance from the atom of interest to the ith other atom carrying charge δq_i. If the ionization potential shift, ΔU, is measured, the atomic charge, q, can be calculated provided that the constant $1/r$ is known and the other charges and distances can be estimated.

The relevance of these remarks to ultraviolet photoelectron spectroscopy is that even with 21.2 eV radiation some inner shell ionizations can be seen, and with 40.8 eV light the range is greatly extended. This means that ultraviolet photoelectron spectroscopy provides a means of deducing the charge distribution in several molecules and thence also the partial ionic characters of the bonds.

The inner shell ionizations that one can observe in the ultra-violet energy range are those of the full d shells of the B-group metals (Cu, Ag, Au, Zn, Cd and Hg with He I), those of the full p shells of the alkali metal and alkaline earth metal atoms (K and Ba with He I) and the full f shells of the third-row transition metals. Ionization from many of these d shells[40,41] and from some f shells[42] has been examined and both the shifts and splittings of the inner shell bands have been studied. As examples of the photoelectron spectra, those of mercury(II) bromide and dimethylmercury are shown in *Figures 4.8* and *4.9*. The d electron ionizations produce three bands in the spectra at ionization potentials above 15 eV; for mercury(II) bromide they are 16.4, 16.8 and 18.3 eV and for dimethylmercury 15.0, 15.4 and 16.9 eV. These bands were originally[43] attributed to $Hg\,5d^{-1}$ ionizations on the following grounds:

(1) They appear in the spectrum of every mercury compound examined.
(2) The relative spacing of the three bands remains almost constant, although the absolute position on the energy scale varies.

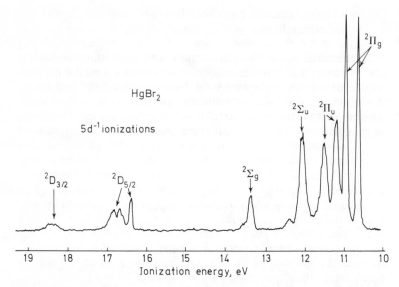

Figure 4.8   Photoelectron spectrum of mercury(II) bromide, showing the 5d electron ionizations. (From Eland[43], by courtesy of Elsevier Publishing Company)

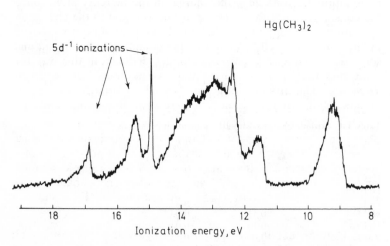

Figure 4.9   Photoelectron spectrum of dimethylmercury, showing the 5d^{-1} ionization bands above 15 eV ionization energy. (From Eland[43], by courtesy of Elsevier Publishing Company)

(3) The spacing of the two outer bands is close to 1.86 eV, the spin–orbit splitting of the ^2D state of Hg^+.

Of the three bands, the one at the lowest ionization potential is always sharp, and it represents ionization from a d orbital perpendicular to the axis of the molecule. None of the valence orbitals of the molecule can interact with this orbital, so it is essentially non-bonding. The ionic state produced has a total electronic angular momentum of $\pm5/2$; it corresponds to one component of the $^2D_{5/2}$ state of the atomic mercury ion. The second band is clearly split in the spectra of some compounds and corresponds to the $J = 3/2$ and $J = 1/2$ components of $^2D_{5/2}$, which do experience some interactions with the valence electrons in the molecule. The third band, which is also sometimes split, corresponds similarly to the formation of $J = 3/2$ and $J = 1/2$ states derived from $^2D_{3/2}$ of Hg^+. The classification of electronic states according to J value rather than according to orbital angular momentum is necessary because the splitting of the ^2D state by spin–orbit interactions is much larger than that caused by the valence interactions.

The shift between the sharp $J = 5/2$ peak and the $^2D_{5/2}$ ionization potential of atomic mercury is a direct measure of the difference between the mercury atom in the molecule and a free mercury atom. The shifts can be equated with changes in potential and used in equation 4.7 to deduce the charge on the mercury atom, once the constant $1/r$ is known. This constant is equal to the change in ionization potential of the d shell produced by unit positive charge in the outer 6s shell, and it can be obtained from the atomic spectrum of mercury[43]. Atomic charges deduced in this way for some mercury(II), zinc and cadmium compounds[44] are given in *Table 4.4*. The atomic charges are closely related to such parameters as the partial ionic characters of the bonds and the

Table 4.4 Atomic charges from $1d^{-1}$ ionization potentials

Compound	Shift eV	Charge on metal (units of e)
$HgCl_2$	1.87	0.42
$HgBr_2$	1.56	0.33
HgI_2	1.15	0.23
$HgMe_2$	0.11	0.03
$HgEt_2$	−0.16	−0.04
$ZnCl_2$	2.04	0.53
$ZnBr_2$	1.69	0.39
$CdCl_2$	1.98	0.50
$CdBr_2$	1.70	0.39

electronegativities of the different atoms and groups, which can readily be derived from the measurements. The change in sign of the charge on mercury between the dimethyl and diethyl compound shows, for instance, that the electron-attracting power of a mercury atom is intermediate between those of the methyl and the ethyl groups. The charges in the chlorides and bromides demonstrate that the electronegativities of zinc and cadmium are about equal, and less than that of mercury[44]. In the spectra of compounds of zinc and cadmium, and also of Ga, In and Tl, the splitting of the d ionization bands is due only partly to spin–orbit coupling. Another major influence is the molecular ligand field which, if it is dominant in a linear molecule, produces $^2\Delta$, $^2\Pi$ and $^2\Sigma^+$ ionic states. The $^2\Sigma$ state will normally be of lowest ionization potential, since the d orbital concentrated along the bonds is most strongly destabilized by ligand charges. Detailed calculations of the ligand-field effects have been made, and it has been shown that the experimental spectra give information on the asymmetric part of the field, from which electric field gradients can also be derived[40].

References

1. HOTOP, H., HUBLER, G. and KAUFHOLD, L., *Int. J. Mass Spectrom. Ion Phys.*, **17**, 163 (1975)
2. BREHM, B., *Nineteenth Annual Conference on Mass Spectrometry and Allied Topics*, Atlanta, Georgia, American Society for Mass Spectrometry, 78 (1971)
3. MURRELL, J.N., KETTLE, S.F.A. and TEDDER, J.M., *Valence Theory*, John Wiley, London (1965)
4. KOOPMANS, T., *Physica*, **1**, 104 (1933)
5. NEWTON, M.D., *J. Chem. Phys.*, **48**, 2825 (1968)
6. RICHARDS, W.G., *Int. J. Mass Spectrom. Ion Phys.*, **2**, 419 (1969)
7. DODDS, J.L. and MCWEENEY, R., *Chem. Phys. Lett.*, **13**, 9 (1972)
8. EVANS, S., GREEN, J.C. and JACKSON, S.E., *J. Chem. Soc., Faraday Trans. II*, **68**, 249 (1972)
9. COX, P.A. and ORCHARD, A.F., *Chem. Phys. Lett.*, **7**, 273 (1970)
10. CLEMENTI, E., *Chem. Rev.*, **68**, 341 (1968)
11. BROGLI, F. and HEILBRONNER, E., *Theor. Chim. Acta*, **26**, 289 (1972)
12. HEILBRONNER, E. and SCHMELTZER, A., *Nouv. J. chimie*, **4**, 23 (1980)
13. KRAUSS, M., *N.B.S. Tech. Note No. 438*, U.S. Government Printing Office, Washington, D.C. (1967)
14. BRUNDLE, C.R., ROBIN, M.B., BASCH, H., PINSKY, M. and BOND, A., *J. Amer. Chem. Soc.*, **92**, 3863 (1970)
15. BRUNDLE, C.R., ROBIN, M.B. and JONES, G.R., *J. Chem. Phys.*, **52**, 3383 (1970)
16. BREHM, B., MENZINGER, M. and ZORN, C., *Can. J. Chem.*, **48**, 3193 (1970)

17. JONSSON, B.Ö. and LINDHOLM, E., *Ark. Fysik*, **39**, 65 (1969)
18. BIERI, G. and ÅSBRINK, L., *J. Electron Spectrosc. Rel. Phen.*, **20**, 149 (1980)
19. PRAND, L., MILLIE, P. and BERTHIER, G., *Theor. Chim. Acta*, **11**, 169 (1968)
20. ÅSBRINK, L., EDQVIST, O., LINDHOLM, E. and SELIN, L.E., *Chem. Phys. Lett.*, **5**, 192 (1970)
21. ÅSBRINK, L., LINDHOLM, E. and EDQVIST, O., *Chem. Phys. Lett.*, **5**, 609 (1970)
22. POTTS, A.W., PRICE, W.C., STREETS, D.G. and WILLIAMS, T.A., *Discuss. Faraday Soc.*, **54**, 168 (1973)
23. CARLSON, T.A. and ANDERSON, C.P., *Chem. Phys. Let.*, **10**, 561 (1971)
24. MATTSSON, L., KARLSSON, L., JADRNY, R. and SIEGBAHN, K., *Phys. Scripta*, **16**, 221 (1977)
25. LINDHOLM, E., FRIDH, C. and ÅSBRINK, L., *Discuss. Faraday Soc.*, **54**, 127 (1973)
26. ÅSBRINK, L., FRIDH, C. and LINDHOLM, E., *Chem. Phys. Lett.*, **52**, 63, 69 (1977)
27. BAKER, C and TURNER, D.W., *Chem. Commun.*, 797 (1967)
28. ELAND, J.H.D. and DANBY, C.J., *Z. Naturforsch.*, **23a**, 355 (1968)
29. BOSCHI, R., MURRELL, J.N. and SCHMIDT, W., *Discuss. Faraday Soc.*, **54**, 116 (1973)
30. CLARK, P.A., BROGLI, F. and HEILBRONNER, E., *Helv. Chim. Acta*, **55**, 1415 (1972)
31. COULSON, C.A. and STREITWEISER, A., JR., *Dictionary of π-Electron Calculations*, Pergamon Press, London (1965)
32. MEYER, W., *J. Chem. Phys.*, **58**, 1017 (1973)
33. BUENKER, R.J., PEYERIMHOFF, S.D. and BUTSCHER, W., *Mol. Phys.*, **35**, 771 (1978)
34. MÜLLER, W., NAGER, Ch. and ROSMUS, P., *J. Chem. Phys.*, to be published
35. LANGHOFF, S.R. and CHONG, D.P., *Chem. Phys.*, **55**, 355 (1981)
36. CEDERBAUM, L.S., *Theoret. Chim. Acta*, **31**, 239 (1973); *J. Physics, B, Atom. Molec. Phys.*, **8**, 290 (1975); CEDERBAUM, L.S. and VON NIESSON, W., *Chem. Phys. Lett.*, **24**, 263 (1974)
37. SCHIRMER, J. and CEDERBAUM, L.S., *J. Physics B, Atom. Molec. Phys.*, **11**, 1889 (1978)
38. SIEGBAHN, K., NORDLING, C., FAHLMAN, A., NORDBERG, R., HAMRINN, K., HEDMAN, J., KOHANSSON, G., BERGMARK, T., KARLSSON, S.E., LINDGREN, I. and LINDBERG, B., *Nova Acta Regiae Soc. Sci. Upsal.*, *Ser. IV*, **20** (1967)
39. FAHLMAN, A., HAMRIN, K., HEDMAN, K., NORDBERG, J., NORDLING, R. and SIEGBAHN, K., *Nature, Lond.*, **210**, 4 (1966)
40. BANCROFT, B.M., COATSWORTH, L.L., CREBER, D.K. and TSE, J., *Physica Scripta*, **16**, 217 (1977); BANCROFT, G.M. and GUPTA, R.P., *Chem. Phys. Lett.*, **54**, 226 (1978)
41. POTTS, A.W. and PRICE, W.C., *Physica Scripta*, **16**, 191 (1977)
42. LEE, E.P.F., POTTS, A.W. and BLOOR, J.E., *Proc. Roy. Soc. Lond.*, **A381**, 373 (1982)
43. ELAND, J.H.D., *Int. J. Mass Spectrom. Ion Phys.*, **4**, 37 (1970)
44. BERKOWITZ, J., *J. Chem. Phys.*, **61**, 407 (1974)

5

Photoelectron band structure—I

5.1 Introduction

The position of a photoelectron band indicates the energy of an ionic state, whereas the structure of the band gives information about the structure and bonding of the ions in that state. If a band has resolved vibrational fine structure we can examine the identities and frequencies of the modes excited on ionization, and the vibrational line intensities. An unresolved band gives less but still useful information in its width and shape. The topics covered in this and the following chapter are the analysis of photoelectron band structures and the deductions that can be made from them, the simpler aspects being covered here, before Chapter 6 concentrates on the complexities of band structure that appear when orbitally degenerate states are reached in ionization.

Photoelectron spectra are primarily spectra of ions, but because of Koopmans' theorem, we can also make deductions from them about the electronic structure of the neutral molecules from which ionization takes place. These deductions depend on the reliable assumption of the Franck–Condon principle and on the less reliable assumption of Koopmans' theorem. They also depend on the applicability of the orbital model, and on an assumed similarity between the normal modes of vibration of the molecule and ion. Both of these assumptions are usually valid for low-lying ionic states, but *may* break down partially even there. For states in the inner valence region, roughly for ionization energies above about 18 eV, these assumptions are likely to break down completely, so that no *simple* deductions about electronic structure can be made from the ionization band shapes. Two characteristics of the inner valence region force this breakdown:

(1) The states observed in the inner valence region mostly require more than one configuration (in terms of orbital

134

occupancy) for their description, so they are not produced just by electron ejection from one orbital.

(2) The bands often consist of several states in close proximity; the vibration structure is not just an overlay of straightforward structure from each electronic state, but is complicated by interference effects—vibronic interactions.

Another matter which is also involved is the question of charge delocalization following ionization. When inner-shell electrons are ionized by X-ray photons, it seems that the charges do not become delocalized over all the equivalent atoms in a molecule on the time scale of the experiment. If a 1s electron is removed from carbon in acetylene, for instance, the kinetic energy of the ejected electron can be calculated accurately only if it is assumed that one carbon atom in the $C_2H_2^+$ ion has a vacancy in its 1s orbital and the other is not affected. When symmetrical charges of $+\frac{1}{2}$ on each carbon atom are assumed, the calculated ionization energy changes by about 6 eV, which is more than the experimental or computational error[1]. On the other hand, ionization of any valence electron from the C_2H_2 molecule certainly results in a symmetrical charge distribution in the ions on the time scale of ultraviolet photoelectron spectroscopy. It is perhaps possible that a changeover occurs as one chooses deeper and deeper lying electrons. Similarly, it is not clear what happens when one lone-pair electron is ionized from a large molecule that contains two equivalent heteroatoms well separated in space. Localization or delocalization must affect the structure of the molecular ions and hence may also have an observable effect on band structures in photoelectron spectra.

In discussing the structure of photoelectron bands, it is necessary to refer repeatedly to vibrational modes or normal modes of vibration. The definition of normal modes and their forms in different molecules cannot be included here and must be studied in textbooks on symmetry or infrared and Raman spectroscopy[2].

5.2 Analysis of vibrational structure

In order to identify the vibrational modes that are excited on ionization one first compares the vibrational intervals observed in a photoelectron band with the ground state vibrational frequencies of the molecule, which are known from infrared or Raman spectroscopy. It is very rare for the frequencies of the same mode in the molecule and ion to differ by more than a factor of two, and much smaller changes are usual. This alone is not sufficient for positive identifications except in very small or highly symmetrical molecules that have few vibrational modes. A useful adjunct is the fact that both the change in frequency and the change in equilibrium bond lengths following ionization are related to the bonding character of the electron removed. These two effects are also, therefore, related to one another, and if a proposed assignment involves a large change in frequency between molecule and ion, excitation of a long progression in that frequency is to be expected on ionization. This idea has been placed on a semi-quantitative basis by Turner[3], who showed that the fractional change in frequency and the difference between adiabatic and vertical ionization potentials are roughly linearly related. A diagram showing the relationship is reproduced in *Figure 5.1* and it can be used to check the suitability of possible identifications.

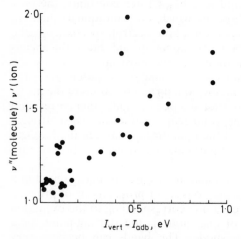

Figure 5.1   Relationship between the change in frequency on ionization and the vibrational excitation energy. (From Turner[3], by courtesy of the Council of the Royal Society)

An important aid to the unravelling of vibrational structure is the existence of selection rules for vibrational excitation in all electronic transitions, including ionization. The selection rules indicate those vibrational modes which should be excited strongly and those excitations which are forbidden in the ionization of molecules with elements of symmetry. These selection rules are based on the Franck–Condon principle and can be explained as follows. If the electronic and vibrational motions can be separated, then in an electronically allowed band* the relative intensity of a vibrational transition from the vibrational level v'' in the molecule to v' in the ion is given by the Franck–Condon factor (FCF), which is equal to the square of the overlap integral between the vibrational wave-functions $\chi_{v''}$ and $\chi_{v'}$:

$$FCF = | <\chi_{v'} | \chi_{v''}> |^2 \qquad (5.1)$$

Within one electronic state, the vibrational wave-functions for levels with different vibrational quantum numbers, v, are orthogonal to one another, that is, the overlap integrals between them are zero. If another electronic state has a potential energy surface of the same shape, the vibrational wave-functions will also be the same, and the overlap integrals will be zero for transitions that involve any change in vibrational quantum number. If there is little change in the potential energy surface on ionization, in other words little change in bond lengths or force constants, the only strong transitions are those in which the vibrational quantum number remains the same. As in photoelectron spectroscopy the target molecules are in their vibrational ground states, this means that adiabatic (0–0) transitions are the most intense. If, on the other hand, there is a change in the shape of the potential energy surface on ionization so that the equilibrium positions of the nuclei are different, then the vibrational mode or modes that correspond most closely to the change in nuclear positions are most strongly excited. This is the basis of the relationship between the localization of bonding character of particular electrons and the structure of ionization bands.

When two or more vibrational modes are strongly excited in a transition, the band structure consists of progressions of progressions, which means that each line corresponding to the excitation of a number of quanta of one mode is the starting-point for a progression in the other mode. The bands can become very complicated, and the resolution in photoelectron spectroscopy has up to now been such that only if one mode is much less strongly excited than the other have bands been fully assigned. Examples of progressions of progressions are seen in the photoelectron spectrum of carbonyl fluoride, shown in *Figure 5.2*.

An important *caveat* must be entered at this point on the nature of the normal modes; they cannot always be assumed to be the

---

*Almost all photoionization bands are electronically allowed in this sense, as the ionizations that are electronically forbidden, for example two-electron processes, cannot be made allowed by vibronic interactions.

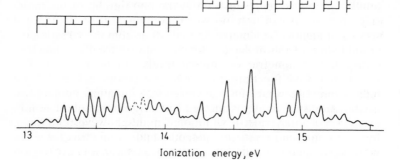

Figure 5.2   Partial photoelectron spectrum of carbonyl fluoride showing progressions of progressions. The vibrational analysis is indicated above. (From Thomas, R.K. and Thompson, H., *Proc. R. Soc., Lond.*, **A327**, 13 (1972), by courtesy of the Council of the Royal Society)

same in the ion as in the molecule. Whenever there is more than one mode of the same symmetry, contributions of different atomic motions to each mode may change radically between molecule and ion, to such an extent that frequency comparisons between molecule and ion, for instance, become meaningless. A dramatic case is the $\tilde{B}\,^2\Sigma^+$ state of HCN^+. The two stretching modes in neutral HCN are of the same symmetry, one being essentially a C–H stretch, the other a CN stretch. In the $\tilde{B}\,^2\Sigma^+$ state of HCN^+ there is only one progression of bound vibrational states, representing an in-phase stretching of both CH and C–N bonds, while the other symmetric mode is a dissociation continuum. Changes of normal-mode nature in larger polyatomic species between molecule and ion are seldom as severe as this, but are probably of very frequent occurrence. They are sometimes referred to as the Duschinsky effect[4], and may have a considerable effect on vibrational line intensities.

5.2.1   Vibrational selection rules

All that has been said up to now applies equally to symmetrical and unsymmetrical molecules. For molecules with some elements of symmetry there are more exact selection rules which help with the interpretation of vibrational structure.

If the overlap integral in equation 5.1 is to be non-zero, the product of the vibrational wave-functions must be fully symmetric. In the language of group theory, the direct product of the representations to which $\chi_{v'}$ and $\chi_{v''}$ belong must be or contain the totally symmetric representation in the point group of the molecule and ion; it can only do so for combinations of vibrational species of identical symmetry. In ionization from the vibrationless ground state of the molecule, which is always totally symmetric, only totally symmetric vibrational levels can be reached. The vibrational wave-functions for symmetric vibrational modes are fully symmetric whatever the vibrational quantum number, so excitation of such modes is allowed with any number of quanta. In excitation of antisymmetric vibrational modes, however, the wave-functions are antisymmetric for odd and symmetric for even vibrational quantum numbers. Such modes can be excited on ionization only in units of two quanta:

$$\Delta v_k = 0, \pm 2, \pm 4 \ldots \tag{5.2}$$

The intensities of the transitions with double quantal excitation are very much less than that of the (0–0) transition, because the vibrational wave-functions in the upper state always have their maxima at the symmetrical position directly above the vibration-less ground state on a Franck–Condon diagram. Even for a change in frequency of an antisymmetric mode by a factor of two, 95% of the total intensity remains in the (0–0) transition. This conclusion applies strictly when there is only one antisymmetric mode of each symmetry class, but is relaxed (the Duschinsky effect) when two or more modes of the same symmetry are present.

Excitation of degenerate vibrational modes on ionization is governed by the same rules as those for the excitation of anti-symmetric modes, and only weak transitions in units of two quanta are allowed. For certain point groups, the odd quantal states of degenerate vibrations are also antisymmetric with respect to at least one element of symmetry and rule 5.2 applies strictly. In other instances, transitions with $\Delta v_k = \pm 3, \pm 5$ may be very weakly allowed, but $\Delta v_k = \pm 1$ is always strictly forbidden. The formal vibrational selection rules may be summarized as follows:

(1) Only totally symmetric modes may be excited with arbitrary number of quanta.

(2) Antisymmetric and degenerate vibrations should be excited only weakly, and with even numbers of quanta in ionization from the $v'' = 0$ ground state.

By and large, these rules give a good description of vibrational structure in the spectra of small molecules, particularly in ionization to low-lying ionic states. The only vibrations strongly excited

[handwritten margin note: not true if ion/neutral is of v. different symmetry e.g. C2v vs. Cs (different bond lengths)]

in ionization of a linear symmetric triatomic molecule like CO_2 or CS_2 is the totally symmetric stretch v_1, for instance, while in $C_{\infty v}$ molecules (COS or HCN, N_2O) both v_1 and the anti-symmetric stretch v_3 are seen. The spectra of bent symmetric triatomics (C_{2v} symmetry) like SO_2 and H_2O show strong excitation of the symmetric stretch and the bending vibration v_2, which are both totally symmetric, but not of the antisymmetric stretch v_3.

When weaker vibrational lines in photoelectron spectra are examined, the formal vibrational selection rules are rather less successful. Weak double-quantal excitation of the bending mode, v_2, is seen in the ground state $\tilde{X} \, ^2\Pi$ of N_2O^+, for instance, but several cases of excitation of the 'strictly forbidden' single quanta of v_2 and v_3 have also been found. Examples[5] are excitation of $1v_2$ in the $\tilde{B}$ states of CS_2^+ and COS^+, and in the $\tilde{C}$ states of CO_2^+ and N_2O^+, and excitation of $1v_3$ in the $\tilde{C}$ states of CO_2^+ and CS_2^+. These examples all refer to the He I ionization, where autoionization is not suspected; at longer wavelengths (e.g. Ne I), autoionization can produce strong excitation of 'forbidden' vibrations, by passing through intermediate states of lower symmetry.

The reason for the breakdown of the formal selection rule, even without autoionization, is *vibronic coupling*. This is a mixing of electronic states induced by nuclear motion; if it occurs, the symmetry-based selection rules apply only to the overall symmetry of a level, which is the product of the purely electronic and purely vibrational symmetries. The effect is that vibrational levels which would otherwise be forbidden appear in the spectrum with intensities dependent on the strength of their coupling to other electronic states whose production is allowed. The *electronic* characteristics of the new vibrational peaks, particularly the electron angular-distribution parameters, β, and the quantum defects in Rydberg series that converge on the new levels, are likely to be characteristic of the electronic state from which they gain intensity in the spectrum, rather than of the electronic state to which they belong. These effects are clearly illustrated in the fourth band of the photoelectron spectrum of CO_2, showing formation of the $\tilde{C} \, ^2\Sigma_g^+$ state. The interloper peak assigned as one quantum of the bending mode, which is of vibronic symmetry $\Pi_u \times \Sigma_g = \Pi_u$, has a β value close to that of the normal peaks of the $\tilde{A} \, ^2\Pi_u$ band ($\beta = 0.8$), instead of the $\beta = 1.2$ characteristic of the allowed $\tilde{C}$ state peaks. The unusually strong peak attributed to excitation of one quantum of v_2 and one of v_3 has vibronic symmetry $\Pi_u \times \Sigma_u \times \Pi_g = \Pi_g$, and its β value is much lower (0.2), close to the $\beta = -0.15$ of $\tilde{X} \, ^2\Pi_g$. A detailed analysis has been given by Domcke[6], and particulars of the Rydberg series and related dissociation characteristics are given by Eland and Berkowitz[5].

If ionization causes a change in equilibrium symmetry between molecule and ion, such as bent to linear, non-planar to planar or vice versa, the preceding rules still apply, but only in respect of symmetry elements that are common to the initial and final state. Hence in a linear to bent transition of a symmetric triatomic molecule, excitation of the bending mode, which is degenerate in the linear form, becomes allowed, but excitation of the antisymmetric stretching mode remains forbidden, except weakly in double quanta.

When ionization produces an orbitally degenerate state of the molecular ion, as it does if ionization is from a degenerate orbital, there is frequently a change in molecular geometry and the vibrational structure may be complex. In transitions to degenerate electronic states, the selection rules previously given apply only if coupling between electronic and vibrational motions in the degenerate state is negligible. Molecules that have orbitally degenerate electronic states also possess degenerate vibrational modes, and interactions that involve the two degeneracies cause complications in the spectra. The complications, when they occur, are severe and comprise the Jahn–Teller effects in non-linear molecules and the Renner–Teller and related effects in linear molecules; these topics are considered in Chapter 6. Coupling of the vibrational and electronic motions means that resolution of the transition moment into electronic and vibrational parts is no longer valid, and the selection rules must be based on the vanishing or non-vanishing of the dipole matrix element $< \Psi|M|\Psi >$. The wave-functions Ψ now describe vibronic states, and the electron continuum is included in the final state wave-function for a photoionization process.

In the photoelectron spectra of linear molecules, there are many examples of ionization to degenerate electronic states where no complications are seen and the normal selection rules are obeyed. In the spectra of non-linear molecules, on the other hand, bands due to degenerate electronic states usually do involve complications that can be attributed to Jahn–Teller effects. Similar complications (pseudo-Jahn–Teller effects) may arise even in bands for non-degenerate states, as discussed in the next chapter.

5.3   Interpretation of vibrational structure

Resolved vibrational structure within a band contains useful information in the vibrational intervals themselves, in the identity of the vibrational modes excited and in the relative intensities of the vibrational lines. All of these allow direct deductions to be made about the nature of the ionic state produced, and also about differences between the ionic state and the molecular ground state from which ionization takes place. The changes in molecular geometry caused by ionization of particular electrons can be deduced if the vibrational structure of a band is resolved; they provide the closest characterization of the bonding power of electrons in molecules possible by photoelectron spectroscopy.

5.3.1 Frequencies and anharmonicities

The change in frequency of a vibration on ionization is related to the change in bond strength and thus to the bonding power of the electron removed, and little more information can normally be obtained from vibrational spacings alone. One exception is the halving of the frequency of a bending vibration, which is observed when the molecular geometry changes from bent or non-planar in the molecules to linear or planar in the ions (see Chapter 6, Section 6.5). When a long vibrational progression is found, it is also possible to look for a variation of the spacing of the levels with the vibrational quantum number, and so to derive the anharmonicity constant $\omega_e x_e$.

The energies of vibrational levels in a diatomic molecule or a single vibrational mode of a polyatomic molecule can often be accurately represented by the expression:

$$G(\upsilon) = (\upsilon + \tfrac{1}{2})\omega_e - (\upsilon + \tfrac{1}{2})^2 \omega_e x_e \tag{5.3}$$

The energy is measured from the minimum of the potential energy surface. For the spacing between adjacent levels

$$\Delta G = \omega_e + 2\omega_e x_e - 2\upsilon\omega_e x_e \tag{5.4}$$

Hence the interval ΔG should be a linear function of the vibrational quantum number υ with a slope of $2\omega_e x_e$. If the spacing increases with increasing υ, the anharmonicity is said to be negative. This nomenclature arises because the potential energy curves for most diatomic molecules cause the levels to converge as they approach the dissociation limit, and such convergence is considered to be normal. Converging progressions are often found in the photoelectron spectra of diatomic molecules; *Figure 5.3* is a graph of ΔG against υ' for H_2^+ as an example. Negative anharmonicity is found most commonly in progressions due to bending vibrations; this is because in such vibrations the restoring

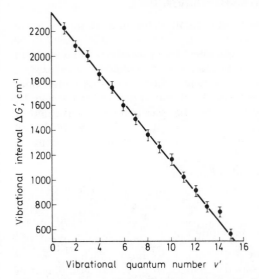

Figure 5.3 Graph of the vibrational interval in H_2^+ $(X\,^2\Sigma_g^+)$ against the upper state vibrational quantum number, showing positive anharmonicity. (From Cornford, A.B., Frost, D.C., McDowell, C.A., Ragle, J.L. and Stenhouse, A.I., in Quayle, A. (Editor) *Advances in Mass Spectrometry, Vol 5*, Institute of Petroleum, London (1971))

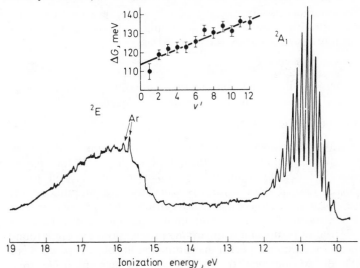

Figure 5.4 Photoelectron spectrum of ammonia with an inset showing negative inharmonicity in the $^2A_1$ band

force does not become weaker as the amplitude increases, but is rather increased by steric interactions when the oscillating groups approach each other. The second bands in the spectra of H_2O, H_2S, H_2Se and H_2Te are examples of this, and the first bands in the spectra of NH_3 and related molecules show the same effect. The increase in the vibrational interval at high vibrational quantum numbers can be seen in the photoelectron spectrum of ammonia in *Figure 5.4*.

5.3.2 Identity of the vibrations excited

If a molecule has several different totally symmetric vibrational modes, a relationship should exist between the localization of bonding or antibonding character in the electron removed and the identity of the vibrational mode that is most strongly excited on ionization. The best examples of a clear relationship of this type are found in the photoelectron spectra of the linear molecules of cyanogen[7], diacetylene[7] and the dihaloacetylenes[8]. In all of these molecules, ionization of the outermost π electron is accompanied by excitation of ν_1 and ionization of the inner π electron by excitation of ν_2. The relationship between the vibrational modes and the orbital structures is shown in *Figure 5.5*.

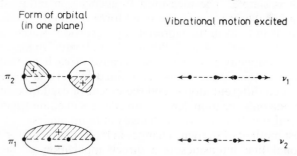

Figure 5.5   The forms of the π orbitals in cyanogen and the vibrational motions excited by ionization from them. The same relationship between orbital structure and motions of the heavy atoms holds for diacetylene, and a similar relationship for dihaloacetylenes

The outermost π orbitals are bonding across the triple bonds and antibonding across the central single bond; accordingly, the mode excited on ionization, ν_1, is one in which the triple bonds contract while the single bond expands. The inner π orbitals are bonding over the whole molecule, but most strongly over the central single bond, and ionization from them excites the symmetrical stretching, vibration v_2 in which the central single bond expands most. More often, the type of vibration excited, whether it is, for instance, a bending or a C–C or a C–H stretching, gives an indication of the nature of the electron removed. Ionization from the non-bonding but angle-determining lone-pair electrons in water or ammonia causes strong excitation of the bending vibrations, while removal of electrons that are more strongly involved in the bonding causes excitation of both bending and stretching vibrations. Some further examples from the photoelectron spectrum of benzene have been mentioned in Chapter 4, where the observation of progressions showing excitation of C–H as well as C–C stretching vibrations was used to help assign some of the bands.

5.3.3   Changes in molecular geometry on ionization

Once the vibrational modes excited in a particular ionization have been identified, one can proceed to an interpretation in terms of the changes produced in the molecules; these changes also reflect the bonding character of the electron removed, subject to the caveats mentioned in the introduction to this chapter. In diatomic molecules, all is simple. The measured frequencies in different states of the molecule or ion give the bond force constants, while the intensity distributions in the vibrational progressions lead to a determination of the changes in equilibrium bond length. In larger molecules, this simplicity is largely lost because in each normal mode of vibration the frequency is determined by several force constants between different atoms, and the extent of excitation of a particular mode on ionization depends on changes in equilibrium length in several bonds and also on changes in bond angles.

The simplest method of deriving changes in molecular geometry from vibrational line intensities is a direct application of the semi-classical Franck–Condon approximation to bands in which only a single vibrational mode is excited, where the motion in that mode is well described by variations in a single molecular coordinate, a bond length or angle. This is automatically true of the diatomic molecules and it is also true of the totally symmetric stretching vibrations in molecules of the forms linear BAB, tetrahedral AB_4, octahedral AB_6, square planar AB_4 and planar AB_3. Bending vibrations of non-linear BAB molecules and the umbrella bending vibration of pyramidal AB_3 molecules are also totally symmetric and can be reasonably described by a single molecular co-ordinate, so the changes in angle following ionization can be represented on a two-dimensional potential energy diagram like that for a diatomic molecule.

Consider the two-dimensional potential energy diagram of *Figure 1.5* with vibrational wave-functions illustrating the Franck–Condon principle. The wave-functions for high vibrational quantum numbers have their greatest amplitude near the potential energy curve itself, which gives the position of the turning points of the classical vibrational motion. The largest Franck–Condon factor for a transition from the ground state, and therefore the maximum intensity in a vibrational progression, occurs when the turning point in the ionic state comes at the same bond distance or angle as the equilibrium position in the ground state of the molecule. The energy of the classical oscillator that represents vibrations in the ion is proportional to the square of the vibrational amplitude at the turning point and can be set equal to the experimental vibrational energy in the ion at the vertical ionization potential. For a stretching vibration in a diatomic molecule,

$$2\pi^2\mu v'^2\delta^2 = (v'_{max} + \tfrac{1}{2})hv' = I_{vert} - I_{adb} \qquad (5.5)$$

where v' is the vibrational frequency in the ion, μ is the reduced mass appropriate for the vibration, v'_{max} is the vibrational quantum number at the maximum intensity in the band and δ is the difference in equilibrium bond length between ion and molecule. The same equation is valid for bending vibrations if δ is replaced by $l\delta\theta$, where l is the bond length and $\delta\theta$ the change in equilibrium bond angle. When the constants and parameters are expressed in convenient units, the equation reduces to

$$\delta^2 = l^2\delta\theta^2 = 5.439 \times 10^5 \frac{(I_{vert} - I_{adb})}{\mu v'^2} \qquad (5.6)$$

with δ and l in ångstroms, $\delta\theta$ in radians, I_{vert} and I_{adb} in electron volts, μ in atomic units and v in cm^{-1}.

Because the similarity between the classical and wave-mechanical oscillators used in deriving this equation exists only for high vibrational quantum numbers, the equation is valid only when large changes of shape and therefore long vibrational progressions are involved. Care must be taken when using it to define the reduced mass μ correctly for the particular mode excited, and on this point Herzberg's book[2] must usually be consulted. The energy of the classical vibrator on the left-hand side of equation 5.5 must also be calculated explicitly in terms of the desired internal co-ordinate whenever a triatomic or larger molecule is involved.

More general methods have been developed to allow changes of molecular geometry to be determined without recourse to the semi-classical approximation, and these can be applied even if the (0–0) transition is the most intense. The observed relative vibrational intensities are compared with Franck–Condon factors calculated in one of several ways, for an estimated change of geometry. The most accurate method of calculation is numerical integration over potential energy surfaces obtained by inversion (RKR method) from known energy levels. Next comes numerical integration over Morse potentials, which can be done if, at least, anharmonicities are known in addition to vibration frequencies. If only the frequencies are known, harmonic oscillator potentials must be used, and in this approximation the changes in geometry can be deduced directly from vibrational intensities, because the Franck–Condon factors have been calculated in analytical form. The method of Heilbronner and co-workers[9] involved the use of several vibrational intensities, while in the simpler technique of Dujardin and Leach[10] only the (0–0) and (1,0) intensities are compared. The change in bond length in a diatomic is given by:

$$\delta = 4.096 \left\{ \frac{I_{10}}{I_{00}} \times \frac{1}{\mu v'} \right\}^{1/2} (1 + \beta) \qquad (5.7)$$

where β is the frequency ratio v'/v'', and the other quantities are in the same units as before. Some bond length changes deduced by the different methods are given in *Table 5.1* for comparison with accurate values known from the analysis of rotational structure in ion emission spectra.

Table 5.1 Structural changes following ionization

Molecule	Ionic state	Change in bond length on ionization, Å			
		Spect.	ref. 10	eqn 5.6	eqn 5.7
H_2	$X\,^2\Sigma_g^+$	0.33	0.35	0.32	0.28
O_2	$X\,^2\Pi_g$	−0.08	−0.09	−0.08	−0.11
	$a\,^4\Pi_u$	0.17	0.20	0.19	0.14
CO	$X\,^2\Sigma^+$	0.04	0.05	–	0.012
	$A\,^2\Pi$	0.12	0.12	0.11	0.104
CO_2	$X\,^2\Pi_g$	0.015	0.015	–	0.016
	$A\,^2\Pi_u$	0.066	0.074	0.062	0.052
	$B\,^2\Sigma_u$	0.018	0.015	–	0.015
CS_2	$X\,^2\Pi_g$	0.010	–	–	0.004
	$A\,^2\Pi_u$	0.051	0.08	0.07	0.060

The agreement shown in *Table 5.1* between bond length changes determined by the different methods is generally good, and suggests that vibrational intensity measurements could provide a reliable way of finding molecular geometries in ionic states and of determining the bonding powers of different electrons in molecules quantitatively. The ion S_2^+ provides an example of this, as its bond lengths in the $X\,^2\Pi_g$ and $A\,^2\Pi_u$ states were first determined by Franck–Condon analysis of photoelectron band intensities[11] and were later confirmed by rotational analysis of the newly discovered emission spectrum[12].

When polyatomic molecules are involved, the changes in normal co-ordinates, which can be determined by the methods described above, are not so simply related to individual bond lengths. The necessary transformations are well documented, however; they normally involve matrix methods[9,13], and are well suited to numerical computation.

5.3.4   Rotational structure of photoelectron peaks

A single vibrational peak in a 'resolved' photoelectron spectrum is equivalent to a vibrational band in an optical spectrum, and is made up of many individual rotational transitions. The rotational lines normally form several regular branches, each branch corresponding to one change of a rotational quantum number; in a linear molecule the most familiar are the $Q(\Delta J = 0)$, $R(\Delta J = +1)$ and $P(\Delta J = -1)$ branches. The structure of a photoelectron peak depends on two things: the nature of the most intense rotational transitions (the selection rule) and the geometry change between molecule and ion. To obtain the actual band contour one must, of course, include the degeneracy factors and the Boltzmann populations of molecular levels before ionization, exactly as in optical spectroscopy. The nature of the geometry changes, which determine the moments of inertia, have been discussed above, and the rotational selection rules were examined in Section 3.4.3. To recapitulate, the basic rule is $\Delta N = 0\pm1\ldots\pm l$, where l is the orbital angular momentum of the electron ionized from a *united atom* model of the molecule.

no longer true in 1990

Even with the advent of molecular beam sources to remove the Doppler broadening, no rotationally well-resolved photoelectron spectra have yet been recorded. The cooling of molecular rotation in supersonic beam expansion is actually counter productive, because for the low J levels which remain populated, the spacing within a branch is very small. The branches may not extend far enough to reveal the characteristic shapes of the band contours, which can, however, be seen in the usual room temperature spectra. They would be best seen using a molecular beam source which removes Doppler broadening *without* rotational cooling.

The most characteristic features of rotational band contours are the tailing to low ionization energy if the ion is larger than the molecule, or to high energy if the ion is smaller. Rotational contours in bands where no change of geometry occurs should be roughly symmetrical, their widths depending on the selection rules in force.

5.4 Unresolved bands

Most photoelectron spectra of molecules larger than triatomic contain some, if not a majority, of bands that have no apparent vibrational structure. Although theoretical reasons for this lack of structure are discussed below, very common practical reasons are undoubtedly poor instrumental performance. A resolution of 10 meV or better is necessary to be sure of observing vibrational lines separately, and a good ratio of signal to statistical noise is also essential. It is now realized that a very complex vibrational structure, which may produce apparently continuous bands, arises frequently even in bands for non-degenerate states of polyatomic ions. Its origin is vibronic coupling effects, in which more than one vibration may be involved. Detailed discussion of these non-adiabatic effects is postponed till the next chapter; here we must note that a great many puzzling, unstructured bands probably arise because of such vibronic coupling between electronic states.

5.4.1 The existence of continuous bands

Reasons often suggested for the occurrence of an unresolved band are as follows.

(1) The band consists of many closely spaced vibrational lines that cannot possibly be resolved. This requires a vibrational spacing less than the width of the lines due to their rotational structure, which is of the order of kT (24 meV) in many instances, or less in others where the rotational selection rule is $\Delta J = 0, \pm 2$. The broadening due to thermal motion of the target molecules, so important for H_2, is much less so for the

larger molecules with which we are concerned here. Vibrations with such low frequencies as 24 meV (200 cm^{-1}) or lower are common in molecules that contain heavy atoms, but much rarer in hydrocarbons, where only torsional vibrations have such frequencies. If only totally symmetric nondegenerate vibrations are considered, frequencies as low as 200 cm^{-1} are unusual unless atoms from the third row of the Periodic Table are involved. If unresolved bands found in the spectra of compounds of first-row elements are to be attributed to overlapping, simultaneous excitation of several modes of vibration must probably be invoked. If the totally symmetric vibrations are of such frequencies that they ought to be resolved, possible reasons for unresolved bands in the spectra of symmetrical molecules are the occurrence of Jahn–Teller complications, which may indicate a degenerate electronic state, or pseudo-Jahn–Teller complications which arise from interactions between non-degenerate states. The first two bands in the photoelectron spectrum of carbon tetrafluoride have no resolved vibrational structure (*Figure 5.6*), although the third band is structured, and the only totally symmetric vibrational mode has a frequency of 904 cm^{-1} (112 meV) in the neutral molecule. The reduction in frequency on ionization could hardly be so great as to prevent

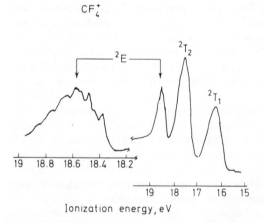

Figure 5.6 The photoelectron spectrum of carbon tetrafluoride, with the ^{2}E band on an expanded scale to show the vibrational structure. (From Pullen, W.E. *et al.*, *Inorg. Chem.*, **9**, 2474 (1970), by courtesy of the American Chemical Society)

resolution of such large quanta, so some explanation is needed. Jahn–Teller effects are, indeed, expected in the ^2T states which comprise the first two bands, and since all symmetric vibrations can be excited on ionization, as well as the Jahn–Teller active vibrations (Chapter 6), very complex vibrational structures are likely. Because ions in these states dissociate, line broadening (explanation (2)) may also contribute.

(2) The lifetime of the molecular ions in a particular state may be so short that a broadening of the energy levels results from the uncertainty principle, $\Delta E \Delta t \approx \hbar$; alternatively, the ionic state may be repulsive and so truly continuous in the Franck–Condon region. The extent of the broadening necessary to produce a continuous band depends on the spacing of the vibrational structure that would otherwise be expected, and this spacing will normally be more than 20 meV. The uncertainty principle, expressed in units of electron volts and seconds, is approximately $\Delta E \Delta t = 10^{-15}$, so a broadening of 10 meV or more corresponds to a lifetime of 10^{-13} s or less. The fluorescence lifetimes of excited ions produced in ultraviolet photoelectron spectroscopy are much longer than this time, about 10^{-8} s, but lifetimes as short as 10^{-13} s towards dissociation are possible, and also towards non-radiative transitions, such as internal conversion or internal vibrational redistribution. Large molecular ions have many possible decomposition pathways and a high density of states to which non-radiative transitions can occur, and on this account bands without structure are to be expected in the photoelectron spectra of polyatomic molecules. Unfortunately, it is just for these molecules that loss of visible structure due to overlapping is almost most likely, and it is therefore difficult to decide experimentally between the two explanations. The best established examples of broadening due to dissociation are all found in the photoelectron spectra of small molecules—for instance, in the $C\,^4\Sigma_u^-$ state of O_2^+, the $A\,^2\Sigma^+$ states of HF and HBr and the $B\,^2\Sigma^+$ state of HCN^+. Some photoelectron bands showing dissociative broadening are illustrated in *Figure 7.3* (p. 207).

Within any one electronic state, the rates of all non-radiative energy flows, including dissociation, increase rapidly with increasing energy. Rapid rate increase is predicted by theory, because of the increasing density of states, and is very well demonstrated experimentally. Furthermore, the most successful theory of uni-molecular decomposition of large molecular ions invokes the assumption that all electronically excited states of the ions relax by internal conversions to the ionic ground state before dissociating. This implies a rule that if loss of structure in a particular band in a photoelectron spectrum is due to rapid dissociation, then all bands at higher ionization potential must be equally continuous. The ions that correspond to higher bands have higher internal excitation energies, and according to the theory they will decompose faster. On this basis, the explanation that the loss of structure in the first photoelectron band of CF_4 is due to fast dissociation is precluded by the presence of resolved structure in the third band. However, there is in fact independent evidence that the quasi-equilibrium theory is not valid for CF_4^+ ions which, in their ground state, do dissociate directly, and probably very rapidly. There are many other molecules whose photoelectron spectra contain continuous bands followed by well resolved bands at higher energy, such as benzene, furan, acetone, methane and neopentane. In seeking the origin of continuous bands in the spectra of such molecules, the above rule should at least be borne in mind.

5.4.2 The shapes of unresolved bands

Even if no vibrational structure can be seen for physical or experimental reasons, the shapes of bands still give a little information. One can distinguish three types of unresolved band shape, which have been designated[14] types 1, 2 and 3 and which are shown in *Figure 5.7*. In type 1 bands, the low ionization

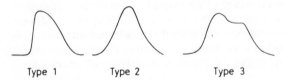

Type 1   Type 2   Type 3

Figure 5.7   Idealized contours of unresolved bands

potential edge is sharp, indicating that the (0–0) transition is still the strongest, or at least its intensity is substantial, say 50% or more of the most intense transition in the band. Type 2 bands may be roughly symmetrical, but their characteristic feature is the lack of any sharp onset. The FCF for the (0–0) transition is very low, and probably this adiabatic transition is not seen at all. Bands of type 3 have envelopes that are distorted by the Jahn–Teller effect and indicate an orbitally degenerate electronic state.

In bands of type 1, the adiabatic ionization transition can still be discerned as well as the vertical ionization transition, and the difference between vertical and adiabatic ionization potentials is a crude measure of the degree of distortion of the molecule caused by ionization. The fact that the adiabatic transition is seen at all suggests that the distortion is relatively small, and one might therefore expect that within one photoelectron spectrum bands of type 1 would be narrower than bands of type 2. This is often true, and exceptions must be examined carefully with the possibility of overlapping bands in mind. In bands of type 2, however, the widths are determined by different factors from those that affect the difference between vertical and adiabatic ionization potentials. The width of a type 2 band is the product of the extension of the vibrational wave-function in the ground-state molecule with the mean slope of the potential energy surface in the ionic state. Neither of these quantities is known beforehand, and the slope of the ionic potential energy surface is a poor indication of the change in molecular geometry. In a polyatomic molecule, both the width of the ground-state wave-function and the slope of the potential energy surface in the ion depend on the identity of the normal mode(s) involved. By assuming that the potential energy surfaces are parabolic (harmonic oscillators) and that a single mode is excited, one can derive an equation for the width, Δ:

$$\Delta \propto k^{3/4}\delta/\mu^{1/4} \tag{5.8}$$

where k is the force constant, assumed to be the same in molecule and ion, μ is the reduced mass and δ is the change in the normal co-ordinate. The derivation of this equation involves such severe approximations that its use in estimating δ from the widths of bands of type 2 cannot be recommended. Its important feature is the inverse dependence of band width on $\mu^{1/4}$, which should be observable as an effect of isotopic substitution, particularly deuteration.

5.5   Orbital bonding character

The relationship between photoelectron band form and electron bonding character is very simple at first sight. Long vibrational progressions, broad bands and bands of type 2 and 3 indicate strong bonding or antibonding character, while sharp bands and bands of type 1 indicate little bonding character. Where vibrational structure is resolved, these ideas can be made quantitative by estimation of the direction and magnitude of changes in bond lengths and bond angles following a particular ionization. However, bonding character indicated in this direct way by the photoelectron spectra does not correspond completely to the chemist's normal idea of bonding and non-bonding electrons.

A first, perhaps obvious, *caveat* is that 'orbital bonding power' is only an approximate theoretical concept, and band width is only an approximate indicator of the true change in molecular shape on ionization. No deductions of orbital bonding power can be attempted in the inner valence region of photoelectron spectra, for instance, where the orbital model fails. In the outer valence region there are a few less obvious pitfalls for the unwary.

First of all, there are lone-pair electrons, which are non-bonding in the sense that their presence does not affect any bond lengths, but which are angle determining. This is true of the lone-pair electrons in ammonia, amines and other Group V compounds and of one lone pair of electrons in water, alcohols, ethers and the related Group VI compounds. Ionization from orbitals that have such angle-determining properties gives broad bands in the spectra, often of type 2, even if it causes no change in bond length. Furthermore, non-bonded interactions between lone-pair electrons can drastically alter the effective bonding power of the electrons (see Chapter 8, Section 8.3).

A second problem can arise when spectra of highly polar compounds are to be interpreted. The orbitals in an ionic compound have the same symmetries as those in a covalent molecule, but the effect of their occupancy on the bonding may be quite different. Ionization of a localized electron, which converts the molecule from A^+B^- to A^+B, has a strong effect on the bond length and gives a broad ionization band. On the other hand, ionization from a molecular orbital that is localized on the metal atom, and whose loss converts A^+B^- to $A^{2+}B^-$, will have little effect on the bond length in a predominantly electrovalent molecule. The first example of such a reversal of the normal ideas of bonding character was found in the photoelectron spectrum of xenon difluoride[15] and even clearer examples are found in the spectra of the thallium and indium monohalides[16,17]. The spectrum of thallium bromide is shown in *Figure 5.8*, where it can be seen that the low ionization potential region contains only one relatively sharp band and one broad band with which it overlaps. On the normal molecular orbital model, we expect ionization from a

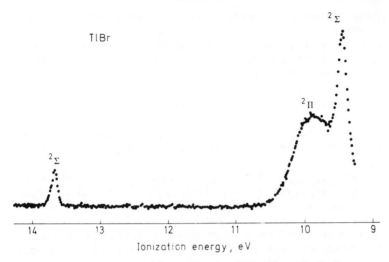

Figure 5.8   He I photoelectron spectrum of thallium bromide. (From Berkowitz[16], by courtesy of the American Institute of Physics)

lone-pair orbital of the halogen atom to produce a $^2\Pi$ state and give two sharp peaks in this region for the $^2\Pi_{3/2}$ and $^2\Pi_{1/2}$ components, which should be separated by about 0.3 eV. In fact the *broad* band in the spectrum represents the $^2\Pi$ states, the reason being that the molecules are initially mostly Tl^+Br^- and removal of an electron localized on the halogen has a strong effect on the bonding. The single narrow peak is due to ionization of a σ electron, which is localized mainly on the Tl^+ atomic ion. In fact, the above description of the spectrum is a simplification, because the splitting between $^2\Sigma_{1/2}$ and $^2\Pi_{1/2}$ is affected by both the molecular bonding ('ligand field') and by spin–orbit interaction, which cannot be treated separately in this case.

Finally, another apparent contradiction of the usual classification of orbitals as bonding or non-bonding is found in the photoelectron spectra of molecules with multiple bonds. According to the photoelectron spectrum of nitrogen (*Figure 1.4*), the $2p\sigma$ orbital is non-bonding, because $2p\sigma^{-1}$ ionization gives a sharp single peak with little structure showing vibrational excitation of the ion. This contradicts the simple molecular orbital model in which $2p\sigma$ is the main σ bonding orbital, which contributes with the two π_u orbitals to the triple bond strength of N_2. The reason for the discrepancy is illustrated in *Figure 5.9*. The presence of the π bonds makes the N–N bond so short that positive and negative

Normal p – σ bonding

Shortened p – σ bond

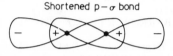

Figure 5.9   The loss of bonding power in pσ orbitals much shortened by simultaneous π bonding. The elongation of p orbitals has been greatly exaggerated in order to emphasize the less favourable overlap that occurs at short bond lengths.

overlap contributions in 2pσ cancel out, making the orbital non-bonding at the molecular internuclear distance. The occupancy of 2pσ does not contribute, therefore, to the force constant (the curvature of the potential energy curve) near the equilibrium internuclear distance, nor does it affect the bond length. It does contribute to the bond dissociation energy, however, because in dissociation the molecule must pass through the region in which the 2pσ orbital regains its full bonding character. Apparent loss of bonding power such as this is a feature of the photoelectron spectra of all small molecules with multiple bonds; another good example is the σ_u^{-1} ionization in CO_2, which gives a very narrow band and causes very little change in bond length (*Table 5.1*).

References

1. SCHWARTZ, M.E., SWITALSKI, J.D. and STRONSKI, R.E., in Shirley, D.A. (Editor) *Electron Spectroscopy*, North Holland, Amsterdam, 605 (1972)
2. COTTON, F.A., *Chemical Applications of Group Theory*, Interscience, New York (1963); HERZBERG, G., *Infrared and Raman Spectra*, Van Nostrand, Princeton, N.J. (1945)
3. TURNER, D., *Phil. Trans. R. Soc., Lond.*, **A268**, 7 (1970)
4. DUCHINSKY, F., *Acta Physicochim. URSS*, **7**, 551 (1937)
5. High resolution spectra of the linear triatomics have been published as follows: CO_2; ELAND, J.H.D. and BERKOWITZ, J., *J. Chem. Phys.*, **67**, 2782 (1977): N_2O; DEHMER, P.M., DEHMER, J.L. and CHUPKA, W.A., *J. Chem. Phys.*, **73**, 126 (1980): CS_2; HUBIN-FRANSKIN, M.J., DELWICHE, J., NATALIS, P. and CAPRACE, G., *J. Electron Spectrosc. Rel. Phen.*, **18**, 295 (1980): CO_2, CS_2 and COS; POTTS, A.W. and FATTAHALLAH, G.H., *J. Phys., B. Atom Molec. Phys.*, **13**, 2545 (1980)

6. DOMCKE, W., *Physica Scripta*, **19**, 11 (1979)
7. BAKER, C. and TURNER, D.W., *Proc. R. Soc., Lond.*, **A308**, 19 (1968)
8. HEILBRONNER, E., HORNUNG, V. and KLOSTER-JENSEN, E., *Helv. Chim. Acta*, **53**, 331 (1970)
9. HEILBRONNER, E., MUSZKAT, K.A. and SCHAUBLIN, J., *Helv. Chim. Acta*, **54**, 58 (1971)
10. DUJARDIN, G., Doctoral Thesis, Université de Paris-Sud, France (1982)
11. DYKE, J.M., GOLOB, N., JONATHAN, N. and MORRIS, A., *J. Chem. Soc., Faraday Trans. II*, **71**, 1026 (1974)
12. CAPEL, A.J., ELAND, J.H.D. and BARROW, R.F., *Chem. Phys. Lett.*, **82**, 496 (1981)
13. SMITH, W.L. and WARSOP, P.A., *Trans. Faraday Soc.*, **64**, 1165 (1968)
14. GLEITER, R., HEILBRONNER, E. and HORNUNG, V., *Helv. Chim. Acta*, **55**, 255 (1972)
15. BREHM, B., MENZINGER, M. and ZORN, C., *Can. J. Chem.*, **48**, 3193 (1970)
16. BERKOWITZ, J., *J. Chem. Phys.*, **56**, 2766 (1972)
17. BERKOWITZ, J. and DEHMER, J.L., *J. Chem. Phys.*, **57**, 3194 (1972)

6
Photoelectron band structure—II: Degenerate ionic states

6.1 Introduction

Whenever an electron is ejected from a fully occupied degenerate orbital in a molecule, the result is an orbitally degenerate doublet state of the corresponding ion. The degeneracy of such a state can be lifted either by coupling between the spin and orbital angular momenta of the unpaired electron, spin–orbit coupling, or by a change in molecular shape, the Jahn–Teller effect. When both of these effects are weak, the photoelectron spectrum contains a single intense band corresponding to the ionization, but the vibrational structure of this band is liable to be complex. When the interactions are stronger there can be as many photoelectron bands in the spectrum as there were electron pairs in the original degenerate orbital, but not more. Orbitally degenerate ionic states can also arise from photoionization out of partially occupied degenerate orbitals, from two-electron transitions or from ionization out of closed shells in molecules that also have an open shell. Orbital degeneracy arising from these processes is not common in photoelectron spectroscopy, but whatever the source of degeneracy, the same splitting mechanisms operate. In some unusual photoionization processes, orbitally degenerate ionic states can be produced that are not also spin degenerate; such states would be susceptible to the Jahn–Teller effect only and not to splitting by spin–orbit coupling. For linear species, on the other hand, only spin–orbit coupling can lift the degeneracy and no Jahn–Teller effect is operative.

6.2 Spin–orbit coupling

If an unpaired electron is in a degenerate orbital where it has orbital angular momentum, the spin angular momentum and orbital angular momentum can combine in different ways and produce new states that are characterized by the total electronic angular momentum. The new states have different energies because the magnetic moments due to electron spin and orbital motion may oppose or reinforce one another. All states with multiplicity greater than one and a non-zero orbital angular momentum are split by this spin–orbit coupling. The simplest examples from photoelectron spectra are the ionizations of the rare gases, which leave ions with the configuration np^5 in the

Table 6.1 Splittings of degenerate states

Point group	Electronic state	Spin–orbit components	Examples	Spin–orbit splitting	Jahn–Teller active modes
C_{3v}	^2E	$E_{3/2} + E_{1/2}$	CH_3I^+	ζ_I	e
C_{4v}	^2E	$E_{3/2} + E_{1/2}$	BrF_5^+		$b_1 + b_2$
$D_{\infty h}$	$^2\Pi_g$	$E_{3/2g} + E_{1/2g}$	HgI_2^+	ζ_I	None
	$^2\Pi_u$	$E_{3/2u} + E_{1/2u}$	XeF_2^+	$c^2_{Xe}\zeta_{Xe}$	None
$C_{\infty v}$	$^2\Pi$	$E_{3/2} + E_{1/2}$	N_2O^+		None
D_3h	$^2E'$	$E_{5/2} + E_{3/2}$	BBr_3^+	ζ_{Br}	e'
	$^2E''$	$E_{3/2} + E_{1/2}$	BBr_3^+	Zero	e'
D_{6h}	$^2E_1$	$E_{3/2} + E_{1/2}$	$C_6H_6^+$ ⎫	Zero in	e_{2g}
	$^2E_2$	$E_{5/2} + E_{3/2}$	$C_6H_6^+$ ⎬	$^2E_{1g}, {}^2E_{2u}$	e_{2g}
T_d	^2E	$G_{3/2}$	CBr_4^+	(None)	e
	$^2T_1$	$G_{3/2} + E_{1/2}$	CBr_4^+	$3/4\zeta_{Br}$	e, t_2
	$^2T_2$	$G_{3/2} + E_{5/2}$	CBr_4^+	$1/2\zeta_{Br}$	e, t_2
O_h	^2E	$G_{3/2}$	SF_6^+	(None)	e_g
	$^2T_1$	$G_{5/2} + E_{1/2}$	SF_6^+		e_g, t_{2g}
	$^2T_2$	$G_{3/2} + E_{5/2}$	SF_6^+		e_g, t_{2g}

The third column gives the species of the multiplet components produced by spin–orbit splitting in the degenerate electronic states (second column) of molecular ions belonging to important point groups (first column). The fifth column gives some estimates of the splitting in terms of atomic splitting parameters, ζ_i, appropriate for the examples cited in the fourth column. The last column contains the species of the vibrational modes that are Jahn–Teller active for the same electronic states. The g and u symmetries of the multiplet components for D_{6h} and O_h are omitted, as they are the same as those of the electronic states; only g vibrations are Jahn–Teller active in g or u electronic states alike.

outermost shell and hence in ^2P states, which split into $^2P_{3/2}$ and $^2P_{1/2}$. Because in this instance the incomplete shell is more than half full, the $^2P_{3/2}$ state, with the higher total angular momentum, is of lower energy than $^2P_{1/2}$, as indicated by Hund's rules[1]. For atomic ions such as these, the degeneracies are equal to $2J + 1$, i.e., 4 and 2, respectively, which leads to the expectation of a 2:1 ratio of peak intensities in the spectra.

When spin–orbit coupling in molecules is considered, the designation of states by the normal symmetry species is not sufficient. In order to determine the number and species of the states produced by spin–orbit coupling, extended point groups, which include the electron spin explicitly[2], must be used. The way in which the normal symmetry species of doublet orbitally degenerate states go over to species of the extended groups is shown in *Table 6.1* for the most important cases encountered in photoelectron spectroscopy.

6.2.1   Linear molecules

In linear molecular ions, all $^2\Pi$, $^2\Delta$, $^2\Phi$ states and, of course, triplet or quartet Π, Δ and Φ states are split; the doublet states give two components characterized by a quantum number Ω equal to $\Lambda \pm S$. The two states are of equal degeneracy because there is only one axis in which angular momentum is quantized, and the two peaks in the spectrum should be of equal intensity. By far the commonest states in photoelectron spectra are doublet states produced by removing one electron from a closed shell, and here the term with higher Ω is of lower energy. If spin–orbit interaction is relatively small and is well described by Russell–Saunders coupling[1], the energies of the spin–orbit components are given by

$$E = E_0 + \zeta \Lambda \Sigma \tag{6.1}$$

where E_0 is the energy in the absence of spin–orbit coupling and Σ is the component of S, the resultant spin angular momentum, along the axis. As Σ takes the values S, $(S - 1)\ldots -S$, in this approximation every term is split into $2S + 1$ equally spaced components, the spacing being equal to ζ in a Π state ($\Lambda = 1$). The spin–orbit interaction parameter, ζ, is characteristic of the molecular orbital in which the unpaired electron moves, and of the atomic orbitals from which it is made up. For a single electron in the coulomb field produced by a nucleus of charge Z, the splitting increases as Z/r^3, or, as r is proportional to Z^{-1}, ζ must increase with Z^4. For atoms with many electrons, the splitting in the valence shells is approximately proportional to Z^2. For elements in the first row of the Periodic Table, splittings of 20 meV or less are normal, and for those in the second row the splittings are about 50 meV. Because of the intervening filling of the d shells of the transition elements, non-metals of the third row have splittings of 200–300 meV and in the fourth row the splittings are 300–600 meV. When elements of the third, fourth and fifth rows are involved, spin–orbit splittings become particularly noticeable in photoelectron spectra.

In a $^2\Pi$ or $^2\Delta$ state of a linear ion, the magnitude of the splitting depends on the proportions of the different atomic orbitals that make up the molecular orbital in which the unpaired electron moves. If the molecular orbital ψ is expressed as a linear combination of atomic orbitals, ϕ_μ, for atoms μ, with coefficients c_μ:

$$\psi = \sum_\mu c_\mu \phi_\mu \tag{6.2}$$

then the effective splitting ζ is given approximately by

$$\zeta = \sum_\mu c_\mu^2 \zeta_\mu \tag{6.3}$$

where ζ_μ are the characteristic splittings of the atomic orbitals, a selection of which are given in *Table 6.2*. Equation 6.3, although only approximate, is extremely useful as it enables one to determine the coefficients c_μ from the spin–orbit splittings observed in the spectra.

Table 6.2 Atomic spin–orbit coupling parameters for atoms and ions

Orbital	Splitting parameter ς, eV						
2p	B	C	N⁺	O	F	Ne⁺	Na
	0.001	0.004	0.011	−0.019	−0.033	−0.064	−0.121
3p	Al	Si	P⁺	S	Cl	Ar⁺	K
	0.009	0.019	0.039	−0.047	−0.073	−0.118	−0.173
4p	Ga	Ge	As⁺	Se	Br	Kr⁺	Rb
	0.068	0.12	0.20	−0.21	−0.305	−0.444	−0.563
5p	In	Sn	Sb⁺	Te	I	Xe⁺	Cs
	0.182	0.27	0.44	0.49	−0.628	−0.871	−0.810
6p	Tl	Pb	Bi⁺	Hg			
	0.644	0.91	1.25	0.52			
3d	Sc	Ti	V	Cr	Mn	Fe	Co
	0.008	0.013	0.020	0.028	0.030	0.048	0.064
3d	Ni	Cu					
	0.074	0.102					

The values for the transition metals are from J.S. Griffith, *The Theory of Transition Metal Ions*, Cambridge University Press (1961), which may also be consulted for the method of deriving these values from atomic spectra. The other values are based on the tables of C.E. Moore, *Atomic Energy Levels*, Vol I (1949), Vol II (1952), Vol III (1957), National Bureau of Standards, Washington, D.C. Several values are taken from the compilation of K. Wittel and R. Manne, *Theoret. Chim. Acta*, **33**, 347 (1974), which may be consulted for ς values of ionized and neutral atoms.

An additional consequence of this simple model is that in a linear molecule containing several atoms with non-negligible spin–orbit splitting in their outer orbitals, the total spin–orbit splitting summed over all molecular π-orbitals should be equal to the sum of atomic ζ values:

$$\sum \Delta E = \sum_{\substack{atom \\ i}} \zeta_i \qquad (6.4)$$

This sum rule is obeyed accurately in the photoelectron spectra of the halo-acetylenes[3], where it has been thoroughly tested. Note that the sum is over all molecular *orbitals*; if some of the π-orbitals built from the atomic orbitals included on the right of equation 6.4 are not occupied, no corresponding ionization bands will be observable, and the rule does not apply.

Table 6.3   Spin–orbit splitting in linear ions

Dominant atom	One heavy atom		Two heavy atoms		
	Ion	Splitting (eV) in $X\,^2\Pi$ or ^2E	Ion	Splittings (eV) in	
				$X\,^2\Pi_{(g)}$	$A\,^2\Pi_{(u)}$
O			O_2^+	0.0242	0.001
			CO_2^+	0.0198	0.0118
F	HF^+	0.030	F_2^+	0.03	
S			CS_2^+	0.0546	0.0218
Cl	HCl^+	0.080	Cl_2^+	0.08	0.02
			ClF^+	0.078	
			$HgCl_2^+$	0.120	
Br	HBr^+	0.333	Br_2^+	0.35	0.23
	CH_3Br^+	0.315	BrF^+	0.322	
	$(CH_3)_3CBr^+$	0.29	$HgBr_2^+$	0.34	0.34
I	HI^+	0.66	I_2^+	0.65	0.80
	CH_3I^+	0.627	ICl^+	0.58	
	$(CH_3)_3CI^+$	0.56	IBr^+	0.58	0.36
			HgI_2^+	0.66	0.40

The simplest examples of spin–orbit splittings are found in the spectra of the halogen hydrides. In these molecules there is only one π orbital, which is wholly localized on the halogen atom, so that ionization leads to $^2\Pi_{3/2}$ and $^2\Pi_{1/2}$ states (strictly $E_{3/2}$ and $E_{1/2}$ in the extended point group), and the splittings between them should be equal to ζ_x. The observed splittings for HCl, HBr and HI given in *Table 6.3* are in excellent agreement with this idea. The spectra of these molecules are particularly simple; they show ionization from the p orbitals of the halogen, two of which form the π orbital while the other forms the H–X σ bond. The bonding character of the pσ orbital is apparent from the vibrational structure of the σ^{-1} ionization bands, which is visible in the photoelectron spectrum of HCl (*Figure 6.1*).

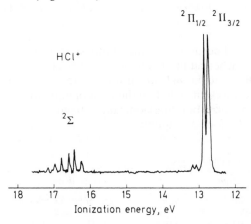

Figure 6.1.   Photoelectron spectrum of HCl ionized by He I light

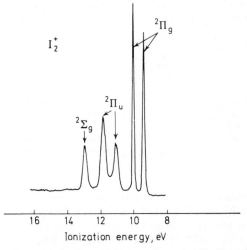

Figure 6.2.   Photoelectron spectrum of iodine showing spin–orbit splitting in the $^2\Pi_g$ and $^2\Pi_u$ ionic states. (From Evans, F. and Orchard, A.F., *Inorg. Chim. Acta*, **5**, 81 (1971), by permission)

The next examples to be considered are the halogens and binary interhalogen compounds, whose measured spin–orbit splittings are also given in *Table 6.3*. Their photoelectron spectra each contain three bands, reflecting the outer orbital structure of the molecules: $\sigma_g^2 \pi_u^4 \pi_g^{*4} \ldots {}^1\Sigma_g^+$ (the designations g and u must be omitted for the interhalogens). The spectrum of iodine is shown in *Figure 6.2*. The sum rule, equation 6.4, ought to apply to the π^{-1} ionizations of the halogens, and inspection of *Tables 6.2* and *6.3* confirms that it is obeyed by all the halogens and interhalogens on which it can be tested, except I_2.

The increased splitting in the ${}^2\Pi_u$ state of I_2^+ is thought to be caused by a spin–orbit induced interaction between the π and σ orbitals[4]. In the extended point group, the unoccupied σ_u orbital has the same species $e_{1/2u}$ as the higher energy component of π_u, so the two orbitals repel each other in the usual manner of interacting orbitals. Similarly, the full σ_g orbital has the same species in the double group as the $\Omega = \frac{1}{2}$ component of π_g, and these orbitals also repel each other. The result is a reduced splitting in ${}^2\Pi_g$ and an increased splitting in ${}^2\Pi_u$, as illustrated in *Figure 6.3*. This is a second-order effect, and such effects are strongest when the interacting orbitals have similar energies.

While this interpretation of the spectrum of I_2 (or a related alternative, see *Figure 6.3*) has been widely accepted, it is not quite certain that it is correct. A recent re-examination of the emission spectrum of Br_2^+ in connection with its photoelectron

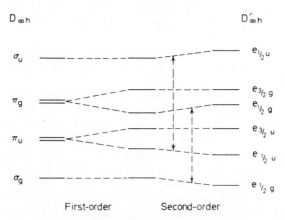

Figure 6.3.   First- and second-order spin–orbit interactions in I_2^+ according to Wittel [4]. See also Jungen, M., *Theor. Chim. Acta*, **27**, 33 (1972), for an alternative interpretation

spectrum[5] suggests a simpler explanation; that the bond length in the $^2\Pi_{1/2u}$ state of I_2 may be substantially greater than in $^2\Pi_{3/2u}$. The Franck–Condon region seen in the photoelectron spectrum would then be further above the potential minimum in $^2\Pi_{1/2u}$ than in $^2\Pi_{3/2u}$, so increasing the observed gap between the photoelectron bands.

The splittings observed in the $^2\Pi$ states of the interhalogen ions are reasonable in terms of equation 6.3 and the expected orbital characters, but because of the likely presence of second-order effects in ICl and IBr it is not appropriate to deduce atomic orbital coefficients. With ClF^+, for which the second-order effects should be small, excellent agreement with the observed splittings has been obtained by the use of a more elaborate, but related, theory[6].

We next consider the 16-electron linear triatomic molecules carbon dioxide, carbon disulphide and the mercury(II) halides. Their valence electronic structure can be written as $\sigma_u^2 \sigma_g^2 \pi_u^4 \pi_g^4 \ldots$ $^1\Sigma_g^+$. The orbital π_g is located entirely on the outer atoms and is non-bonding, while π_u is delocalized over the whole molecule with greatest density at the central atom, and is bonding. Because the electrons in π_g are located on the outer atoms, the splittings in the $^2\Pi_g$ states should be equal to the atomic splitting parameters for the outer atoms, as indeed they very nearly are. The splittings in the inner $^2\Pi_u$ states of CO_2^+ and CS_2^+ are considerably smaller, because of the low ζ value for carbon 2p compared with that of oxygen 2p or sulphur 3p. The situation with mercury(II) bromide and iodide is similar, but the characteristic splitting in the Hg 6p orbital is estimated to be large and reduces the splitting in $^2\Pi_u$ compared with $^2\Pi_g$ only in HgI_2^+.

Xenon difluoride is also a linear molecule, but has 22 valence electrons. Its molecular orbital structure deduced from the photoelectron spectrum (Chapter 4, Section 4.5.2) is $\sigma_u^2 \pi_u^4 \pi_g^4 \sigma_g^2 \pi_u^{*4}$. The outermost occupied orbital, π_u^*, is the antibonding counterpart of π_u, which in this molecule, as in the previous molecules, is bonding and has its greatest density at the central atom. The π_g orbital is again non-bonding and located on the outer atoms only. The spin–orbit parameter for xenon 5p is much larger than that for fluorine 2p, so that it is in the $^2\Pi_u$ states that large splittings are to be expected. The splitting in the outer $^2\Pi_u$ state of XeF_2^+ is found to be 0.47 eV. Then, from equation 6.3 and the atomic splitting parameter for xenon 5p (0.871 eV), the percentage of xenon 5p character in the π_u^* orbital must be $0.47/0.87 \times 100 = 54\%$. For the bonding and antibonding orbitals π_u and π_u^*, the wave-functions can be written approximately as

$$\psi_{\pi_u^*} = c_1\phi_{Xe5p} - c_2\phi_{(F + F)} \tag{6.5}$$

$$\psi_{\pi_u} = c_2\phi_{Xe5p} + c_1\phi_{(F + F)} \tag{6.6}$$

The percentage of xenon 5p character in the π_u orbital must be 46% and the spin–orbit splitting is predicted to be 0.4 eV, in exact agreement with the experimental value (0.40 ± 0.07 eV). The photoelectron spectrum of krypton difluoride has also been measured and analysed in a similar way[7].

Other linear molecules whose photoelectron spectra contain $^2\Pi$ bands split by spin–orbit coupling are the mono- and di-haloacetylenes containing up to four $-C \equiv C-$ groups[3]. For these molecules, the use of equation 6.3 with atomic orbital coefficients obtained from semi-empirical molecular orbital calculations gives excellent agreement with the experimental splittings.

6.2.2   Non-linear molecules

In non-linear molecules, the electrons have orbital angular momentum other than zero only in degenerate orbitals. Orbital degeneracy based on symmetry can exist only in molecules with at least a three-fold axis, so that the molecular point group contains degenerate irreducible representations. In order to determine the number and species of the new terms produced by spin–orbit coupling in multiplet orbitally degenerate states of non-linear molecules, it is essential to use the extended point groups; the most useful data are given in *Table 6.1*. However, the number and symmetries of the new terms unfortunately give no indication of the magnitude of the spin–orbit splittings, except for the ^2E states of tetrahedral and octahedral molecules where there is only one component and the splitting is zero. When one atom or set of equivalent atomic orbitals has the dominant characteristic splitting, an approximate value of the molecular splitting can sometimes be estimated on a model similar to the one used for linear molecules; some estimates of this type are shown in the last column of *Table 6.1*. One striking entry in this column indicates that in $^2E''$ states of D_{3h} molecules the splitting is identically zero, although two species are generated in the extended group. This effect can be explained in general terms as follows. The splitting in axially symmetric molecules is proportional to the product of the projections of the orbital and spin angular momenta in the symmetry axis. An e'' orbital, in BI_3^+, for instance, is made up by combining out-of-plane (π-type) p orbitals of the iodine atoms, and the axes of these p orbitals are parallel to the three-fold rotation axis. The projection of orbital angular momentum in this axis is identically zero and no spin–orbit splitting can result. The same is true of out-of-plane π orbitals in other planar symmetric molecules, such as benzene. It cannot be concluded, however, that $^2E''$ states are never split by spin–orbit interaction, because second-order effects, as discussed for I_2^+, are very likely to cause splittings, although they are usually smaller than the first-order splittings.

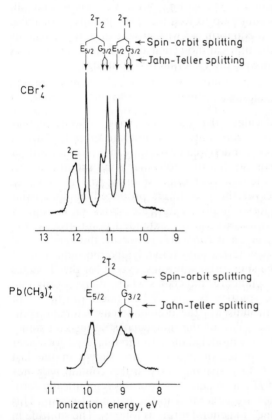

Figure 6.4   Partial photoelectron spectra of carbon tetrabromide and tetramethyl lead showing spin–orbit splitting effects. (CBr_4 from Green, J.C., Green, M.L.H., Joachim, P.J., Orchard, A.F. and Turner, D.W., *Phil. Trans. R. Soc., Lond.*, **A268**, 111 (1970), by courtesy of the Council of the Royal Society; $Pb(CH_3)_4$ from Evans *et al.*, *J. Chem. Soc., Faraday Trans. II*, **68**, 905 (1972), by courtesy of the Chemical Society)

Examples of spin–orbit interactions in non-linear molecular ions are found in the photoelectron spectra of the tetrahedral AB_4 molecules. The photoelectron spectrum of CF_4 (*Figure 5.1*) shows that three electronic states, $^2T_1$, $^2T_2$ and ^2E, arise from ionization out of the halogen lone-pair orbitals, and in these states of CF_4^+ the spin–orbit splitting is negligible. In CBr_4^+, however, substantial splittings are expected, and for comparison the lone-pair ionization region of the spectrum is illustrated in *Figure 6.4*. According to *Table 6.1*, the ^2T states should be split into two components and the ^2E state should remain degenerate, giving a total of five ionic states. The observation of five bands in the CBr_4 spectrum is in agreement with this prediction, and the unsplit ^2E band can be recognized at once. The small additional splittings on two of the five bands are also expected, because the G states produced by spin–orbit coupling are still doubly degenerate and are subject to Jahn–Teller splittings (but not to further spin–orbit splitting). The magnitudes of the experimental energy separations between the spin–orbit split states of CBr_4^+ agree with the estimates in column five of *Table 6.1* and the characteristic splitting parameter, ζ_{Br}, for bromine 4p electrons. In the spectrum of $Pb(CH_3)_4$, which is also shown in *Figure 6.4*, the spin–orbit split band corresponds to ionization from an orbital in which the p orbitals of the Pb atom play a large part. The splitting in this instance into $G_{3/2}$ and $E_{5/2}$ is similar to the splitting of a ^2P state of an atomic ion, and the components should be separated by $\frac{3}{2}\zeta_{Pb}$ if the orbital were purely Pb 6p.

The photoelectron spectrum of BI_3, shown in *Figure 6.5*, provides an example of second-order effects[8]. The first three orbitals from which ionization occurs are of a_2', e' and e'' symmetry, so that according to *Table 6.1* there should be only four ionization bands showing that the $^2E'$-state is split, but not $^2E''$. In fact, five peaks are seen in the halogen lone-pair ionization region, and their number alone shows that the $^2E''$ state is split by a second-order effect. A possible identification of the individual bands, and an indication of the interaction between the $E_{3/2}$ components of $^2E'$ and $^2E''$, are also given in *Figure 6.5*.

The simplest cases of spin–orbit splittings in degenerate states of non-linear molecular ions would appear to be the lone-pair ionizations of the methyl halides. The lone-pair electrons are in e orbitals, so ionization gives ^2E states, which split into two components, $E_{3/2}$ and $E_{1/2}$, of equal statistical weight. There is another e orbital in the molecules made up from carbon 2p orbitals and responsible for the CH bonding, but conjugation of the lone-pair e

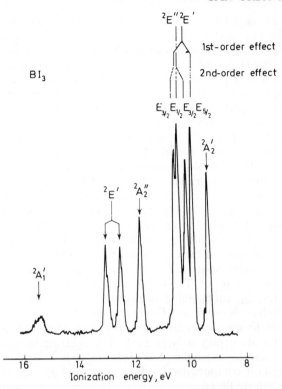

Figure 6.5   Photoelectron spectrum of boron tri-iodide showing a second-order spin–orbit splitting. The analysis indicated is from King *et al.*[8]

electrons with it is weak and the magnitude of the splitting should be ζ_x, as in a linear molecule. This simplicity makes it possible to recognize the existence of a new complication. The spectra of methyl iodide and methyl bromide shown in *Figure 6.6* do contain two peaks in the expected region separated by ζ_I or ζ_{Br}, but in the spectrum of methyl bromide their intensities are not equal. This complication arises because the ^2E states can have their degeneracy lifted not only by spin–orbit coupling but also by the Jahn–Teller effect, as is usual. In MeBr$^+$, the Jahn–Teller splitting is smaller than the spin–orbit splitting, but manifests itself by making allowed the excitation of otherwise forbidden vibrations. It happens that one of the vibrationally excited levels of a normally forbidden progression starting from the $E_{3/2}$ state is of

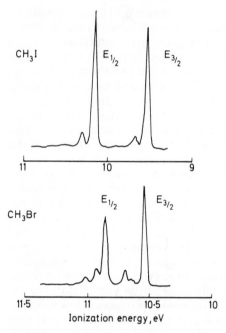

Figure 6.6   Halogen lone-pair ionization bands in the photoelectron spectra of methyl iodide and methyl bromide. (From Ragle, J.L., Stenhouse, I.A., Frost, D.C. and McDowell, C.A., *J. Chem. Phys.*, **53**, 178 (1970), by courtesy of the American Institute of Physics)

the same symmetry as the vibrationless $E_{1/2}$ state, and similar in energy. The result is an unnoticeable shifting of the levels and a strong borrowing of intensity from the $E_{1/2}$ peak into the vibrational structure of the $E_{3/2}$ peak. If deuterium is substituted for hydrogen, giving CD_3Br, the vibrational frequencies are changed sufficiently to reduce the effect noticeably, and two peaks of almost equal intensity appear in the spectrum for $E_{1/2}$ and $E_{3/2}$.

After Jahn–Teller effects have been considered in more detail, the competition between them and spin–orbit splittings is discussed again in Section 6.4.

6.2.3   Spin–orbit coupling without degeneracy

According to the preceding discussion, no spin–orbit splitting should be observed in the ionic states of molecules with less than a three-fold symmetry axis, as such molecules contain no orbitals that are degenerate because of symmetry. This is apparently contradicted by the fact that no discontinuous variation of the photoelectron spectra is found on going from methyl iodide (C_{3v}) to ethyl iodide (C_s), or from isobutyl iodide (C_1) to t-butyl iodide (C_{3v}). In all instances, the spectra contain two sharp peaks at an ionization potential characteristic of iodine and separated by about 0.6 eV, the normal spin–orbit splitting for an iodine ion in a linear environment. The same lack of discontinuity occurs in the series of alkyl bromides. One possible explanation is that the conjugative interactions of the halogen $p_{x,y}$ orbitals with the orbitals of the alkyl moieties are so weak that the halogens experience a cylindrically symmetrical field. This explanation is contradicted, however, by the observation of vibrational structure on the lone-pair peaks, which indicates the existence of some bonding interaction of the halogen $p\pi$ orbitals with the remainder of the molecule. An explanation of this difficulty has been given by Brogli and Heilbronner[9], who showed that the constancy of the splitting is a result of two opposing effects. Conjugation reduces the spin–orbit splitting by progressively reducing the cylindrical symmetry of the field, and also by adding contributions from lighter atoms to the molecular orbitals, but it simultaneously produces a new splitting. If the spin–orbit interaction is zero or very weak compared with the conjugative interaction, there is still a splitting, which is visible, for example, in the photoelectron spectrum of vinyl chloride. This is a splitting between the halogen p orbitals, p_x and p_y, which are made non-equivalent and therefore non-degenerate by the conjugative interaction. In a molecule such as this with C_s or lower symmetry, one halogen p orbital always conjugates more strongly than the other with the remainder of the molecule, so the two p orbital energies are no longer the same. As the conjugative interaction is increased continuously, the reduction in spin–orbit splitting and the increase in the new splitting caused by conjugation compensate for one another until the conjugation becomes very strong. The model proposed by Brogli and Heilbronner[9] also explains why, in the spectrum of cyclopropyl bromide and other molecules in which conjugation is strong, one of the two peaks corresponding to ionization from the lone-pair orbitals has broad vibrational structure while the other is sharp. The sharp peak corresponds to the atomic p orbital of the halogen, which does not interact with the remainder of the molecule, and whether this is the peak at higher or lower ionization potential will depend on the relative energy of the interacting orbitals, as indicated in *Figure 6.7*.

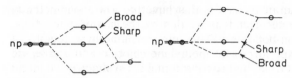

Figure 6.7 Molecular orbital diagrams showing two idealized cases of conjugative interactions between halogen lone-pair p orbitals and other occupied orbitals of a molecule. The designations of 'sharp' and 'broad' refer to the characters of the corresponding photoelectron bands

There is a continuous transition from the rather weak conjugation and dominant spin–orbit coupling of the n-alkyl halides to the strong conjugation with one lone-pair orbital of the halogen atom in unsaturated halogen compounds such as vinyl chloride or the halobenzenes. The number of bands observed for ionization from the lone-pair orbitals of a single bromine or iodine atom is always two, equal to the original orbital degeneracy, irrespective of whether the degeneracy is lifted by spin–orbit coupling, conjugative interaction with molecular orbitals of lower symmetry or, as we shall see below, by Jahn–Teller effects.

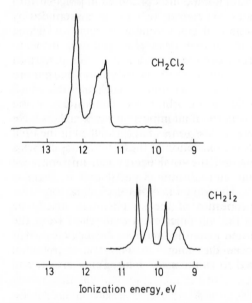

Ionization energy, eV

Figure 6.8 Halogen lone-pair ionization bands in the photoelectron spectra of methylene dichloride and di-iodide

Another group of molecules that have too low a symmetry to possess degenerate orbitals is typified by the methylene halides, CH_2X_2. The non-bonding valence electron ionization regions of the photoelectron spectra of methylene chloride and iodide are depicted in *Figure 6.8*; before considering the symmetries, it might have been guessed that the separation of the two bands in the spectrum of CH_2Cl_2 into four in the spectrum of CH_2I_2 was due to spin–orbit splittings. This naïve idea is at least partly correct, because spin–orbit splitting can arise from *accidental* degeneracy as well as symmetry-based degeneracy. In other words, when two orbitals are nearly degenerate, the second-order effects can become as strong as first-order effects.

6.3   The Jahn–Teller effect

The theorem of Jahn and Teller[10] states that a non-linear molecule in a degenerate electronic state is unstable towards distortions which remove the degeneracy. Although this applies in general to both spin and orbital degeneracy, the effects due to spin are always negligibly small, and we are concerned in practice with orbitally degenerate states. Whenever such a state is produced by ionization of a non-linear molecule, usually by removal of one electron from a degenerate orbital, the positive ion may distort to a lower symmetry, thereby becoming more stable. The distortion is brought about by, or is equivalent to, excitation of one or more degenerate* vibrational modes of the undistorted molecule, which are called the Jahn–Teller active vibrations. The species of the active vibrations for molecules of all important point groups have been tabulated by Herzberg[2] and some are reproduced in the final column of *Table 6.1*. As the excitation of these vibrations causes a change in electronic energy, the total energy can no longer be separated into electronic and vibrational parts; that is, there is strong vibronic coupling. The wave-functions also can no longer be separated so all the properties of the system must strictly be considered in terms of the vibronic levels that result from the coupling of vibrational and electronic motion. Nevertheless, it is helpful to distinguish between changes in the effective potential energy surfaces, referred to as the *static* Jahn–Teller effect, and

---

*In a square-planar molecule, the Jahn–Teller active vibrations are not degenerate but are the two simple vibrations of species b_{1g} and b_{2g}. These act together in exactly the same way as the two components of a degenerate vibration.

complications of the vibrational (vibronic) structure of the state, called the *dynamic* Jahn–Teller effect.

The strength of the Jahn–Teller effect is measured in terms of a dimensionless parameter D, which is so defined that the product of the frequency of the active vibration with D and Planck's constant is equal to the Jahn–Teller stabilization energy, the reduction in energy on going from the symmetrical nuclear configuration to the new equilibrium positions. There is not just one but several new equilibrium positions, and the total original symmetry of the molecule is retained when all the new equilibrium positions are taken together. This concept can be illustrated by the hypothetical case of methyl chloride, a C_{3v} molecule, in an ionic state with a strong Jahn–Teller effect. In this ^2E state of CH_3Cl^+, the equilibrium position of the chlorine atom is no longer on the symmetry axis of the CH_3 group as ν_6 is the active vibration. There are three equivalent positions of minimum energy through which the chlorine atom can pass if it is moved around, but not on, the axis of the CH_3 group. In each single position the original symmetry of the molecule is lost, but the system of all three together still has the full C_{3v} symmetry. The Jahn–Teller stabilization energy, $h\nu D$, is the difference between the energies of the minima and the symmetrical position, and if D is much less than unity the zero-point energy in the active vibration will be sufficient to take the system from one minimum to another. The photoelectron spectrum will then contain no direct evidence of the new potential energy surfaces but only disturbance of the vibrational structure, and it can be said that there is no static effect but only a dynamic Jahn–Teller effect. Different authorities define the static and dynamic Jahn–Teller effects in slightly different ways[2,11], but the observational distinction given here is sufficient for the present purpose.

6.3.1 Jahn–Teller effects in photoelectron spectra

The dynamic Jahn–Teller effect involves splitting of the vibrational levels by vibronic interactions when active vibrations are excited, but this splitting is not easily observed in photoelectron spectroscopy. The simple presence of progressions that show excitation of the Jahn–Teller active modes is much more noticeable, and is the most sensitive indication of the existence of Jahn–Teller effects. In the absence of vibronic coupling, the excitation of these modes is effectively forbidden (see Chapter 5, Section 5.2.1) because they are degenerate or antisymmetric.

Their excitation under the conditions of the Jahn–Teller effect can be understood in two ways. Firstly, selection rules based on vibronic wave-functions instead of the vibrational overlap integrals must be used, and when this is done it is found that the transitions are allowed. Secondly, on going from the symmetry of the undistorted molecule to a lower symmetry by a Jahn–Teller effect, one component of the active vibration that brings about the distortion becomes a totally symmetric vibration in the new symmetry. Its excitation is then allowed on ionization, and if the change in equilibrium nuclear positions is substantial, strong excitation is likely. If the change in shape is small and there are no other complications, the intensity of the line showing excitation of one quantum of the active vibration divided by the intensity of the (0–0) transition should be equal to the parameter D. The excitation of degenerate modes on ionization is hence the first indication of Jahn–Teller effects. Examples already given are the first bands in the spectrum of benzene and in that of methyl bromide.

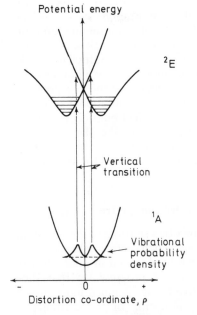

Figure 6.9   Section through the potential energy surfaces involved in a transition from a simple ground state to a ^{2}E ionic state undergoing a static Jahn–Teller effect

In the benzene and methyl bromide ionizations, the Jahn–Teller distortion is small, as the (0–0) vibrational transitions are still the strongest. When the vibronic interaction is stronger, the relevant parts of the potential energy surfaces must be considered in more detail. *Figure 6.9* shows the potential energy as a function of the distortion co-ordinate, ρ, for a transition from a non-degenerate ground state to a doubly degenerate ionic state.

The distortion co-ordinate, ρ, is compounded from the two normal co-ordinates, q_1 and q_2, of the active vibration, which are perpendicular to one another. The definition of ρ is:

$$\rho = (q_1^2 + q_2^2)^{1/2} \qquad (6.7)$$

Now, it can be proved[2,11] that if only linear terms are taken in the vibronic interaction, the potential energy depends only on ρ and not on the individual values of q_1 and q_2, so that the potential energy surface depicted in *Figure 6.9* is cylindrically symmetrical and must be imagined as having rotational symmetry about the central vertical axis. It is the neglected quadratic and higher terms that produce separate minima in the potential energy surface, such as the three for methyl chloride ions mentioned earlier. The potential energy surface in the upper state has its minimum at a

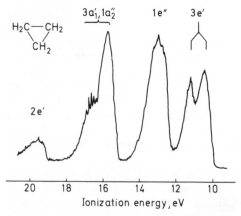

Figure 6.10   The He I photoelectron spectrum of cyclopropane showing Jahn–Teller splitting in the $3e'^{-1}$ ionization band. The $1e''^{-1}$ and $2e'^{-1}$ ionizations cause much smaller Jahn–Teller splittings, which are not apparent in the spectrum. The relative band intensities are apparently distorted by the effects of autoionization at 584 Å, since they are completely different in the spectrum taken with HE II radiation[12]. (From Evans *et al.*[13], by courtesy of Elsevier Publishing Company)

non-zero value of ρ while the minimum in the lower state is at $\rho = 0$, but its probability density, which is shown in *Figure 6.9*, is at a non-zero value of ρ because of the cylindrical symmetry in the q_1, q_2 space. The probability density is obtained by multiplying the square of the wave-function by $2\pi\rho$, the volume of the space available at ρ. Vertical transitions take place from the position of highest probability density of the ground-state vibration as shown in *Figure 6.9*, and because of the Jahn–Teller distortion they cross the upper potential energy surface at two places. There are now two vertical transitions of different energies and the photoelectron band contour may have two separate maxima. Several instances of ^2E states showing this type of splitting have been found[12,13] in photoelectron spectra and an example is shown in *Figure 6.10*. This is the origin of the typical Jahn–Teller band contour, that is, of bands of type 3 (Chapter 5, Section 5.4.2).

By using the semi-classical Franck–Condon approximation and harmonic oscillator potentials, an expression for the splitting, ΔE, between the two observed intensity maxima can be obtained[11] in terms of the parameter D and the frequency of the active vibration, ν; the frequency is assumed to be the same in the ion as in the ground state of the molecule:

$$\Delta E = 2h\nu D^{1/2} \tag{6.8}$$

The splitting between the maxima is smaller than the Jahn–Teller stabilization energy $h\nu D$ provided that D is greater than four, but for smaller values of D the splitting between the maxima is greater than the stabilization. This behaviour is confirmed by an exact calculation of the expected intensity patterns[14]. Unless vibrational structure is resolved, the value of ν needed to deduce D from equation 6.8 must be obtained from the infrared or Raman spectrum with the help of a theoretical prediction of the identity of the single active mode.

In discussing the splitting of the bands, it has been assumed that the active mode is the only mode to be excited strongly on ionization. This may sometimes be so, but there is no reason why totally symmetric modes should not also be excited, just as in a normal transition. A noticeable static Jahn–Teller effect is likely to occur only if the degenerate orbital from which ionization takes place is strongly bonding or antibonding, and excitation of totally symmetric vibrations is therefore to be expected.

When one or more symmetric modes are excited in addition to the Jahn–Teller active mode, or when more than one degenerate

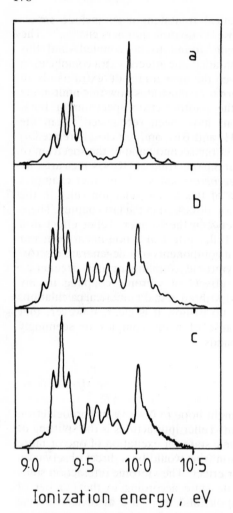

Figure 6.11. Part of the photoelectron spectrum of butatriene showing the energy range of the ion states $^2B_{3u}$ and $^2B_{3g}$. (a) Calculated spectrum, including only the coupling of the two states by the active mode; (b) spectrum calculated with additional excitation of a symmetric mode (tuning mode), which modulates the vibronic coupling; (c) experimental spectrum. Note how the experimental spectrum appears to contain a third 'mystery' band, due entirely to the non-adiabatic multi-mode effects. (Adapted from Cederbaum, L.S., Koppel, H. and Domcke, W., *Int. J. Quantum Chem.: Quantum Chem. Symposium*, **15**, 251 (1981)

mode is active, the theoretical treatment must include simultaneously all the modes whose occupation numbers change[15]. The different modes are generally found to be coupled, and this coupling produces strong non-adiabatic effects, extra complication of vibrational states, and even the appearance of 'extra bands' in photoelectron spectra. *Figure 6.11* illustrates how this multimode vibronic coupling affects the photoelectron spectrum of butatriene. Similar complications have been recognized[16,17] in the photoelectron spectra of NH_3 and BF_3, and are closely related to non-adiabatic effects found in the second band of the spectrum of ethylene and the first band of the spectrum of HCN, which arise by vibronic coupling of *non-degenerate* states[15,18]. Further examples are provided by the failure of the simple selection rules in the spectra of the linear triatomics, discussed in the last chapter. There is no essential difference between the Renner–Teller effect in a linear molecule, the Jahn–Teller effect in a non-linear one, nor between vibronic coupling of components of a degenerate electronic state compared with vibronic coupling of non-degenerate states. Unfortunately, the effects of vibronic coupling in any instance cannot be predicted without actual numerical calculation. From what has been done up to now it is clear, however, that vibronic coupling is the cause of many complex or seemingly continuous photoelectron bands.

6.3.2 Vibronic splittings

The other effect that one might hope to observe in photoelectron bands that show strong Jahn–Teller interactions is the splitting of the vibronic levels in the ionic state for excitation of one or more quanta of the active vibration; this would be a direct observation of the dynamic Jahn–Teller effect. The vibronic interaction splits each level in the degenerate state according to the number of quanta in the active vibration, and there are as many vibronic levels as there are symmetry species that result from multiplication of the electronic and vibrational species in the original symmetry. In an E state of a C_{3v} molecule the following species result from excitation of the first few quanta of an e active vibration:

	Vibrational species	*Vibronic species*
$v' = 0$	a_1	E
$v' = 1$	e	$E + A_1 + A_2$
$v' = 2$	$e \times e$	$E + E + A_1 + A_2$

As usual, this group theory indicates only the number and names of the states that may be present, and nothing about their spacings. In the approximation of a cylindrically symmetrical potential energy surface (*Figure 6.9*), it has been shown for this particular instance of an E state in C_{3v} that the A_1 and A_2 levels are degenerate[19], and a simple equation has been given for the energies[11]. The form of the vibrational structure that might actually be observed in the spectra also depends on the selection rules, as not all the new vibronic levels can be reached in direct photoionization. In ordinary optical transitions, at least for small or moderate vibronic coupling, the normal dipole selection rules imply that only one vibronic component of each level can be reached in absorption starting from the vibrationless ground state[2]. The splittings cannot be observed in absorption unless more than one quantum of an active vibration is already excited in the molecule before the optical transition occurs, that is, in hot bands. The way in which this conclusion must be modified for strong vibronic coupling or for photoionization, where the outgoing electron wave can carry different amounts of angular momentum, is not yet known. It is possible that some splittings may be observable, but their absence must be taken as most likely *a priori*. If any splittings were found, the angular distribution of the photoelectrons might be different for the different vibronic components.

6.3.3   Triply degenerate states

The discussion up to this point has concentrated on doubly degenerate states, because for these states the Jahn–Teller effects are relatively easy to explain. In molecules of tetrahedral or octahedral symmetry there are triply degenerate as well as doubly degenerate orbitals, and also triply and doubly degenerate vibrations. In general several modes will be active, and all the multi-mode Jahn–Teller complexity is to be expected. As far as the doubly degenerate (E) states are concerned, the preceding discussion is fully applicable, but in triply degenerate (T) states the situation as regards band shape and vibronic structure is even more complicated. A T state is susceptible to distortion via either the e or the t vibrational modes or a mixture of the two. Application of the semi-classical Franck–Condon approximation leads to the conclusion that ionization to a ^2T state in which only an e mode is active should give a single band in the spectrum,

while activity of a t mode should give a band with three maxima
even if only single active modes, and no totally symmetric modes
are involved. According to the Franck–Condon approximation,
the central maximum coincides with the energy of the upper state
at the symmetrical position, and the two outer maxima are
symmetrical about it. These conclusions about the band shape
were confirmed by a quantum mechanical calculation by Dixon[20]
for CH_4^+ (^2T), the case that has been studied most extensively. The
photoelectron spectra of methane, silane, germane and stannane
(*Figure 6.12*[21]) do show three maxima or shoulders, in good

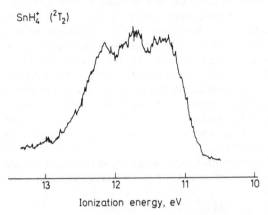

SnH_4^+ ($^2T_2$)

13   12   11   10

Ionization energy, eV

Figure 6.12. $^2T_2$ band in the photoelectron spectrum of stannane,
showing the three intensity maxima produced by the Jahn–Teller effect.
(From Potts and Price[21], by courtesy of the Council of the Royal Society)

agreement with the qualitative and also the quantitative predictions, but since these were all single-mode calculations made
before the importance of multi-mode vibronic coupling was realized, they should be regarded with great caution.

In methane ions formed by t_2^{-1} ionization, the most stable state is
predicted to be one reached by distortion brought about by an e
type vibration[20], and the predominant vibrational structure near
the onset of the ^2T band does seem to be a progression in the e
vibration, ν_2. However, the vibrational structure is complex,
conceivably including some vibronic splittings[22], and it has not yet
been satisfactorily explained. The complexities of the vibrational
structure might also be due to the presence of only a very small or
zero barrier to inversion through the square-planar (D_{4h}) configuration in methane ions[21]. The rule that the species of the

vibronic levels in the upper state are given by the product of electronic and vibrational symmetries holds for T states as well as E states, but here the splittings and selection rules are, at present, even less well understood.

6.3.4   The magnitude of Jahn–Teller distortions

If a photoelectron band is attributed to a degenerate ionic state with single-mode Jahn–Teller distortion, the semi-classical Franck–Condon approximation can be used to deduce the magnitude of the changes of bond length or bond angle that occur, as in normal bands. The energy of the ionic state in the symmetrical position is given by the point midway between the two maxima for a ^2E band, or by the central maximum for a ^2T band, and this energy takes the place of the vertical ionization potential. It is very difficult to be sure experimentally that the adiabatic ionization potential is seen in the spectrum, but equation 6.8 which relates Jahn–Teller band splitting to the stabilization energy for ^2E states, may be of use. The stabilization energy, hvD, is equivalent to the difference between the vertical and adiabatic ionization energy for a normal band.

Potts and Price[21] have made calculations of the changes in shape following t_2^{-1} ionization in the Group IV hydrides using the approximate expression 5.6. They calculated the larger HXH angles in CH_4^+, SiH_4^+, GeH_4^+ and SnH_4^+ to be 165, 150, 149 and 149 degrees, respectively, at the lowest equilibrium positions, that is, in the most stable states (all $^2B_2$ states) produced by the Jahn–Teller splitting. They also used the same method to calculate the maximum bond angles reached at different points in the bands and were able to explain the loss of vibrational structure in the SiH_4^+ and GeH_4^+ bands by the attainment of the square planar configurations of the ions in which the angles concerned reach 180 degrees. The loss of resolved vibrational structure at such a point is due to a disturbance of the vibrational levels and the halving of the frequency above the barrier of a potential energy surface with more than one minimum (see Section 6.5).

6.4   Jahn–Teller *versus* spin–orbit effects

Just as for spin–orbit interactions, accidental degeneracy of electronic states is also a basis for Jahn–Teller effects. One interesting theoretical case of this is degeneracy of u and g states in a linear symmetrical BAB molecule, which could lead to a Jahn–Teller distortion in which one AB bond becomes longer than the other[19]. No example of this is yet known, but a similar effect might occur in an ionic state of allene[23].

It is clear that most states of molecular ions produced by ionization from degenerate orbitals are susceptible to spin–orbit splittings and also to Jahn–Teller effects. The two effects are, in a sense, competing to lift the degeneracy, and details of the photo-electron spectrum depend on which effect is dominant. The strengths of the two interactions depend on different factors, spin–orbit splittings on the characteristics of the atomic orbitals involved and Jahn–Teller splittings on the bonding power of the electron removed. When one type of splitting is much stronger than the other, either normal Jahn–Teller or spin–orbit split bands are seen in the spectrum, but when they are of about the same magnitude new complications can appear that have yet another name, the Ham effect[11]. The changes expected in photoelectron bands as the splitting mechanism goes over from spin–orbit to Jahn–Teller interaction are roughly as follows.

(1) *Spin–orbit » Jahn–Teller*. The spacings between the spin–orbit split components are larger than the quanta of the Jahn–Teller active modes and an uncomplicated spin–orbit effect is observed, as with CH_3I^+ and CI_3H^+.

(2) *Spin–orbit > Jahn–Teller*. If the spin–orbit splitting is comparable with the energy of the Jahn–Teller active quanta, anomalous intensity distributions may be seen owing to intensity borrowing, as in the first ionization bands in the spectra of CH_3Br and CH_3Cl. This is the region of the Ham effect, in which the same components are seen as in (1), but with anomalous intensities and also with shifts of the levels producing an apparent reduction of the spin–orbit splitting, possibly by a large factor. Detailed examination of these effects in CH_3Cl^+ and related ions has been made quite recently[24].

(3) *Jahn–Teller » Spin–orbit*. When the Jahn–Teller effect is dominant and a static effect is produced, the spin–orbit interaction is quenched.

6.5   Renner–Teller effects and multiple potential energy minima

Linear molecules or ions in Π, Δ or Φ electronic states undergo no Jahn–Teller distortion, but vibronic coupling between states arises, and is called the Renner–Teller effect. Vibrational levels in which one or more quanta of degenerate bending vibrations are excited are split into several components by interaction of electronic and vibrational motion. In the ionization of linear molecules, however, the selection rule against excitation of bending vibrations $\Delta v_k = 0$, ($\pm 2, \pm 4...$), is not relaxed very much even for strong vibronic coupling, so this effect does not play an important role in their photoelectron spectra. The splitting has, however, been clearly observed in the photoelectron spectrum of N_2O. The structure seen in the spectrum depends not only on the vibronic splittings but also on the selection rules for excitation of the individual new vibronic levels on ionization.

Bending vibrations of linear ions are strongly excited on photo-ionization if the molecule is bent but the ion is linear, or if a large change in equilibrium angle is caused by ionization. The second ionization band in the photoelectron spectrum of water is of this type, as the ion is linear in the $^2A_1$ state produced by ionization of a $2a_1$ electron while the ground-state molecule is bent. Although the bending vibration is strongly excited, the electronic state of the ion is not degenerate, so no simple Renner–Teller effect results. Nevertheless, the second ionic state of H_2O^+ has a striking feature in that the frequency of the bending mode v_2 in this state, and also in the related Rydberg states, is only about half that in the neutral molecule. This drastic change in frequency is characteristic of a bent to linear transition because of the lifting of the inversion degeneracy. In the bent configuration, the state is degenerate in the sense that an equivalent configuration can be reached by bending the H atoms over on to the other side of the oxygen atom through the linear position. The graph of the potential energy as a function of the bending co-ordinate therefore has two equivalent minima (*Figure 6.13*) and all vibrational levels below the potential barrier are doubly degenerate on this account. Above the potential energy barrier, the previously degenerate levels are split, so twice as many vibrational levels now occupy the same energy intervals and the frequency is apparently halved. In an ionization process of a molecule going from a bent to a linear configuration or from a non-planar to a planar configuration, one therefore expects the frequency of the mode that corresponds most closely to inversion to be halved, if the force constants remain the same. Such halving of the frequency between molecule and ion has been found in the ground states of the ions PH_3^+, AsH_3^+ and SbH_3^+ as well as in the $^2A_1$ state of H_2O^+. If, in a particular state, an ion is only slightly bent, so that vibrational levels above as well as below the potential energy barrier can be reached in ionization, a change

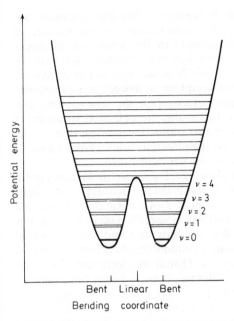

Figure 6.13. Potential energy surface with a double minimum, showing the apparent doubling of vibrational frequency above the barrier

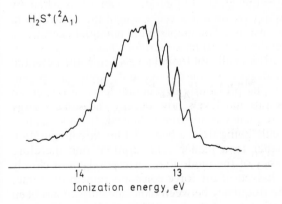

Figure 6.14. Second band in the photoelectron spectrum of hydrogen sulphide, showing the change in vibrational structure above the barrier of a double-minimum potential. (From Potts and Price[25], by courtesy of the Council of the Royal Society)

of vibrational spacings from hv' to $hv'/2$ should be seen within the spectral band. Such effects have been recognized in the second bands, which are a_1^{-1} ionizations, in the photoelectron spectra of H_2S (*Figure 6.14*), H_2Se and H_2Te[25].

Semi-classical Franck–Condon calculation of the change in angle from the difference between vertical and adiabatic ionization potentials confirms in each instance that the changeover takes place when the vibrational excursions are sufficient to make the ions approximately linear at the end of their motion. In earlier studies on hydrogen sulphide with lower resolution and signal-to-noise ratio, it seemed that the structure of the band simply broke off above the barrier, and this is still the apparent situation in the spectra of hydrogen selenide and hydrogen telluride. The vibrational structure above the barrier in H_2S^+ ($^2A_1$) is very complex, and only a partial analysis has been possible[26]. Once the ion attains the linear configuration, the $^2A_1$ state can interact with higher vibronic levels of the $^2B_1$ ionic ground state, because $^2A_1$ and $^2B_1$ combine to form the degenerate $^2\Pi$ state in a linear ion. This gives rise to a dynamic Renner–Teller effect and an increased complexity of the vibronic structure.

References

1. CONDON, E.U. and SHORTLEY, G.H., *The Theory of Atomic Spectra*, Cambridge University Press, Cambridge (1935)
2. HERZBERG, G., *Electronic Spectra and Electronic Structure of Polyatomic Molecules*, Van Nostrand, Princeton, N.J. (1966)
3. BIERI, G., HEILBRONNER, E., JONES, T.B., KLOSTER-JENSEN, E. and MAIER, J.P., *Physica Scripta*, **16**, 202 (1977), and references therein
4. WITTEL, K., *Chem. Phys. Lett.*, **15**, 555 (1972)
5. HARRIS, T., ELAND, J.H.D. and TUCKETT, R.P., *J. Mol. Spectrosc.*, **98**, 269 (1983)
6. ANDERSON, C.P., MAMANTOV, G., BULL, W.E., GRIMM, F.A., CARVER, J.C. and CARLSON, T.A., *Chem. Phys. Lett.*, **12**, 137 (1971)
7. BRUNDLE, C.R. and JONES, G.R., *J. Chem. Soc. Faraday Trans. II*, **68**, 959 (1972)
8. KING, G.H., KRISHNAMURTHY, S.S., LAPPERT, M.F. and PEDLEY, J.B., *Discuss. Faraday Soc.*, **54**, 70 (1973)
9. BROGLI, F. and HEILBRONNER, E., *Helv. Chim. Acta*, **54**, 1423 (1971)
10. JAHN, H.A. and TELLER, E., *Proc. R. Soc., Lond.*, **A161**, 220 (1937)
11. STURGE, M.D., *Solid State Phys.*, **20**, 92 (1967)
12. LINDHOLME, E., FRIDH, C. and ÅSBRINK, L., *Discuss. Faraday Soc.*, **54**, 127 (1973)
13. EVANS, S., JOACHIM, P.J., ORCHARD, A.F. and TURNER, D.W., *Int. J. Mass Spectrom. Ion Phys.*, **9**, 41 (1972)
14. LONGUET-HIGGINS, H.C., ÖPIK, U., PRYCE, M.H.L. and SACK, R.A., *Proc. R. Soc., Lond.*, **A244**, 1 (1958)

15. CEDERBAUM, L.S., KÖPPEL, H. and DOMCKE, W., *Int. J. Quantum Chem.*, **15**, 251 (1981)
16. HALLER, E., CEDERBAUM, L.S., DOMCKE, W. and KÖPPEL, H., *Chem. Phys. Lett.*, **72**, 427 (1980)
17. HALLER, E., KÖPPEL, H., CEDERBAUM, L.S., von NIESSEN, W. and BIERI, G., *J. Chem. Phys.*, **78**, 1359 (1983)
18. KÖPPEL, H., CEDERBAUM, L.S. and DOMCKE, W., *J. Chem. Phys.*, **77**, 2014 (1982)
19. ÖPIK, L.H. and PRYCE, M.H.L., *Proc. R. Soc., Lond.*, **A238**, 425 (1957)
20. DIXON, R.N., *Molec. Phys.*, **20**, 113 (1971)
21. POTTS, A.W. and PRICE, W.C., *Proc. R. Soc., Lond.*, **A326**, 165 (1972)
22. RABALAIS, J.W., BERGMARK, T., WERME, L.O., KARLSSON, L. and SIEGBAHN, K., *Physica Scripta*, **3**, 13 (1971)
23. HASELBACH, E., *Chem. Phys. Lett.*, **7**, 428 (1970)
24. KARLSSON, L., JADRNY, R., MATTSSON, L., CHAU, F.T. and SIEGBAHN, K., *Physica Scripta*, **16**, 225, 248 (1977)
25. POTTS, A.W. and PRICE, W.C., *Proc. R. Soc., Lond.*, **A326**, 181 (1972)
26. DIXON, R.N., DUXBURY, G., HORANI, M. and ROSTAS, J., *Molec. Phys.*, **22**, 977 (1971)

7
Reactions of positive ions

7.1 Introduction

In earlier chapters we have seen how photoelectron spectra show the energies and structure of ionic states, and how they indirectly reveal the characters of the different molecular orbitals. But a photoelectron spectrum is also something more; it is the *internal energy distribution* of ions produced by photoionization at a particular wavelength. We shall concentrate here on the consequences of this aspect of photoelectron spectroscopy, which adds a new dimension to photoionization as a tool in the study of ion reactions. The outcomes and rates of almost all chemical reactions, ionic or neutral, depend on the internal states of the reactants, and the study of the molecular detail of chemical reactions, 'reaction dynamics' becomes possible when known non-thermal state distributions can be selected. Most methods of ionization produce non-thermal ion state distributions, but only in photoionization is the actual distribution known, thanks to photoelectron spectroscopy. This power of photoelectron spectroscopy alone would allow photoionization to open up a photophysics of ions, at least as rich as the photophysics of molecules. In fact, molecular ions have two special advantages in addition. First, they are detectable as single particles, like electrons and photons. This enables us, using coincidence methods, to select single ions in known initial states over the whole range of internal energies available in photoelectron spectroscopy, and to study their reactions. Both bimolecular and unimolecular reactions can be examined, the latter representing perhaps the most fundamental processes of chemical reaction kinetics. Secondly, as we shall see below, molecular ions have simpler electronic state term schemes than most neutral molecules, and this reduces the number of complications which can arise from internal energy transfer.

With these factors in their favour, molecular ions offer a testing ground upon which some of the most important basic concepts of physical chemistry can be proved. Examples of the questions to be answered are:

(1) Do reaction rates and pathways depend on the specific internal states of molecules, or only on the total energy?
(2) Can we influence the outcome of reactions by pumping reactants to specific quantum states?
(3) How quickly is internal energy of a molecule transferred between all its internal modes?
(4) How does the energy transfer rate depend on the amount of energy available, or on the size of the molecules?

7.2   Ions and molecules

If we are to approach these general questions from the experimental study of molecular cations, or if we want to use knowledge of neutral molecules to illuminate the study of ions, we must ask how ions and molecules can be expected to differ in their behaviour. The presence of the electric charge evidently modifies interparticle potentials by adding a charge-induced dipole contribution and, for polar molecules, also a charge–dipole potential. These potentials, which fall off as r^{-4} and r^{-2}, respectively, are of longer range than the van der Waals forces (r^{-6}) between chemically non-interacting species and of much longer range than chemical binding (overlap) forces. On the other hand, although they are dominant at large internuclear distances, their effect at normal bonding distance is less than that of chemical bonding, which is essentially the charge–charge electrostatic interaction.

In order to give an idea of the magnitude of the different contributions to inter- and intra-molecular potentials, the contributions from chemical bonding and different long-range potentials are compared in *Table 7.1* at specific internuclear distances. For the purposes of calculation the dipole moments are assumed to be 0.3 Debye (a fairly polar bond) and polarizabilities are all set at 4×10^{-30} m^3 (e.g. Xenon atom, SO$_2$ molecule).

The ionic potential substantially outweighs the potential due to London dispersion forces at 0.5 nm, while the ion-locked dipole potential exceeds all others at 1 nm and more. The major effect of these long-range forces is to make the cross-sections for bimolecular reactions involving ions much larger than those for reactions of neutral particles. At ordinary bonding distances—that is within a molecule—the figures are not very meaningful, since the charge produced by a valence electron vacancy (as opposed to an inner shell vacancy) is not localized on this scale. Nevertheless, the charge-induced dipole potential is evidently not negligible at these distances, and we can expect some effects of polarization on the structure of ions as compared with their parent molecules. The long range of the ionic forces will introduce coupling between atoms and groups within molecules that are relatively distant, and not directly bonded. Static effects of this sort can probably be

Table 7.1

	0.2 nm	*0.5 nm*	*1 nm*
Strong bond	4 eV	–	–
Weak bond	1 eV	–	–
London forces	1.3 eV	5.3 meV	0.08 meV
Charge-locked dipole	0.2 eV	36 meV	9 meV
Charge-induced dipole	1.9 eV	46 meV	1.9 meV

expressed by changes in the shape of the potential energy surface, and are probably not significant. Dynamic effects of such long-range coupling could be more serious, because the dynamical behaviour of molecules is strongly influenced by the way energy is stored in or flows between internal modes. The flow of vibrational energy is critical, as in most models it determines reaction rates. Because the flow of vibrational energy is mediated by anharmonic coupling, it can only be made *easier* in ions, by comparison with neutral molecules, by the presence of the charge.

Another form of internal energy flow is conversion between different electronic states in a single molecule, which is often a crucial step in molecular reaction sequences. There are several mechanisms of internal conversion (IC) or intersystem crossing (ISC), depending on the nature of the states to be coupled, the most common being spin–orbit coupling (for $\Delta S = \pm 1$ transitions) or vibration–electronic coupling (Born–Oppenheimer breakdown). There is no obvious reason why either of these should be modified by the presence of a charge, so we may assume that they are governed by exactly the same consideration in ions as in neutral molecules, except in so far as they are influenced by the general difference in ion and molecule term schemes, discussed later.

7.3   State selection by coincidence methods

The ideal tool in the investigation of state-to-state reaction dynamics would be molecules or ions produced in single, known quantum states. This idea can be approached for ions, by adding to photoelectron spectroscopy what are known as *coincidence* techniques.

In photoionization using a non-pulsed source of uv light, both photoions and the corresponding photoelectrons are being produced continuously, at random instants. When a photoelectron is detected, however, we know that a photoion was formed at a precise moment, some 20 to 100 ns earlier. The exact detection delay is composed of the flight time of the photoelectron, dependent on its energy, on the transit times of electrons in the electron multiplier used for detection, and on propagation delays in cables and electronic circuits, all of which are known. This knowledge of the precise instant of birth of a photoion can be used to distinguish that particular ion, or its reaction products, from all others.

In the usual form of the technique[1], the arrival of a photoelectron starts a time-to-amplitude converter, which emits a pulse whose height is proportional to the time interval between a start and a stop signal. The stop signals are provided when the product ion or photon is detected, so the pulse height represents the time delay between photoelectron and final product. The height-coded pulses are fed to a multi-channel analyser, which sorts and stores them. A spectrum of time intervals between photoelectron and product detection is thus built up, and if the products have a defined time relationship to photoion formation, a peak will appear in the spectrum. This apparatus is shown schematically in *Figure 7.1*. In another form of the technique[2] the rate of formation of ions is made to be slow compared with the rate of diffusion out of the source region, and a drawout field is applied to the source as soon as a photoelectron is detected. Only those photoions which were partners to the detected photoelectrons will then be accelerated into a beam.

Coincidence techniques select photoions by detecting the photoelectrons; using a photoelectron spectrometer we arrange to detect photoelectrons of a single energy, and thus select ions of a single internal energy, equal to $hv - KE - I$. If the photoelectron spectrum has been analysed, we also know all the analysis can tell us about the initial quantum state of the ions. The coincidence method makes it possible to investigate the reactions of these state-selected ions, provided the reaction products can be detected

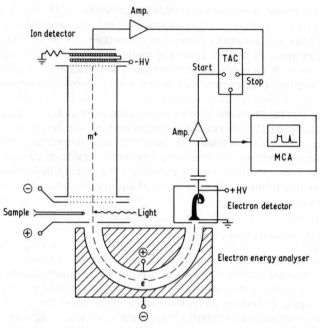

Figure 7.1.   Scheme of an apparatus for photoelectron–photoion coincidence spectroscopy (PEPICS). The TAC is a time-to-amplitude converter, which emits pulses whose amplitudes are proportional to the time between any start and the next stop signal. The pulses are sorted in the MCA (multi-channel analyser), which builds up a spectrum of time delays between photoelectron and photoion detections

as single particles with a defined time relationship to the photoions' production. When all this is done using a fixed wavelength of ionizing light, such as He I, the technique is called PEPICS (photoelectron–photoion coincidence spectroscopy). When the wavelength of light is varied, and electrons of zero energy are detected (threshold photoelectron spectroscopy) the technique has been called[3] PIPECO. Threshold electron detection has the advantage of greater sensitivity, but the disadvantage that the identities of the ionic states populated are not known (Chapter 3, p. 98).

7.4   Internal state changes

The simplest reactions of isolated molecules or ions are internal processes, and it is vital to examine these first, because, as we shall see, they almost invariably precede or compete with the ion reactions to which the coincidence methods of state selection are applied. Ions are generally formed in non-stationary states, and undergo internal evolution from the instants of their formation. Because all such changes are unimolecular they exactly conserve energy, angular momentum and parity (or relevant symmetry). They need not long retain any other memory of their initial state, however. The mechanisms by which they tend to lose their original state identity are the energy flows mentioned before; IVR (internal vibrational redistribution), IC (internal conversion) and ISC (intersystem crossing). We must briefly review current knowledge of these processes before we can evaluate experimental results on the observable unimolecular reactions of ion light emission and ion dissociation.

7.4.1 Vibrational energy flow

The vibrational energy of a polyatomic molecule is stored in the different normal modes of vibration, which are weakly coupled together by anharmonic terms in the molecular potential. Absorption of light, including photoionization, populates the totally symmetric modes preferentially but, because of the anharmonic coupling, energy may flow from any mode into any other combination of modes that preserve energy and relevant symmetry. Direct experiments[4,5] have shown that the rate of this internal vibrational redistribution increases rapidly with increasing energy within an electronic state, after reaching about $10^8 \, s^{-1}$ (competition with fluorescence) at an onset energy of only a few thousand wavenumbers ($3000 \, cm^{-1}$ or $375 \, meV$) in molecules of the size of benzene or naphthalene. Theory indicates that the onset should correspond roughly to the energy at which the widths of the vibrational levels are equal to their average spacing, so it should come at lower energy in larger molecules and at higher energy in smaller ones. Quantitative comparison with the theory shows that the vibrational density of states alone is not sufficient to account for the rates, and it is postulated that rotational energy also plays a part[4]. These direct experiments thus tend to confirm the assumption of the statistical theories of unimolecular reactions, that vibrational–rotational energy randomization is complete in a time which is short compared with the reaction time. In view of the effects of the charge in improving coupling, we must expect the integrity of initial ionic vibrational states to be lost even more rapidly than that of the equivalent neutral molecule states at the same energy.

IVR must be assumed to precede reaction of all but the smallest (diatomic or triatomic) ions, unless the contrary can be demonstrated.

7.4.2   Electronic energy flow

An isolated molecule in an excited electronic state may undergo internal conversion to a lower state of the same spin multiplicity. In either case, the initial electronic excitation energy is converted into vibrational energy in the lower state, and the rate of the transfer process can be approximately expressed by the *energy gap* law:

$$k_{nr} \propto \exp\left(-\frac{\Delta E}{kh\nu''}\right) \tag{7.1}$$

Here E is the electronic energy gap, ν'' is the frequency of the 'acceptor mode'—usually the highest frequency vibration in the lower state—and k is a constant for a series of related molecules. This rule, which was first discovered empirically and later justified theoretically[6], arises from the importance of the vibrational overlap between the initial and final states. The quantity $E/h\nu''$ is the minimum change in the number of vibrational quanta that must occur on transition.

Because of the energy gap law, a fundamental difference between polyatomic molecules and ions arises from the difference in their typical electronic energy level patterns. *Figure 7.2* illustrates the difference, which arises because molecular ions are radicals, not closed shell species, and that the energy gap between the highest occupied and lowest unoccupied orbitals in a molecule (HOMO–LUMO gap) is almost always wider than the gaps between individual occupied orbitals. Excitation of a neutral molecule requires crossing the gap, whereas excitation of a radical cation does not.

The two vital characteristics of the ion term scheme in *Figure 7.2* are that the first doublet–doublet gap is rather narrow, and that the first quartet lies *above* the first excited doublet. The result of the small first gap is that, in most ions, internal conversion brings all excited ions right down to the ground electronic state, whereas in molecules internal conversion usually stops at the first *excited* singlet (Kasha's rules). This immediately explains why few molecular ions exhibit fluorescence. In the exceptional cases of fluorescing ions, the higher energy of the quartet state means that

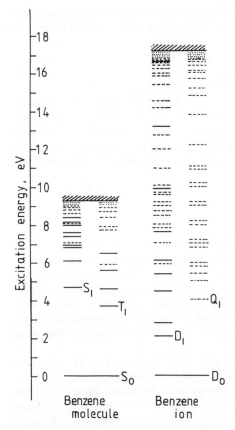

Figure 7.2.   Energy levels of benzene, and its radical cation.
Spectroscopically known states are drawn as solid lines, while estimated
and calculated state positions are dotted lines

the *only* non-radiative pathway from the emitting state is internal
conversion to the ground state. This greatly simplifies theoretical
treatment of the competition between radiative and non-radiative
deactivation, and makes molecular ions an excellent testing
ground for the theory of non-radiative transitions[7].

The energy gap law and the above remarks are generally valid
for polyatomic ions, whose internal energy flows can be described
by the 'statistical limit' of non-radiative transition theory. In
molecules with four atoms or less, energy transfer between states
depends critically on details of the energy level diagram, strengths

of coupling, and accidental degeneracies. In the 'resonance limit' (diatomic molecules) and 'intermediate cases' of non-radiative transition theory more restricted energy transfer takes place, and its rate and effects vary rapidly from one level to another. Quantum interference (beats) and non-exponential decay are characteristics of the intermediate cases, and have been identified in decays of some fascinating small molecular ions. The conservation laws give rise to selection rules for the non-radiative transitions, which are actually restrictive in the small and symmetric molecules. The electronic selection rules, called the Wigner–Witmer rules, have been known for a long time and are well presented by Hasted[8]; the vibronic selection rules are less well known, but have been codified by Howard and Schlag[9].

7.5   Models of ion dissociation

Molecular dissociation is also a form of non-radiative transition and, as such, is subject to the same conservation laws (selection rules) as the processes discussed above. In order to understand the experimentally observed characteristics of ion dissociations, such as reaction rates, choice of products or energy disposal, we try to model them in terms of motion over potential energy surfaces, or in terms of the non-radiative transition steps which lead up to dissociation itself. One classification, illustrated in *Figure 7.3*, is into *direct dissociation*, or one of several sub-classes of *predissociations*. Direct dissociations are the simplest, since the mechanism conceptually involves only a single step; pre-dissociations require one or more non-radiative transitions within the ion before dissociation itself can take place.

7.5.1   Direct dissociation

If the state of a diatomic ion reached directly in photoionization is repulsive (unbound) or a repulsive part of a bound surface, the molecular ion will dissociate immediately and there can be no vibrational structure in the photoelectron spectrum (*Figure 7.3(a)*). Conversely, if it can be proved that lack of vibrational structure in a photoelectron band is due to dissociation, then the potential energy surface reached in ionization is effectively unbound even if according to a normal model of the electronic structure it is expected to be a bound state. An otherwise bound state may be effectively repulsive because of interaction with a

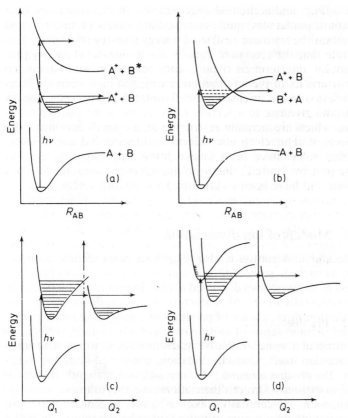

Figure 7.3. Potential energy curves illustrating some important dissociation mechanisms. (a) Direct dissociation; (b) electronic pre-dissociation; (c) vibrational pre-dissociation; (d) internal conversion with vibrational pre-dissociation. In (c) and (d) the co-ordinates Q_1 and Q_2 represent different molecular motions in a polyatomic molecule

repulsive state involving curve crossing or avoided crossing. The products will fly apart with most of the excess energy of the molecular ion above the dissociation limit as translational energy, as there is insufficient time available for it to be redistributed among internal modes before the fragments separate. The potential energy curves representing this process in *Figure 7.3* are suitable only for diatomic molecules; for polyatomic molecules, they must be imagined as two-dimensional cuts through multi-dimensional surfaces with a reaction co-ordinate as the horizontal scale. They retain their simple meanings for dissociations and spectra of polyatomic species only if this reaction co-ordinate and the vibrational motions excited by ionization are the same. It is unlikely that the change in equilibrium molecular geometry produced by ionization of a polyatomic molecule will correspond exactly and exclusively to motion in a reaction co-ordinate; direct dissociation in the strict sense can be defined as a process in which it very nearly does so.

True direct dissociation as defined above can occur only if the removal of an electron has a strong and specific influence on the bonding in the molecule. A close relationship between the identity of the products and the bonding character of the ionized electron is therefore to be sought in such instances. Unfortunately, there are as yet no clearly characterized direct dissociations of ions for which this idea can be tested. The detection of a particular product can be considered to be significant only if an alternative decomposition is energetically possible, and this is not so in the few direct dissociations of polyatomic ions that have been recognized up to now.

7.5.2 Pre-dissociation

If a molecular ionic state is definitely bound, as it has vibrational structure in the spectrum, but nevertheless dissociation takes place, the process is called pre-dissociation. Herzberg[10] has classified pre-dissociations into three ideal cases, as follows.

In *Case I*, pre-dissociation occurs by rearrangement of electronic energy; there is a non-radiative transition from the bound state to a continuous state, that is, from one potential energy surface to another. If the two electronic states have the same symmetry species, the pre-dissociation is *homogeneous*; if they are of different symmetry, it is *heterogeneous*. Electronic pre-dissociation is probably the most common mechanism by which small molecular ions formed in photoionization decompose. The way in which the excess energy is divided between the degrees of freedom of the products, including translation, depends on the details of the potential energy surfaces, especially at the configuration where the transition takes place between them. It is possible for a large fraction of the energy to appear as kinetic energy, but alternatively internal vibrational or rotational energy of the products may be favoured. Some correlations between the bonding power of an electron ionized and the identity of the products formed may be sought, as the nature of the electron ionized determines the forms of the initial ionic potential energy surface and of the initial vibrational motion. However, the existence of such correlations will also depend on several other factors, particularly the forms of surfaces that lead to different products and potentially cause the pre-dissociation, and the strengths of their interactions with the bound potential surface.

In *Case II*, pre-dissociation takes place on a single electronic energy surface by rearrangement of the vibrational energy. The excited molecule has sufficient energy to dissociate but the energy is initially in vibrational modes that do not correspond to the reaction co-ordinate for dissociation. Most thermally induced unimolecular reactions are such vibrational pre-dissociations and involve the ground electronic state only. There is very little evidence to show how common this mechanism may be among molecular ion dissociations, but it is probably less important for small ions than electronic pre-dissociation. A more distant relationship between the identity of the products and that of the electron removed must be expected in vibrational pre-dissociations than is possible in *Case I*, as the vibrational energy is removed from the mode excited on ionization into other modes, which presumably correspond more closely to different reaction co-ordinates. According to theories of unimolecular reactions, the excess energy should be distributed between all the degrees of freedom of the products, in favourable instances in a statistical manner.

Case III, in which dissociation is the result of the rotational energy which a molecule possesses in excess of a dissociation limit, will not be considered further here.

7.5.3 Internal conversion plus vibrational pre-dissociation

Because of its supposed prevalence, this mixed mechanism must be considered separately, although it is a sub-case of pre-dissociation. According to the quasi-equilibrium theory of mass spectra (QET), all excited molecular ions relax rapidly by conversion of their electronic excitation energy into vibrational energy of the molecular ion in its electronic ground state, after which fragmentation follows by vibrational pre-dissociation. The first step is a series of internal conversions between electronic states of the isolated ion, restricted only by conservation of energy and angular momentum. In this mechanism, all traces of the identity of the electron originally ionized are lost and the abundances of different products should depend only on the form of the potential energy hypersurface for the ionic ground state. The excess energy must be distributed statistically among all the internal degrees of freedom of the fragments.

Potential energy curves intended to illustrate these three mechanisms are shown in *Figure 7.3*, but it must be emphasized that the representation is very crude. At least two cuts must be made through the multi-dimensional potential energy surfaces in order to indicate vibrational pre-dissociation at all, whereas the molecules themselves have a choice from an infinite number of such cuts. Very many more sub-cases of pre-dissociation can be imagined than are represented in *Figure 7.3*, and a wider selection has been illustrated by Mulliken[11].

7.5.4   Correlation rules

Direct dissociation may be expected if the state of the molecular ion reached in photoionization goes over directly to a lower dissociation limit (*Figure 7.3(a)*). The symmetry species of the molecular ionic state must be identical with a species that can be obtained by combining the products; the correlation rules indicate those species of states of the molecular ion which can be obtained by combining particular products, and therefore whether direct dissociation to these products is possible or not. The correlation rules, also called Wigner–Witmer rules, are given by Herzberg (reference 10, p. 281), whose book is a most useful source of the symmetry tables needed in applying these rules; for diatomic molecules, the rules are presented in a convenient form by Hasted[8]. In essence, a point group is chosen that corresponds to the symmetry that is conserved in the dissociation, and the appropriate tables (reference 10, p. 574) are used in order to find the species of the molecular state and the states of the separated fragments in this group. The direct products of the representations to which the states of the fragments belong (reference 10, p. 570) then give the orbital species that can result from their combination. For the spins the rule is simply

$$S = S_1 + S_2, S_1 + S_2 - 1 \ldots S_1 - S_2 \qquad (7.2)$$

The multiplicity is, as always, equal to $2S + 1$, and corresponding pairwise combination is valid for more than two fragments. An example of the use of the rules is provided by the dissociation of methyl chloride ions in their first excited state, $^2A_1$, corresponding to the continuous second band in the photoelectron spectrum:

$$CH_3Cl^+(^2A_1) \rightarrow CH_3^+(^1A_1') + Cl(^2P_u) \tag{7.3}$$

The dissociation can be assumed to take place along the C–Cl axis, so that the whole molecular symmetry (C_{3v}) is conserved. The ground state of planar CH_3^+ goes over to $^1A_1$ in C_{3v}, while the ground-state chlorine atom gives $^2A_1 + {}^2E$. The direct product of A_1 with $A_1 + E$ is again $A_1 + E$ and the spin rule allows only doublets, so a $^2A_1$ state does arise from the combination of the products. A direct dissociation is possible and is probably the reason for the continuous nature of the second band in the spectrum. For the related fragmentation of ground state CF_4^+ ions (Chapter 5, Section 5.4.1),

$$CF_4^+(^2T_1) \rightarrow CF_3^+(^1A_1') + F(^2P_u) \tag{7.4}$$

C_{3v} symmetry may still be conserved and direct dissociation is possible through the ^2E components because in C_{3v} symmetry $^2T_1$ (of T_d) goes over to $^2A_2 + {}^2E$.

In the photoelectron spectrum of hydrogen sulphide, the second band shows an apparent breaking-off of vibrational structure at 13.3 eV (*Figure 6.14*), which happens to coincide with the dissociation limit for the process

$$H_2S^+ \rightarrow S^+(^4S_u) + H_2(^1\Sigma_g^+) \tag{7.5}$$

This coincidence has given rise to suggestions that the loss of vibrational structure might be due to rapid dissociation, but as the states of H_2S^+ reached in photoionization are all doublets a direct dissociation is forbidden by the spin rule. It is now known that the change in vibrational structure at 13.3 eV has a different origin, as described in Section 6.5.

The correlation rules, as with all considerations that are based purely on symmetry, indicate only the combinations which are possible and those which are impossible. In order to establish whether a particular state of the products of a dissociation goes over directly to a particular molecular state, further information is required. The most useful guide is the *non-crossing rule*, which is also based on symmetry. This rule states that in a potential energy diagram for a diatomic molecule, no curves of the same symmetry species can cross, but rather they avoid each other, thus producing two new curves. The rule is based on the idea that there is always an interaction between two states of the same symmetry species,

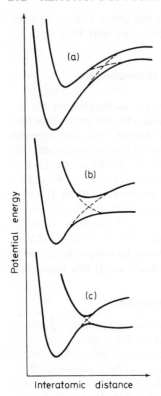

Figure 7.4. Potential energy curves for a diatomic molecule illustrating the non-crossing rule. The dashed lines indicate the unperturbed curves in each instance and the full lines the effective potential energy curves. (a) Interaction between two bound states; (b) and (c) interactions between a bound state and a repulsive state, very strong and weak, respectively

although they may be non-interacting states in an approximate model of the system. The interaction is represented by a matrix element, $<\Psi_1|\hat{P}|\Psi_2>$, which must be non-zero if the operator $\hat{P}$ contains all the terms that are omitted in the approximate model. From the rule, it follows that the lowest state of a given symmetry in a diatomic molecule must go over either directly or by an avoided crossing to the lowest state of the same symmetry obtainable by combining dissociation products. Furthermore, higher states of the same symmetry must likewise go over to the higher dissociation limits of correct symmetry in their natural energetic order. The shape of the potential energy curves produced, however, depends very much on whether the interaction involved is weak or strong, as illustrated in *Figure 7.4*. Even two electronic states of exactly the same symmetry species may interact only weakly if, for instance, they differ in their electron configurations. If the interaction is weak, the rate at which the system can pass from one of the original states to the other is low, and the lifetime of a molecule in an initial bound state may be long.

7.6   Experimental results on ion dissociation

The unimolecular dissociation of a single molecule can be described by the chemical nature of the products, the angles at which the products separate in the molecular frame, the time between energization and dissociation, and the ways the excess energy and angular momentum are shared between the products. Because of the non-deterministic way individual molecules behave, we expect to find *distributions* in all of these properties, even if many molecules are excited to exactly the same initial quantum state. In fact, our experimental techniques do not yet allow us to select single quantum states of excited ions, but photoelectron spectra do show us, and the photoelectron coincidence technique allows us to select, individual vibrational levels of single electronic states.

7.6.1   Chemical nature of products—branching

When a molecular ion dissociates, at least one product species is an ion whose mass can be determined by mass spectroscopy. A mass spectrometer combined with a photoelectron spectrometer provides for the coincidence technique called photoelectron–photoion coincidence spectroscopy (PEPICS), in whose simplest form the mass spectrometer consists of no more than a flight tube where the ions separate according to their different velocities. Since flight times to the fixed ion detector are proportional to the square roots of the ion masses, mass spectra showing the decay of state-selected ions can be taken.

The formation of a particular set of chemical products by ion dissociation is significant only when other competing dissociation pathways are energetically accessible. For H_2S^+ ions in the first excited state $\tilde{A}^2A_1$, only S^+ ($+H_2$) is possible energetically (and is formed), but from the second excited state, $\tilde{B}^2B_2$, both S^+ and HS^+ could be formed, but only HS^+ is actually produced[12]. The fact that the less exothermic reaction is preferred means that the reaction is controlled by specific features of the $\tilde{B}$ state potential energy surface, rather than purely by the quantity of energy available. There can be no internal conversion from $\tilde{B}$ to $\tilde{A}$, and the inference is that the HS^+ forming reaction is relatively rapid. From a chemical point of view it seems reasonable that an electron vacancy in an S–H bonding orbital leads to HS^+–H cleavage. The reaction has been studied experimentally by several groups, and theoretical calculations of the potential hypersurfaces have also been undertaken[13].

The ion $C_2F_6^+$ provides a second example of significant branching behaviour. Its ground state is unstable, and PEPICS experiments show[14] that the product ion is CF_3^+. As soon as the selected photoelectron energy is changed slightly to select the first excited state of $C_2F_6^+$, however, the dissociation product changes to $C_2F_5^+$. This discontinuous change proves that no internal conversion from the first excited state to the ground state precedes fragmentation, contradicting the assumption of the usual statistical theory of polyatomic ion dissociation. This was actually the first direct proof of 'isolated state behaviour' in mass spectrometry.

In the majority of polyatomic ion dissociations which have been studied by the coincidence techniques of state selection, the product ion identities and yields seem to be determined 'statistically'. This does not mean that absolutely all energetically possible products are formed, but that the competition between the channels that are actually open is governed primarily by the total probability (volume of the phase space) for each channel at a particular total energy. Unfortunately, the theories tend to involve many parameters, so it is difficult to decide between different theories (e.g. pure phase-space or statistical adiabatic channel theory) on the basis of present evidence.

7.6.2   Product angular distributions

If we could prepare energized H_2S^+ molecular ions not only in a known quantum state but also with a definite orientation in space, we might expect to find a clear relationship between the starting position and the angles at which S^+ and HS^+ products are detected. On the other hand, slow dissociation, allowing many rotations and possibly internal rearrangements (isomerization) before fragmentation, would tend to erase memory of the initial orientation.

In fact, detection of a photoelectron emitted into a single laboratory direction with a defined energy *does signal formation of an orientated ion*. This poorly appreciated aspect of photoionization can be understood by imagining a molecule held fixed during the ionization process. The departing electron cannot pass through the molecule in all directions with equal ease; in fact, the electron distribution pattern will reflect the shape of the molecule, with emphasis from the localization of the orbital. If the electron energy is high enough to give it an appropriate wavelength, the outgoing wave will be diffracted by the molecule; at all events, the distribution will be highly anisotropic. When we select photoelectrons ejected in a single direction (into a single slit or aperture) we are selecting molecular ions whose orientation is just as anisotropic as the photoelectron pattern from a space-fixed molecule. It is therefore to be expected that fragment ion distributions will *generally* be anisotropic in the laboratory frame, when measured with respect to the direction of the departing photoelectron. Even a long lifetime allowing many rotations before dissociation does not completely abolish an initial anisotropy, because rotation cannot supply or remove angular momentum in any axis[15]. Any forward–backward asymmetry does vanish within a few rotations, however, and the distribution is generally smoothed leaving only a $P_2(\cos\theta)$ term.

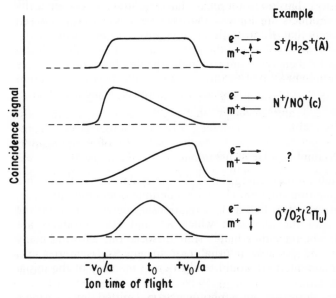

Figure 7.5.   The effects of anisotropic fragment ion distributions upon coincidence time-of-flight peak shapes in PEPICS coincidence experiments. It is assumed that a single kinetic energy, larger than kT is released in the dissociation, and the figures show expected peak shapes for isotropic (top) and for different anisotropic distributions of fragments ions with respect to photoelectrons

Forward–backward asymmetry means that a fragment ion is not equally likely to depart in the same direction as the electron, and in the opposite direction; this is the simplest form of asymmetry, and was the first to be detected[16]. *Figure 7.5* shows how it manifests itself in the photoelectron–photoion coincidence spectrum, as a strong late-early asymmetry. The origin of this spectral signature is that daughter ions leaving in a direction opposed to that of the departed photoelectron fly straight towards the ion detector, and so arrive relatively early, while ions which follow the electrons must have their initial velocity reversed, and so arrive late. There is always some inequality between the early and late arrivals because of apparatus effects, but this can be thoroughly allowed for, and the real forward–backward asymmetry remains.

Ion fragmentation angular distributions are a very promising field for future research: because of the effect of rotations in partially washing-out the anisotropy, measurements on rotationally cold molecular beams would be very informative. They would even allow estimates of unimolecular rates in the range 10^{10}–10^{11} s^{-1} to be made, from study of the effect of rotational temperature on the observed anisotropies.

7.6.3   Ion dissociation rates

Ion dissociations which take less than 10^{-12} s or so are almost certain to give anisotropic product angular distributions; they also cause detectable line broadening, even in photoelectron spectra. Although 'continuous' photoelectron bands are often the result of vibronic coupling complications, some bands in spectra of small molecules show broadening which is unambiguously due to short lifetimes; three examples are given in *Figure 7.6*.

HF^+

The first excited state of HF^+ is a $^2\Sigma^+$ state that arises from the ionization of an electron from the H–F bonding σ orbital. The second band in the photoelectron spectrum[17] shows vibrational structure from the onset at 19.09 eV up to 19.43 eV, where it breaks off to yield to a continuum. The lowest dissociation limit is for the production of H^+ (^1S_g) + F (^2P_u) atoms in their ground states, and calculation and experiment agree that it lies at 19.44 eV. The fact that the vibrational structure disappears exactly at the dissociation limit shows that this is a direct dissociation—that is, ionization above the limit goes to an unbound part of the upper

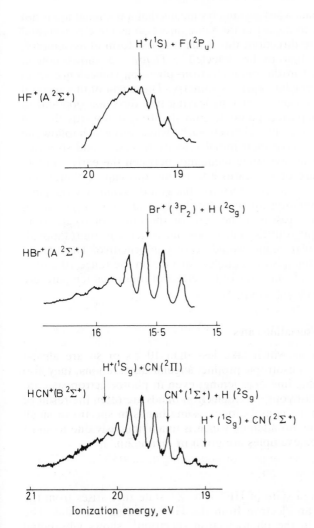

Figure 7.6.   Three photoelectron bands which show broadening due to rapid dissociation. The arrows give the positions of dissociation limits for formation of the products named (HF from Brundle[17], by courtesy of North Holland Publishing Company; HBr from Schneider and Smith[19], by courtesy of the North Holland Publishing Company; HCN from Baker, C. and Turner, D., *Proc. R. Soc., Lond.*, **A308**, 19 (1968), by courtesy of the Council of the Royal Society)

potential energy surface. The products combine according to the correlation rules to give a $^2\Sigma^+$ state and a $^2\Pi$ state. The $^2\Pi$ combination correlates directly with the ground state of HF^+, which is $X^2\Pi$, while the $^2\Sigma^+$ combination goes over directly to the A $^2\Sigma^+$ state of HF^+, which dissociates. This is confirmed by correlation of the individual orbitals and by a detailed numerical calculation[18], and so the dissociation of HF^+ $(A^2\Sigma^+)$ ions is definitely simple and direct, as depicted in *Figure 7.3(a)*.

HBr^+

The first excited state of HBr^+ is a $^2\Sigma^+$ state that corresponds to ionization of an H–Br bonding σ electron. The lowest dissociation limit is calculated to be 15.59 eV and represents the formation of the products H (^2S_g) + Br^+ $(^2P_2)$. This dissociation limit is well below the onset of observable broadening in the photoelectron spectrum[19], which first sets in for the $v' = 4$ line of the $^2\Sigma^+$ band at 15.9 eV. The emission spectrum of HBr^+ (A $^2\Sigma^+$) ions produced by photoionization at 584 Å has been measured[19,20], and the only transitions found in it are from the $v' = 0$ and $v' = 1$ levels of HBr^+, both of which are below the dissociation limit. Hence all HBr^+ ions that are produced with energies above the dissociation limit dissociate faster than they can radiate, thus in less than about 10^{-9} s, but only at the vibrational level $v' = 4$ does the dissociation rate become fast enough to cause broadening in the photoelectron spectrum. This is clear evidence that the process is a pre-dissociation, probably involving a curve crossing at or a little above the $v' = 4$ level. In connection with the study of the emission bands, it has been shown[20] that the pre-dissociation is caused by a $^4\Pi$ state that is obtained by combining the products. The other states produced by combining them are $^{2,4}\Sigma^-$ and $^2\Pi$, so that no homogeneous dissociation is possible. The interaction between the A $^2\Sigma^+$ state and the $^4\Pi$ state of HBr^+ must be brought about by spin–orbit coupling, which is strong for the bromine atom.

HCN^+

As the $-CN$ group is sometimes considered as a pseudo-halogen atom it is not surprising that there is a superficial similarity between the behaviour of HCN^+ and those of the halogen acid ions. The similarity is deceptive, however, because the dissociation involves some purely polyatomic effects. The first band in the photoelectron spectrum is complex because of vibronic interaction between the $\tilde{X}^2\Pi$ ground state of HCN^+ and the nearby $\tilde{A}^1\Sigma^+$ state[21]. The second band, shown in *Figure 7.6*, was originally interpreted as a simple $4\sigma^{-1}$ ionization, giving a $\tilde{B}^2\Sigma^+$ state of HCN^+, but subsequent calculations have shown that it is actually more like an inner-valence band. At least two electron configurations are needed to describe the ionic state, and the configuration mixing is a strong function of the bond lengths[22]. The potential surface of the $\tilde{B}^2\Sigma^+$ state contains a saddle point, and differs so much from that of neutral HCN that the vibrational motion is totally different (Duschinsky effect, p. 138). The Wigner–Witmer rules indicate that $\tilde{B}^2\Sigma^+$ correlates to $H + CN^+$ at 19.43 eV, while the products actually formed from the dissociation of HCN^+ excited to the third band, $H^+ + CN$, correlate to the $\tilde{A}^2\Sigma^+$ state. The formation of H^+ thus requires an internal conversion between $\tilde{B}$ and $\tilde{A}$, which are of the same symmetry and cannot cross. It is thought[22] that the conversion may go via an intermediate $^2\Pi$ state, by vibronic coupling involving the vibration v_2. The effect of the bending vibration is to convert surface crossings between $^2\Sigma$ and $^2\Pi$ states into conical intersections[23], providing lines on the surfaces where interconversion is possible. This is a complex mechanism, so it is perhaps not surprising that considerable vibrational structure persists in the photoelectron spectrum above the H^+ threshold.

The vibrational structure of the HCN^+ third band cannot be interpreted in the usual way because of the non-adiabatic effects introduced by the effect of the bond lengths on the electronic configuration. It can, however, be transformed to yield a description of the time evolution of the wave packet describing HCN^+ excited to the third band[24]. This is an example of a very general relationship between spectroscopy and dynamics which has been developed by Heller and applied particularly to molecular ions by Lorquet[25]. When effects of rotational envelopes, hot bands and spin–orbit splitting have been removed, the Fourier transform of a spectral band yields the time evolution of the correlation function that describes overlap of the wave packet at every instant with its initial position in the newly-formed ions. In HCN^+ $\tilde{B}^2\Sigma^+$ the time evolution in the first 10^{-13} s is found to be decidedly non-exponential: the wave packet starts at first to execute an in-phase C–H and C–N stretching oscillation but rapidly spreads out and separates into a part which undergoes very rapid dissociation and a part which decays more slowly after being trapped in a shallow well on the surface. It is not yet clear how this global description can be related to state specific measurements on branching, angular distributions or energy release.

7.6.4   Slow ion dissociations

If ions dissociate too slowly to cause line broadening the PEPICS technique can be used to determine their lifetime distributions directly by measurement of the time-of-flight distributions of fragment ions. When a photoelectron is detected, we know that an ion of definite internal energy was formed in the ionization region some 100 ns earlier (flight time of the electron), and immediately it was formed the ion will have started its acceleration towards the mass spectrometer, under the influence of the source electric field. The acceleration is inversely proportional to the mass of the charged particle, so the parent ion speeds up least rapidly, and a lighter fragment ion more rapidly. If an ion dissociates during acceleration it will gain an intermediate velocity, and appear at the detector at an intermediate time. Lifetimes from a few tens of nanoseconds to tens of microseconds can be detected if the mass difference between parent and fragment is large, and the lifetime distribution can be determined by a transformation of the observed time-of-flight distribution[24].

When a lifetime distribution is examined, it may be found to form a decaying exponential distribution,

$$N(t) = A \exp(-t/\tau) \tag{7.6}$$

If this is true (and it is not always so) it is correct to extract the mean lifetime τ and thus also the decay rate constant, $k = \tau^{-1}$. The magnitude of the rate constant can then be determined as a function of the initial internal energy of the ions by changing the chosen photoelectron energy. This technique thus provides a direct way of testing theories of unimolecular reactions, such as RRKM theory, which 'predict' rates as functions of internal energy. Rate constants deduced in this way are shown in *Figure 7.7* for a dissociation of pyridine[26], which seems to be very well described by a statistical RRKM-type model. Rate constants have been measured for several polyatomic ion dissociations, including dissociation of ions prepared from molecules of the same molecular formula, but of different structure. The dissociation rates of C_2H_2 loss from ions of cyclo-octatetraene and styrene, both $C_8H_8^+$, for instance, are exactly the same when measured at the same energies with respect to the dissociation products[27]. This means

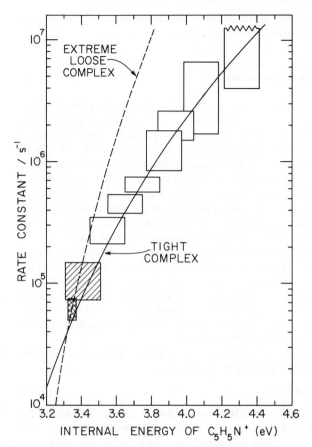

Figure 7.7.   Rate constants for the unimolecular reaction $C_5H_5N^+$ (pyridine ion) $\rightarrow C_4H_4^+ + HCN$ as a function of the internal energy of the parent ion, derived mainly from photoelectron–photoion coincidence experiments. The data are compared with RRKM calculations assuming 'tight' or 'loose' activated complexes

that the isomeric ions rearrange to a common form before dissociating, and comparison with RRKM calculations suggests that the common form has stilbene$^+$ structure. Similar behaviour has been found in several cases. The identical ionic behaviour of initially different neutral isomers implies that all of their ions which have enough energy to dissociate, sample a common isomeric phase space. Certain other isomers of the same molecular formula may behave differently, because they perceive barriers to isomerization and, of course, there is no suggestion that ions rearrange to an equal extent at energies *below* the dissociation limit. Nevertheless, these findings demonstrate that isomerization of gas-phase carbocations is probably very common, just as it is in solution chemistry.

7.6.5   Energy disposal

When an energized ion dissociates, all its energy in excess of the minimum needed for dissociation is divided among the internal degrees of freedom of the fragments, or else goes into their relative kinetic energies. The part that goes into kinetic energy is easily characterized by the coincidence method, because it shows up in the fragment ion time-of-flight peak shapes. If a fragment is shot out straight towards the ion detector, for instance, it inevitably arrives there earlier than a zero-initial-energy fragment of the

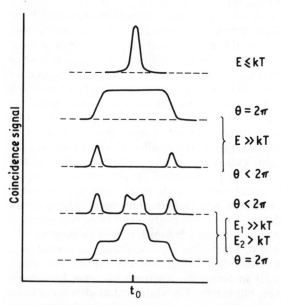

Figure 7.8.   The effects of fragment ion kinetic energy E and of the angle from which ions are collected on time-of-flight peak shapes. Isotropic angular distributions are assumed. Comparison with *Figure 7.5* shows that kinetic energy distributions can be deduced from peak shapes only if the angular distributions are known

same mass, whereas if it is shot off in the opposite direction it must be turned right around by the ion source electric field before getting underway towards the detector, and it arrives late. When there is release of translational energy the peaks are therefore broadened; the kinetic energy release distribution together with the angular distribution determines the actual peak shape, as shown symbolically in *Figure 7.8*. If the angular distribution is known and independent of the kinetic energy (both unlikely!), or if it is perfectly isotropic (almost impossible!) the initial kinetic energy release distribution can be deduced from an observed coincidence time-of-flight peak shape. In practice, we often have to *assume* that the angular distribution is isotropic, because this is the only means of making progress. Unless the dissociation is very fast (peak broadening), distributions are likely to be only slightly anisotropic even with respect to the photoelectron direction, so the error is small. Conversely, if we want to determine an angular distribution from an observed peak shape, we have to know the energy release distribution.

In view of the ease of energy transfer within energized ions, which apparently sets up the random internal energy distributions assumed by the successful statistical reaction rate theories, we can expect energy partitioning to be essentially random too, at least in decays of large molecules. The simplest assumption is that of equipartition; the reaction co-ordinate is one degree of freedom equivalent to the other internal ones in an 'activated complex', so the average energy kinetic release should be equal to the total excess energy divided by the number of degrees of freedom. This number is normally taken to be the number of vibrations, n_{vib}, in the undissociated ion. This simple model predicts that the average energy release should be proportional to the excess of energy available, which is usually found to be true[28], and that the slope should be n_{vib}^{-1}, which is *not* usually confirmed. The average kinetic energy release is very often greater[29] than equipartition predicts, suggesting that energy randomization is incomplete.

The simplest form of kinetic energy distribution expected on a statistical model is essentially a Boltzmann distribution, very like a decaying exponential in form; distributions like this have been found in a few cases, but rarely. The statistical models are a good starting point for discussion of energy release distributions, but they need several refinements to enable them to match observations satisfactorily, even in decays of the large ions to which they can reasonably be applied. First, theories which do not include angular momentum conservation as well as energy conservation fail badly on the low energy parts of the release distribution. For a rotating ion, dissociation with zero kinetic energy release is impossible, whereas in energy-only theories it is the most probable outcome. Newer models[30], incorporating angular momentum conservation, describe the low energy parts of the observed distributions much better. Second, a distinction can be made between excess internal energy of the parent ion, and activation energy of the reverse reaction, the ion–molecule combination. Any reverse activation energy is released as the fragments separate, and there is little or no opportunity for this energy to be partitioned into all the internal modes of the separating molecular fragments.

The energy disposal in dissociations of large polyatomic ions is characterized only to a limited extent by the kinetic energy release distribution alone, and it is not surprising that simplified theoretical models can be made to fit the facts. When a triatomic molecular ion decays, on the other hand, the number of possible fates of any excess of energy is much more restricted, and measurement of the kinetic energy release distribution provides a more sensitive barometer of the reaction dynamics. The H_2S^+ ion decays[12] provide an interesting paradigm (*Figure 7.9*). As already mentioned, H_2S^+ in its first excited state, $\tilde{A}^2A_1$ decays forming S^+ + H_2 exclusively. The kinetic energy release in this reaction is found

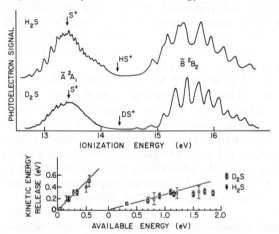

Figure 7.9.   Characteristics of the unimolecular dissociations of H_2S^+ and D_2S^+ from $\tilde{A}\,^2A_1$, yielding S^+, and from $\tilde{B}\,^2B_2$, yielding HS^+. Arrows on the photoelectron spectra show the thermochemical thresholds and the lower figure shows the kinetic energy released in each decay as a function of the energy available in excess of each threshold

to be almost single-valued, and equal to 100% of the available energy, with experimental error. Thus, *none* of the available energy is partitioned into rotation or vibration of H_2. When the second excited state $\tilde{B}^2B_2$ dissociates, by contrast, the major (perhaps exclusive) products are $HS^+ + H$, and the kinetic energy release takes the form of a broad distribution, in which just one-third of the available energy appears, on average. Since non-linear H_2S has just three vibrations, this average energy release agrees with an equipartition model, despite the small size of the ion.

Some complex explanations of the behaviour of H_2S^+ ions have been given[31]; one naïve explanation of the kinetic energy release distributions can be given in geometrical terms[12]. Suppose that in decay of the $\tilde{A}^1A_1$ state the S^+ and H_2 fragments retreat from each other *along the molecular symmetry axis*, retaining C_{2v} symmetry. The repulsion between them will then act directly on the centre-of-gravity of the H_2 molecule, and cannot cause it to rotate or vibrate. In formation of $HS^+ + H$, on the other hand, assume that dissociation take place along the line of the S–H bond in the $\tilde{B}^2B_2$ state, which is strongly bent. The energy release will act on the HS^+ fragment asymmetrically, and inevitably cause it to rotate (angle not 0° or 180°) and to vibrate (angle not 90°). The wide range of H–S^+–H angles produced by the initial ionization to excited levels of the bending vibration will evidently produce a broad distribution. This sort of explanation can be applied to many small molecular ion dissociations, and provides a simple form of insight into the ion reaction dynamics.

The fact that the formation of S^+ from H_2S^+ gives a very sharply distributed and large kinetic energy release, even though the dissociation is known to be slow from the existence of metastable ions in the mass spectrum of H_2S for S^+ formation and from the essentially isotropic angular distribution[16] of S^+, proves that a dissociation need not be fast to give a non-statistical form of energy release. In general, the observation of sharp kinetic energy distributions which directly demonstrate incomplete energy partitioning can lead to one or more deductions about mechanism:

(1) Reaction is on a single electronic energy surface, because internal conversion inevitably involves energy exchange.
(2) 'Late' energy release occurs (equivalent to 'reverse activation energy'), with consequent poor exchange.
(3) Alternatively, very rapid (quasi-direct) dissociation occurs, allowing no opportunity for energy exchange.

Sharp distributions representing large fractions of the available energy, such as have been observed in the CH_3^+-X dissociation of CH_3F and CH_3Cl, for instance, are a direct demonstration that *part* of the reaction is non-statistical. It is tempting, sometimes even a reasonable extrapolation, to deduce that the whole reaction is of a state-specific (i.e. non-energy sharing) type.

7.7   Ion fluorescence

In a photoelectron spectrum we see the formation of molecular ions in their different states; if the ions fluoresce, the emission spectrum and its time variation can give a detailed view of the evolution of the undissociated excited ions. If an ion dissociates to form an excited fragment which subsequently emits, its spectrum may give details of the internal energy distribution, that is, a view of energy disposal in the reaction, unobtainable by any other method.

Until 1975 very few molecular ions, other than diatomics, were known to yield emission spectra. Photoelectron spectroscopy provided the impetus for change by allowing the wavelengths of ion emission bands to be predicted, simply by subtracting photoelectron energies. About a hundred polyatomic ion emitters were known[32] by 1981, and the list continues to grow, though the diversity is limited as many of them are chemically related. The majority of the new ionic emission bands have been discovered by Maier and his group, using controlled electron-impact excitation and techniques of optical spectroscopy. The very first new polyatomic ion emission was first seen in a photoelectron spectrometer, however, in a coincidence experiment[33] to which the acronym PEFCO (photoelectron–fluorescence coincidence) has been applied. The photoelectrons are detected, as in a normal spectrometer, and the ionization region is also viewed by a sensitive photomultiplier. Photons are detected in coincidence with photoelectrons, and if they are accumulated in the usual way using a time to amplitude converter and multi-channel analyser, the coincidences form a (usually) decaying exponential curve of the lifetime distribution. Besides measurement of the lifetime, the experiment allows the quantum yield of ion fluorescence from each upper level to be measured directly. Because intensities are low, it has not been feasible to record dispersed fluorescence spectra from single upper levels in coincidence, but this may come. Meanwhile, a more sensitive, but cruder, technique is to record emission photons in coincidence with photoions (PIFCO) rather than with photoelectrons[34]. The improved sensitivity stems from the fact that ions can be gathered and detected with near 100% efficiency, whereas an efficiency of one in 10^4 is good for energy-resolved photoelectrons. Another advantage of PIFCO is that the chemical identity of the emitter is unambiguous, because the ions are mass analysed. This distinguishing power was vital in showing that the emission seen after excitation of SO_2^+ comes not from the parent ion, as at first thought, but mainly from the SO^+ fragment. This PIFCO technique allows lifetimes and quantum yields to be determined too, but does not select the initial state of the molecular ion.

To illustrate the applications of these techniques we shall consider the results of photon coincidence experiments on a few interesting representative molecules.

7.7.1   Diatomic ions

If excited diatomic ions fluoresce from a particular level, they are expected to do so with near unit quantum efficiency. The density of states is so low that non-radiative transitions other than dissociation are extremely rare, and are confined to particular rotational levels. The possible competition between emission and dissociation for certain levels of, for instance, O_2^+ $b^4\Sigma_g^-$ or HBr^+ $A^2\Sigma^+$ could well be examined by means of coincidence studies of emission yields and lifetimes from selected states. The intense and convenient diatomic ion emissions are most useful as standards for calibration, the most easily observed of all being N_2^+ $B^2\Sigma_u^+$ – $X^2\Sigma_g^+$, with its origin at 3914 Å, quantum yield of unity and lifetime of 60 ns.

7.7.2   Triatomic ions

There is a fascinating variety of behaviour among excited states of triatomic ions, with fluorescence and dissociation closely linked.

The CO_2^+ ion emits from both the $\tilde{A}^2\Pi_u$ and $\tilde{B}^2\Sigma_u^+$ states, and a surprise result, which came up in one of the first PIFCO experiments[35], was that the quantum yield is apparently less than unity from the $\tilde{B}$ state, and correspondingly more than unity from the $\tilde{A}$ state. (The same paradox had, in fact, been evident earlier, from comparison of ionization and fluorescence cross-section measurements[36]). Later, photoelectron spectroscopy, PIFCO and threshold electron–photon coincidence experiments on CO_2^+ and on the isotopic variants $^{13}C^{16}O_2^+$ and $^{12}C^{18}O_2^+$ revealed[37] that the peaks in the photoelectron spectrum normally identified with the $\tilde{B}^2\Sigma_u^+$ state actually represent formation of a 'mixed' state of both $\tilde{A}$ and $\tilde{B}$ character. There is an accidental near-degeneracy between levels of $\tilde{A}$ of the right symmetry and angular momentum and the (000) level of $\tilde{B}$; the levels are mixed, but since accidental degeneracy is involved, the extent of mixing varies from one isotopic form to another. When photoelectrons normally interpreted as representing $\tilde{B}$ are selected in a coincidence experiment, coincident fluorescence signals are found in the spectral regions characteristic of both $\tilde{A}$ and $\tilde{B}$ emission. This situation can be looked at either in terms of energy transfer from $\tilde{B}$ to $\tilde{A}$ or, more properly, as a breakdown of the 'zero order' description of $\tilde{B}$ and $\tilde{A}$ as distinct states. However, high resolution spectroscopic studies show that only some rotational levels are involved in the corresponding perturbations, and the situation is very complicated at the level of individual quantum states[38]. The general conclusion is that one must be wary of interpreting photoelectron bands, even of triatomic molecules, in terms of pure 'zero order' states.

The N_2O^+ molecular ion is isoelectronic with CO_2^+, and emits from the $\tilde{A}^2\Sigma^+$ state, equivalent to CO_2^+ $\tilde{B}^2\Sigma_u^+$. Some of the very first photoion-photoelectron coincidence experiments[39] revealed that while the ions prepared in the (000) level of $\tilde{A}$ remain as N_2O^+, those prepared in higher vibrational levels end up partly as N_2O^+ but partly as NO^+. This implies that the quantum yields and lifetimes of the fluorescence should be a function of vibrational level. Much more recently this has been confirmed directly by PEFCO experiments[40], which show sharply different lifetimes for the different levels of $\tilde{A}$. As in all competitive unimolecular processes, only one lifetime can be measured for a single level, and it is related to theoretical lifetimes by:

$$\frac{1}{k_{\text{obs}}} = \frac{1}{k_{\text{nr}}} + \frac{1}{k_{\text{rad}}} \tag{7.7}$$

In the case of N_2O^+ $\tilde{A}$, k_{rad} can be taken as equal to the decay constant of the non-pre-dissociated (000) level, since radiative decay constants vary only slowly with vibrational quantum number in the absence of competing pathways. The measured fluorescence lifetimes can thus be used to deduce the competing non-radiative rate constants for each level (*Table 7.2*) which are for pre-dissociation in this case. The dissociation from levels involving the 'antisymmetric stretch' is much more rapid than that from those with excitation in symmetric stretch or bending vibrations. Notice how this unimolecular reaction, despite being very slow indeed on a molecular level, shows extremely strong initial preparation effects. This underlines the fact that in a small molecule with little vibrational excitation the requirements of energy and angular momentum conservation effectively forbid internal energy transfer.

Table 7.2   Decay of N_2O^+ ($\tilde{A}\ ^2\Sigma^+$)

Level v_1,v_2,v_3	k_{pred}	Products (where known)
1,0,0	2.2×10^7	N_2O^+ ($\tilde{X}$); 44%
		NO^+ (v =4) + N; 56%
0,0,1	1.5×10^6	$O^+ + N_2$; trace
1,1,0	1.5×10^6	N_2O^+, NO^+ (v = 4), O^+; proportions unknown
1,0,0	1.5×10^6	N_2O^+ ($\tilde{X}$); 70%
		NO^+ (v = 4) + N; 30%
0,2,0	1.4×10^7	$O^+ + N_2$; trace
0,1.0	1.2×10^6	
0,0,0	$<2 \times 10^5$	N_2O^+ ($\tilde{X}$) + hv; no dissociation

The pre-dissociation rate constants are from Klapstein and Maier[40], the product identifications from Lerme, Abed, Holt, Larzilliere and Carre (in press) and from Brehm et al.[39]. It is significant for the mechanism that the NO^+ product ion is formed mainly in $v' = 4$ irrespective of the initial vibrational level.

The ion SO_2^+ has two more electrons, and is bent in all its known states, in accordance with Walsh's rules. The third band in the photoelectron spectrum contains three overlapping electronic states, and one might well ask, in view of experience with CO_2^+, whether they are completely unmixed. When photoelectrons from this third band are selected, the main process found to occur in the ions is dissociation to SO^+, but certain specific levels yield S^+, and some very few ions remain as SO_2^+. Sensitive ion-photon coincidence experiments[41] confirm the existence of an extremely weak SO_2^+ fluorescence, presumably from this band, but show much stronger emission from the SO^+ fragment. It is, however, not energetically possible for SO^+ ions formed from SO_2^+ in the third band of the photoelectron spectrum to be excited, and threshold electron–photon coincidence measurements reveal that a higher inner-valence state $\tilde{F}$ of SO_2^+ is the one that dissociates to excited SO^+ ($A^2\Pi_u$). This was the first discovery of an ionic dissociation reaction leading to an emitting product.

7.7.3   Polyatomic ions

In all the ion fluorescences mentioned hitherto, the lifetime distributions could be described by single exponential decays; this is not so for the fluorescence of the halo-acetylene ions, typified by $ClCCH^+$; monochloracetylene[7,42]. Emission is from the $\tilde{A}^2\Pi$ state to the ground state $\tilde{X}^2\Pi$, and all other states populated in photoionization are fully dissociated. Nevertheless, the lifetime distribution is strongly non-exponential in both the photon–photoion coincidence experiments and the classic electron-beam excitation. The lifetime distribution can be fitted as a sum of three exponentials and the individual decay constants, and their relative amplitudes have been interpreted in terms of the intermediate 'strong coupling' case of radiationless transition theory. The coupling is between the excited state and the ground state: as in the case of CO_2^+, the levels populated in photoionization can be seen as $\tilde{A}$ states with some vibrationally excited $\tilde{X}$ character mixed in. Here, in a four-atom molecule, the density of states is such that each zero-order $\tilde{A}$ level may communicate with several $\tilde{X}$ levels, which are thus also in communication with each other. Every excitation populates a *coherent superposition* of the communicating levels, whose time evolution involves interference effects leading to the observed non-exponential decay. The details of the interpretation go beyond the scope of this book; it is interesting to speculate whether the decay dynamics, studied hitherto for the whole $\tilde{A}$ state together, may not vary from one vibrational level within $\tilde{A}$ to another.

The statistical limit of radiationless transition theory is typified by the fluorobenzene cations, the hexafluorobenzene ion being the first ionic emitter to be discovered by coincidence methods. The lifetime distributions from selected levels of the emitting $\tilde{B}$ state of $C_6F_6^+$ are found to be mono-exponential, and give mean lifetimes which decrease more or less monotonically from 49 ns for the $\tilde{B}\ 0°$ level to 9 ns for a level about 1 eV higher in energy[43]. Over the same range of levels the quantum yield of fluorescence decreases from unity to 7%. There is no possibility of ion dissociation in this energy range, so the non-radiative competing pathway is internal conversion to the ground state of $C_6F_6^+$. The non-radiative rate constant can be deduced from the lifetimes and quantum yields ($k_{nr} = (1 - \phi_F)\tau_F^{-1}$), and is found to be a roughly exponential function of the vibrational energy in the $\tilde{B}$ state. The experimentally determined non-radiative rates have been modelled quite successfully using the rather well developed theory of the 'statistical case'[44]. Even when photoelectrons from C_6F_6 corresponding to the $\tilde{C}$ state of $C_6F_6^+$ are selected, fluorescence emission is still observed. Although this emission has not been spectrally resolved, it is concluded from its other characteristics and comparison with a similar phenomenon in sym-$C_6F_3H_3^+$ that the $\tilde{C}$ and $\tilde{B}$ states are mixed. Here is at least one probable further example of the mixing of excited states as first seen in CO_2^+, having similar consequences. While the fluorescence technique makes the mixing detectable in only a few cases, it must surely be part of a full description of other ion reactions too.

7.8 Bimolecular ion reactions

Ion–molecule reactions are of great importance in the ionosphere, in other planetary atmospheres and in comet tails, and are thought to be responsible, in the main, for molecular synthesis in the dark interstellar clouds[45]. According to one theory, extraterrestrial synthesis is the ultimate basis for the emergence of life[46], so there is no lack of incentive to understand these reactions. In particular, if we are to extrapolate from rate constants measured in the laboratory to the very low temperatures and pressures of space we need to know state-specific reaction cross-sections; some of these can be provided by photoelectron coincidence experiments.

A photoion state is selected in the usual way, whereupon the ion can be accelerated to a definite energy and can be made to collide with neutral molecules in a separate, second chamber. The products of any ion reaction can be mass-analysed, and the time of their arrival at a particle detector will still bear a definite relationship to the original photoelectron arrival time, so they can be counted in coincidence. Experiments of this sort were first carried out in the early 1970s, but systematic studies began only in the 1980s. Almost all the recent work has used the threshold photoelectron technique because of the much better signal-to-noise ratio which it offers in coincidence experiments: thus, one group calls the technique TESICO (threshold electron secondary ion coincidence).

7.8.1 The role of internal energy

According to the usual conception of reaction mechanisms in terms of motion over potential energy surfaces, the rates of *exo-ergic* reactions should be little affected by the internal energy of the reactants. In *endo-ergic* reactions, on the other hand, internal (vibrational) energy of the reactant may have an enormous effect on the rate, and often the same amount of energy is much more effective as vibration than as relative kinetic energy. Because many ion–molecule reactions are exo-ergic (this is why they occur in the cold of interstellar space), the state selection of reactants in many of the commonest reactions shows little dependence of the cross-sections on internal energy. This is the case for such reactions as:

$$CH_4^+ + CH_4 \rightarrow CH_5^+ + CH_3$$

and

$$NH_3^+ + NH_3 \rightarrow NH_4^+ + NH_2$$

the latter of which has been examined by the photoelectron coincidence method[47]. The reaction cross-section drops as the vibrational excitation energy of the NH_3^+ ion increases, and because the drop, although small, significantly exceeds the variation predicted by statistical models it is concluded that no long-lived complex is involved. The fundamentally important proton transfer reaction

$$H_2^+ + H_2 \rightarrow H_3^+ + H$$

has also been examined by the coincidence method[48]; its cross-section decreases with increasing v and low collision energies, and becomes independent of v at high ones.

Proton transfer in ammonia ions (and generally) is accompanied by the *charge* transfer reaction:

$$NH_3^+ + NH_3 \rightarrow NH_3 + NH_3^+$$

where reacted and unreacted ions can be distinguished experimentally by their different velocities. This reaction is obviously thermoneutral and, indeed, the cross-section is found to rise as the vibrational quantum number of NH_3^+ increases. The variation is not very steep, however, and is much smaller than the variation in Franck–Condon factors. A much more dramatic variation is found for the reaction[49]

$$H_2^+(\upsilon) + Ar \rightarrow H_2 + Ar^+$$

where the cross-section at low collision energies is very much larger for $\upsilon = 2$ than for other vibrational levels. This is explained by 'resonance' enhancement. It happens that while $Ar^+(^2P_{3/2})$ is intermediate in energy between H_2^+ ($v = 1$) and ($v = 2$), $Ar^+(^2P_{1/2})$ is almost exactly at the same energy as H_2^+ ($v = 2$), being lower by only 16 meV. Only when the relative translational energy is substantially increased does the cross-section for $v = 1$ become comparable with that for $v = 2$. If D_2 is substituted for H_2 no such resonant enhancement is found, because the Ar^+ levels both lie between D_2^+ vibrational energies.

The (H_2^+ + Ar) charge transfer reaction is also accompanied by an exo-ergic proton transfer[50]:

$$H_2^+(v) + Ar \rightarrow ArH^+ + H$$

At low collision energy it is found that while the charge transfer cross-section is enhanced at $v = 2$, the proton transfer cross-section is diminished, proving that the two channels are in competition.

The inverse of the charge transfer reactions, namely

$$Ar^+ + H_2 \rightarrow Ar + H_2^+$$

has also been examined by the same method[50]. The effect of the near resonance at $v = 2$ is to make the cross-section seven times larger for $Ar^+(^2P_{1/2})$ in this reaction than for $Ar^+(^2P_{3/2})$. In the similar reactions:

$$Ar^+ + N_2 \rightarrow Ar + N_2^+$$

and

$$Ar^+ + CO \rightarrow Ar + CO^+$$

there is no possibility of resonance effects, but nevertheless the experiments[51] show a marked difference in cross-section between the two spin–orbit states of Ar^+. There seem to be some other factors involved, and it is hoped that future work will reveal them. These are only the very first bimolecular reactions to have been studied by the photoelectron coincidence technique of state selection, and there will undoubtedly be many fascinating developments in this area.

References

1. BREHM, B. and VON PUTTKAMER, E., *Adv. Mass Spectrom.*, **4**, 591 (1967); ELAND, J.H.D. and DANBY, C.J., *Int. J. Mass Spectrom. Ion Phys.*, **8**, 143, 153 (1972); DANNACHER, J., *J. Chem. Phys.*, **29**, 339 (1978)

2. ELAND, J.H.D., *Rev. Sci. Inst.*, **49**, 1688 (1978)
3. STOCKBAUER, R., *J. Chem. Phys.*, **58**, 3800 (1973); WERNER, A.S., TSAI, B.P. and BAER, T., *J. Chem. Phys.*, **60**, 3650 (1974)
4. PARMENTER, C.S., *J. Phys. Chem.*, **86**, 1735 (1982)
5. COVALESKIE, R., DOLSON, D.A., PARMENTER, C.S. and STONE, B.M., *J. Photochem.*, **17**, 165 (1981); HALBERSTADT, N. and TRAMER, A., *J. Chem. Phys.*, **73**, 6343 (1980)
6. SIEBRAND, W.J., *J. Chem. Phys.*, **44**, 4055 (1966); JORTNER, J., RICE, S.A. and HOCHSTRASSER R.M., *Adv. Photochem.*, **7**, 149 (1969)
7. DUJARDIN, G., LEACH, S., TAIEB,G., MAIER, J.P. and GELBART, W.M., *J. Chem. Phys.*, **73**, 4987 (1980)
8. HASTED, J.B., *Physics of Atomic Collisions*, Butterworths, London (1974)
9. HOWARD, W.E. and SCHLAG, E.W., *J. Chem. Phys.*, **68**, 2679 (1978)
10. HERZBERG, G., *Electronic Spectra and Electronic Structure of Polyatomic Molecules*, Van Nostrand, Princeton, N.J. (1966)
11. MULLIKEN, R.S., *J. Chem. Phys.*, **33**, 247 (1960)
12. ELAND, J.H.D., *Int. J. Mass Spectrom. Ion Phys.*, **31**, 161 (1979)
13. HIRSH, G., and BRUNA, P.J., *Int. J. Mass Spectrom. Ion Phys.*, **36**, 37 (1980)
14. SIMM, I.G., DANBY, C.J. and ELAND, J.H.D., *Int. J. Mass Spectrom. Ion Phys.*, **14**, 285 (1974)
15. JONAH, C., *J. Chem. Phys.*, **55**, 1915 (1971)
16. ELAND, J.H.D., *J. Chem. Phys.*, **70**, 2926 (1979)
17. BRUNDLE, C.R., *Chem. Phys. Lett.*, **7**, 317 (1970)
18. RAFTERY, J. and RICHARDS, W.G., *J. Phys, B, Atom Molec. Phys.*, **5**, 425 (1972)
19. SCHNEIDER, B.S. and SMITH, A.L. in Shirley, D.A. (Editor) *Electron Spectroscopy*, North Holland, Amsterdam (1972)
20. HAUGH, M.J. and BAYES, K.D., *J. Phys. Chem.*, **75**, 1472 (1971)
21. CEDERBAUM, L.S., KOPPEL, H. and DOMKE, W., *Int. J. Quantum Chem.*, **15**, 251 (1981)
22. HANSOUL, J.P., CALLOY, C. and LORQUET, J.C., *J. Chem. Phys.*, **68**, 4105 (1978)
23. HERZBERG, G. and LONGUET-HIGGINS, H.C., *Disc. Faraday Soc.*, **35**, 77 (1963)
24. ELAND, J.H.D. and SCHULTE, H., *J. Chem. Phys.*, **62**, 3835 (1975)
25. LORQUET, J.C., DELWICHE, J. and HUBIN-FRANKSIN, M.J. *J. Chem. Phys.*, **76**, 4692 (1982)
26. ELAND, J.H.D. and BERKOWITZ, J., *Int. J. Mass Spectrom. Ion Phys.*, **28**, 297 (1978)
27. SMITH, D., BAER, T., WILLETT, G.D. and ORMEROD, R.C., *Int. J. Mass Spectrom. Ion Phys.*, **30**, 155 (1979)
28. COOKS, R.G. and BEYNON, J.H. in MACCOLL, H. (Editor). *International Revs of Science* **5**: *Mass Spectrometry*, Butterworths, London (1975)
29. ELAND, J.H.D., *Adv. Mass. Spectrom.*, **7**, 17 (1979)
30. POWIS, I. *J. Chem. Soc., Faraday Trans. II*, **77**, 1433 (1981), and references therein
31. BRUNA, P.J., HIRSCH, G., PERIC, M., PEYERIMHOFF, S.D. and BUENKER, R.J., *Mol. Phys.*, **40**, 521 (1980)
32. MAIER, J.P., *Chimia*, **34**, 219 (1980)
33. BLOCH, M. and TURNER, D.W., *Chem. Phys. Lett.*, **30**, 344 (1975)
34. DUJARDIN, G., LEACH, S. and TAIEB, G., *Chem. Phys.*, **46**, 407 (1980)

35. ELAND, J.H.D., DEVORET, M. and LEACH, S., *Chem. Phys. Lett.*, **43**, 97 (1976)
36. SAMSON, J.A.R. and GARDNER, J.L., *J. Geophys. Res.*, **78**, 3663 (1963)
37. LEACH, S., DEVORET, M. and ELAND, J.H.D., *Chem. Phys.*, **33**, 113 (1978)
38. LEACH, S. in Levine, R. and Jortner, J. (Editors) *Molecular Energy Transfer*, Halsted, New York (1976)
39. BREHM, G., ELAND, J.H.D., FREY, R. and KÜSTLER, A., *Int. J. Mass Spectrom. Ion Phys.*, **13**, 251 (1974)
40. KLAPSTEIN, D. and MAIER, J.P., *Chem. Phys. Lett.*, **83**, 590 (1981)
41. DUJARDIN, G. and LEACH, S., *J. Chem. Phys.*, **75**, 2521 (1981)
42. ALLAN, M., KLOSTER-JENSEN, E. and MAIER, J.P., *J. Chem. Soc., Faraday Trans. II*, **73**, 1406, 1417 (1977)
43. MAIER, J.P. and THOMMEN, F., *Chem. Phys.*, **57**, 219 (1981); DUJARDIN, G., Thesis, University of Paris (1982)
44. DUJARDIN, G. and LEACH, S., *Chem. Phys.*, **46**, 407 (1980); *J. Chem. Phys.*, **79**, 658 (1983)
45. KLEMPERER, W., *Physics Today*, **28**, 32 (1976)
46. HOYLE, F. and WICKRAMASINGHE, C., *Space Travellers: The Bringers of Life*. Enslow Publishers, Hillside, N.J. (1981)
47. BAER, T. and MURRAY, P.T., *J. Chem. Phys.*, **75**, 4477 (1981)
48. KOYANO, I. and TANAKA, K., *J. Chem. Phys.*, **72**, 4858 (1980)
49. TANAKA, K., KATO, T. and KOYANO, I., *J. Chem. Phys.*, **75**, 4941 (1981)
50. TANAKA, K., DURUP, J., KATO, T. and KOYANO, I., *J. Chem. Phys.*, **73**, 586 (1980); *J. Chem. Phys.*, **74**, 5561 (1981)
51. KATO, T., TANAKA, K. and KOYANO, I., *J. Chem. Phys.*, **77**, 337 (1982)

8
Applications in chemistry

8.1 Introduction

The major application of ultraviolet photoelectron spectroscopy is, and always has been, to open up molecular electronic structure to inspection and analysis. After almost two decades the *caveats* required in using molecular orbitals as the basis of such analysis have started to become more apparent; the importance of electron correlation in the inner valence region, expressed as the failure there of the single configuration model, is a very necessary reminder that molecular orbitals are not the be-all and end-all of molecular electronic structure. Orbitals will nevertheless continue to dominate all discussion of photoelectron spectra, and many applications involve use of the spectra to define the 'energies' and forms of orbitals. One can only hope for the future that when a practically useful many-electron description of electronic structure is evolved, photoelectron spectroscopy will take a leading part in its development.

Many aspects of molecular orbitals have been examined by photoelectron spectroscopists with diverse interests in organic and inorganic chemistry, and a number of specialist reviews have been published[1]. A very few such topics are introduced in this chapter as examples; any readers who have persevered up to this point will have no difficulty in pursuing the subjects that interest them in the literature. There have also been applications of the technique as a physical tool, in analysis for instance, and in reaction dynamics. It seems possible to make a partial listing of the major and exotic applications as follows:

(1) Relationship of ionization potentials to molecular orbitals and chemical structure (this chapter and throughout the book).

(2) Determination of bond lengths and angles in ionic states by band shape analysis (Chapters 5, 6).

(3) Energy distributions and state selection in ion reaction dynamics (Chapter 7).

(4) Prediction of gas-phase ion spectra (Chapter 3).

(5) Interpretation of ion spectra in condensed phases (this chapter).

(6) Quantitative and qualitative analysis (this chapter).

(7) Interpretation of multiphoton ionization mechanisms (Chapter 3).

(8) Characterization of surfaces and adsorbates (this chapter).

A few other applications not listed above and not discussed in this book are the determination of electron affinities by photodetachment, the determination of X-ray and ultraviolet spectral line energies, and the interpretation of structured charge-transfer spectra in solution.

8.2   d Orbitals in bonding

There are two situations in which d orbitals of transition metal atoms give rise to easily recognizable bands in photoelectron spectra. In one case the d orbitals are full and rather strongly bound, behaving almost as core orbitals, with small perturbations due to chemical bonding. This situation is typified by the mercury-(II) compounds mentioned in Chapter 3 and by the Au, Cd and later B-metal compounds. The 4f electrons in the lanthanide trichlorides behave similarly, showing atomic-like orbital energies[2]. The second relatively simple situation is found in transition metal complexes, in many of which the d orbitals are outermost so giving bands at the lowest (sometimes at very low) ionization potentials. The complexes containing metals of formally zero oxidation number are typical here; record low ionization potentials are those of *bis*-cyclopentadienyl complexes and bis-benzene chromium[3]. In both these situations the d orbitals are only weakly involved in bonding, and can be recognized as giving rise to distinct bands in the photoelectron spectra. There are other compounds, however, where the d orbitals are heavily involved in bonding, and therefore are mixed strongly with other orbitals of correct symmetry. The Cu(II) halides[4], and the triatomic dihalides of the transition metals from Ti to Ni are in this category: the many bands in their photoelectron spectra[5] represent ionization from bonding orbitals of considerable d character. The spectra can hardly be interpreted without the help of detailed quantum mechanical calculations, including correlation effects.

8.2.1   Transition metal complexes

The most volatile transition metal complexes are the mainly covalent complexes with σ-donating and π-accepting ligands such as CO or PF_3 or with organic π systems. As examples of the spectra of this type of compound, those of some carbonyls and trifluorophosphine adducts will be discussed here. The bonding in these complexes involves the donation of σ electrons from the ligands into empty metal orbitals, accompanied by back-donation from metal d orbitals into empty ligand π^* orbitals of appropriate symmetry. These effects are co-operative, as the more charge is transferred in one direction by one mechanism the greater is the inducement for it to be replaced by the other mechanism, thus restoring electroneutrality. The ligands must be both σ donors and π acceptors, and of these properties that of accepting π electrons seems to be the most important for the stability of the compounds. The molecular field produced by the ligands is strong, and the complexes are almost all of low spin. The metals that form these complexes occur in the second half of the transition series and are much more common in the first than in the second and third transition series. These are the metals that have several occupied d orbitals of relatively high energy from which donation can take place.

For the interpretation of the photoelectron spectra, these qualitative ideas must be translated into observable effects on molecular orbital energies. The orbitals involved are the filled d and empty s and p atomic orbitals for the metal, and the full σ and empty π^* orbitals for the ligands. Compound formation should cause stabilization of both the ligand σ orbitals and the metal d orbitals compared with their energies in the metal atom and free ligand molecules. If problems of local charges and Koopmans' approximation are neglected, this should lead to an increase in both sets of ionization potentials, visible in the photoelectron spectra.

Figure 8.1 shows the photoelectron spectra of $Mo(CO)_6$, $Mo(PF_3)_6$ and of the ligand PF_3. The band at lowest ionization potential in the spectra of the two complexes shifts by only 0.7 eV

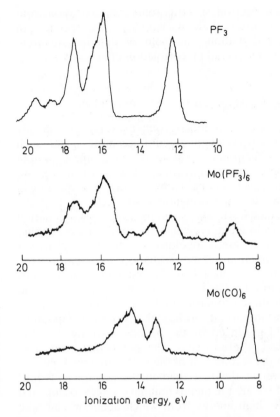

Figure 8.1.   He I photoelectron spectra of phosphorus trifluoride,
molybdenum hexakistrifluorophosphine and hexacarbonyl molybdenum

when the ligand is changed and must be attributed to ionization
from the metal d orbitals. As the complexes are of low spin, all of
the six d electrons are in t_{2g} orbitals and the d electron ionization
bands are single. The electron configuration of atomic molybdenum and that of the molybdenum in the complexes are so different
that the d electron ionization potentials in the two states cannot be
compared directly. The metal d orbital ionization potentials in the
CO and PF_3 complexes can be compared, however, and as PF_3
causes the greater stabilization, it seems to be a better π acceptor
than CO. In the high ionization potential region between 15 and
20 eV there is little difference between the photoelectron spectrum
of PF_3 and that of its molybdenum adduct. This means that

compound formation has only a weak effect on the energy of the fluorine lone-pair orbitals or on the P–F bonding orbitals. The band at 12.2 eV in the PF_3 spectrum represents ionization from the lone pair located mainly on the phosphorus atom, the orbital from which σ donation occurs. In octahedral symmetry, the six ligand lone-pair orbitals become t_{1u}, e_g and a_{1g} molecular orbitals, which can be stabilized by interaction with empty molybdenum p, d or s orbitals, respectively. The three bands in the $Mo(PF_3)_6$ spectrum at 12.4, 13.5 and 14.5 eV are identified by their relative areas with ionization from these three orbitals in the order given. It can be seen that all three orbitals are stabilized relative to the lone pairs of free PF_3, in accordance with their bonding character. In the $Mo(CO)_6$ spectrum, only one band in the σ bonding region can be seen (13.2 eV) and this band probably represents the t_{1u} orbital. The other σ bonding orbitals presumably overlap with the part of the spectrum attributed to ionization from orbitals located in the CO molecules.

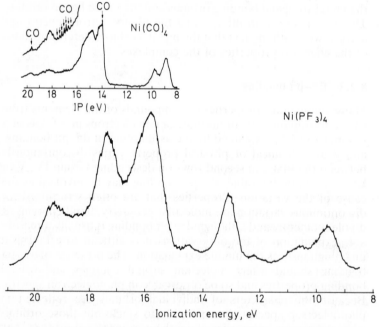

Figure 8.2.   He I photoelectron spectra of nickel carbonyl and nickel tetrakistrifluorophosphine. (Spectrum of nickel carbonyl by courtesy of D.R. Lloyd)

Figure 8.2 shows the photoelectron spectra of $Ni(PF_3)_4$ and $Ni(CO)_4$. As nickel in the zero oxidation state has a completed d shell, both the t_2 and e orbitals of these tetrahedral complexes are full. The first bands again represent d electron ionizations and are split into two components with approximate relative areas of 3:2, as expected for t_2^{-1} and e^{-1} ionizations. The splitting between the states $^2T_2$ and ^2E, which crudely indicates the strength of the ligand field, is about the same in the PF_3 and CO complexes, but once again the ionization potential of the PF_3 compound is higher, showing that PF_3 is a better π acceptor than CO. The analysis of the remainder of the $Ni(PF_3)_4$ spectrum is similar to that given for $Mo(PF_3)_6$; again, the PF_3 lone-pair σ-donating orbitals are stabilized in the complex.

The photoelectron spectra of these complexes illustrate a generalization that was made by Evans *et al.*[6] in connection with the pentacarbonylmanganese derivatives, namely that the spectra of the metal complexes can often be divided into three regions. In order of increasing ionization potential come the metal d orbitals, the metal-to-ligand bonding orbitals and then pure ligand orbitals. This rule is useful in interpreting the photoelectron spectra and accords well with the fact that the metal d orbitals determine many of the chemical properties of the complexes.

8.2.2   dπ–pπ bonding

Many 'anomalous' properties of compounds of the elements from silicon to sulphur with atoms that contain electrons in orbitals of π symmetry can be explained by the assumption of dπ–pπ bonding, and if any chemical or physical property varies discontinuously between the first and second rows on descending Group IV, V or VI of the Periodic Table, dπ–pπ bonding may be invoked as the cause of the variation. Properties that are often scrutinized for discontinuous variation are molecular geometry, bond energies or dipole moments, and although dπ–pπ bonding is usually a reasonable explanation of the observations it is difficult to establish it unambiguously as the unique explanation. The presence of dπ–pπ bonding should affect molecular orbital energies and orbital bonding properties and so be observable in photoelectron spectra. Because the characters of individual orbitals are reflected in photoelectron spectra, it is possible to single out those orbitals whose symmetry properties allow them to involve d orbitals, and this procedure results in a more specific test of d orbital participation. The involvement of d orbitals can be established from photoelectron spectra strictly only by comparison with theoretical models which include or neglect d orbitals in a properly even-handed manner. Nevertheless, the special symmetry properties of d orbitals do permit qualitative conclusions directly from spectra in some particular cases. The second band in the photoelectron spectrum of sulphur dioxide[7], for instance, contains overlapping progressions that belong to two electronic states of the ion, $^2B_2$ and $^2A_2$. According to the vibrational analysis, one of the orbitals involved, $5b_2$ or $1a_2$, is strongly bonding between S and O and the other is S–O non-bonding, while occupancy of both the orbitals has a strong effect on the bond angle. Now, according to the orbital symmetries, the $1a_2$ orbital is completely C–O non-bonding in the absence of sulphur d orbital participation, and $5b_2$ is only weakly S–O bonding. It appears that $d\pi$–$p\pi$ bonding must be effective in at least one of these orbitals in order to account for the S–O bonding character found. This is confirmed by an SCF molecular orbital calculation[8], which shows that the S–O bonding orbital is indeed $1a_2$, which has the lower ionization potential, and that it owes its bonding character to overlap with sulphur d orbitals.

A series of compounds in which the special symmetry properties of d orbitals play an important role are the cyclic phosphonitrilic halides, $(PNX_2)_n$:

The electronic structure of these compounds resembles that of the aromatic hydrocarbons in that it can be described in terms of separate σ and π systems. All phosphonitrilic derivatives with $n = 3$ and the phosphonitrilic fluorides with $n = 3$–6 have their PN rings planar or nearly so, and all P–N bond lengths equal. Two π systems are distinguished, one in the plane of the ring (π_s) and the other out of the ring plane, as in aromatic hydrocarbons (π_a). The in-plane system is *homomorphic*, which means that in an orbital in which all overlaps are favourable, the p wave-functions on two consecutive nitrogen atoms have the same sign. The out-of-plane π system is *heteromorphic* because the symmetry of the d_{xz} orbitals involved means that consecutive nitrogen p wave-functions must have opposite signs for favourable overlap. The molecular energy diagram for a heteromorphic system is different from that for a homomorphic system, and a heteromorphic system can be aromatic with any number of delocalized electrons[9]. The phosphonitrilic halides are indeed aromatic for all values of n, as shown by their chemical properties. Branton et al.[10] have measured the photoelectron spectra of a series of phosphonitrilic fluorides and have also measured the first ionization potentials of other phosphonitrilic derivatives by an electron impact method; they compared their experimental ionization potentials with orbital energies for the two π systems calculated by a Hückel procedure. The ionization potentials agree with the calculated orbital energies sufficiently well to confirm the $d\pi-p\pi$ model, and the alternation in first ionization potentials with n shows that the homomorphic system is energetically outermost, in agreement with previous findings. Because of overlap between ionization bands from the two systems of π orbitals, less sharp structure is seen in the spectra of the phosphonitrilic fluorides than in those of aromatic hydrocarbons.

8.3   Non-bonded interactions

There are a number of electronic interactions between atoms or groups within molecules which are not represented by bonds in chemical formulae and are often omitted from simple molecular orbital models. They may, nevertheless, be strong and have an important effect on the electronic structure, particularly on the nature of the outermost orbitals. Examples are the interactions of heteroatom lone pairs in large organic molecules, hyperconjugation and homoconjugation. These topics are all related to one another and have been studied extensively by photoelectron spectroscopy. For a discussion of the theoretical ideas involved, two reviews[11] can be recommended.

8.3.1   Heteroatom lone pairs

In the photoelectron spectra of organic molecules that contain heteroatoms with lone pairs, the lone-pair ionization bands can often be identified either by their low ionization potentials or their relatively narrow contours. Very narrow bands are rarely seen, however, and if the molecules are conjugated, thus possessing occupied π orbitals that also have low ionization potentials, the lone-pair ionizations can be recognized only after model calculations and comparison with the photoelectron spectra of structurally related compounds. The surprising result that emerges is that if a molecule contains two equivalent lone pairs, there is not just one band in the photoelectron spectrum showing degeneracy of the lone-pair orbitals but two or more, even if the heteroatoms are separated by a number of bonds. Furthermore, the splitting does not decrease monotonically as the heteroatoms are placed farther away from one another in a series of compounds, but passes through a minimum and rises again.

An example of such splittings is provided by the photoelectron spectra of the sulphur ring compounds shown in *Figure 8.3*. There are considered to be two mechanisms that underlie this splitting, namely, *through-space* and *through-bond* interations. If there are two equivalent lone pairs in a molecule described by atomic orbital wave-functions ϕ_1 and ϕ_2, then two symmetry-adapted molecular orbitals can be formed from the atomic orbitals:

$$\psi_s = 1/\sqrt{2}\,(\phi_1 + \phi_2) \tag{8.1}$$

$$\psi_a = 1/\sqrt{2}\,(\phi_1 - \phi_2) \tag{8.2}$$

If the atomic orbitals interact directly through space, the symmetrical combination ψ_s will have the lower energy (higher ionization potential) when the overlap integral $S_{ab} = <\phi_1|\phi_2>$ is positive, but the unsymmetrical combination will have the lower energy if S_{ab} is negative. This through-space interaction will usually be dominant if the two heteroatoms are neighbours, for instance, in the disulphides (S_{ab} positive), *trans*-azo compounds (S_{ab} negative), *cis*-azo compounds (S_{ab} positive), and it often remains dominant if they are separated by only one carbon centre. If the interaction is predominantly through-space, it should produce new orbitals with energies symmetrical about the energy of the original lone pairs or, more generally, the centre of gravity of the lone-pair ionization bands should not be shifted by this interaction alone.

The existence of through-bond interaction between lone pairs was first predicted by Hoffmann, Imamura and Hehre[12] by using extended Hückel theory. In particular, they found that for the diazabicycloalkanes,

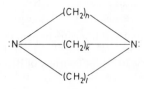

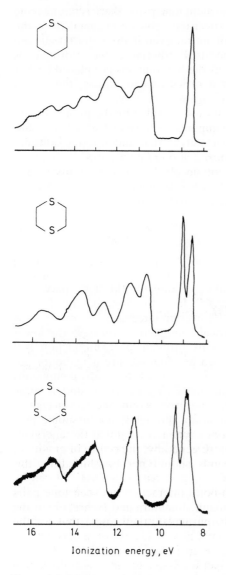

Ionization energy, eV

Figure 8.3. He I photoelectron spectra of pentamethylene sulphide, 1,4-dithiane and 1,3,5-trithiane. (From Sweigart, D.A. and Daintith, J., *Sci. Prog. Oxf.*, **59**, 325 (1971), by courtesy of Blackwell's Scientific Publications Ltd.)

the through-space interaction with S_{ab} positive dominates when h, k and l are unity, but for h, k and l larger than unity a second-order interaction through the C–C and C–H bonding σ orbitals predominates. It is mainly an interaction with C–C σ orbitals of suitable symmetry and energy, and it effectively delocalizes the lone pair away from the nitrogen atoms over the rest of the molecule. This through-bond interaction makes the new orbital containing mainly a symmetrical combination of lone pairs energetically outermost, giving the opposite ordering to that expected on a through-space mechanism, and it also shifts the centre of gravity of the bands. The effects of the through-space and through-bond interactions on the lone-pair orbital energies are shown schematically in *Figure 8.4*.

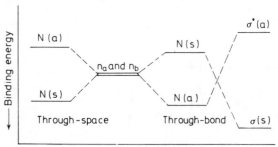

Figure 8.4. Schematic molecular orbital energy diagram illustrating the effects of through-space and through-bond interactions on the ionization potentials of lone-pair orbitals

The predictions of through-bond interaction for the case $h = k = l = 2$ (1,4-diazabicyclo[2.2.2]octane, DABCO) have been elegantly confirmed by Heilbronner and co-workers[13,14]. Their photoelectron spectra of DABCO and two related compounds are shown in *Figure 8.5*, in which the splitting and shift to higher ionization potentials of the lone-pair bands in DABCO can be clearly seen. They were able to show, by an analysis of the vibrational fine structure of the two bands in terms of the structural changes following ionization, that the outermost orbital is indeed the symmetrical combination. The splitting between the two lone-pair ionization bands in DABCO and the shift of the centre of gravity of the two bands relative to the ionization energy of the lone pair in quinuclidine had been calculated theoretically as 1.6 and 0.37 eV, respectively, and these predictions were confirmed by experiment, where values of 2.1 and 0.57 eV, respectively, were found. The same effects can be seen qualitatively in the

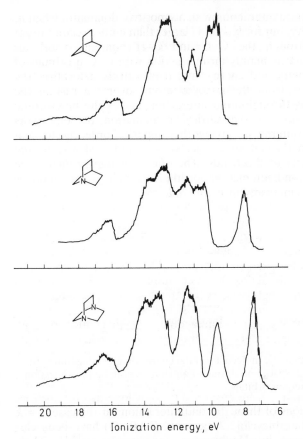

Figure 8.5. The photoelectron spectra of bicyclo[2.2.2]octane, quinuclidine and DABCO. (From Bischof *et al.*[13], by courtesy of Pergamon Press)

spectrum of 1,4-dithiane compared with that of pentamethylene sulphide (*Figure 8.3*).

The lone-pair interactions in nitrogen compounds have been studied intensively. Compounds that have been investigated include several with azo groups, both *cis-* and *trans-*substituted[15–17], azabenzenes[18,19], ethylenediamine[13], piperazine[13] and some hydrazines[17]. The interpretation of the spectra generally follows from comparison with empirical calculations that have been suitably parameterized. The analysis of the photoelectron spectra of the azabenzenes is still to some extent controversial, but the proper inclusion of the lone-pair interactions is clearly of crucial importance. The splittings between the lone-pair bands in the spectra of the diazines according to Gleiter *et al.*[18] are 2.0 eV for the *ortho* compound (pyridazine), 1.5 eV for the *meta* compound (pyrimidine) and −1.7 eV for the *para* compound (pyrazine). These values show an alternation in magnitude which is characteristic of the transition from through-space to through-bond interaction, and the negative sign shows the consequent reversal in the order of the symmetrical and antisymmetrical orbital combinations.

The interactions of equivalent oxygen lone pairs in dicarbonyl compounds have been examined, and it has been shown that the through-bond interaction is dominant[20]. Calculated lone-pair orbital energy splittings agree well with the measured photoelectron spectra in instances when there is no doubt about the band identifications. The oxygen and sulphur lone-pair ionizations in some cyclic ethers and sulphides have also been studied[21] and the observed splittings can be interpreted in a similar manner. The through-space interaction between sulphur atoms seems to be stronger than that between oxygen atoms, perhaps because of the greater size of the sulphur orbitals, whereas the reverse may be true of the through-bond interaction. The magnitude of both effects must depend markedly on molecular geometry, and in an open-chain molecule the different accessible conformations may have very different interactions and so give rise to overlapping structure in the lone-pair region of the photoelectron spectrum. For this reason, it is more profitable to study lone-pair interactions in the relatively rigid ring compounds. Numerical values of the splittings between the lone-pair ionizations of a few interesting molecules are given in *Figure 8.6*.

The lone-pair interactions between equivalent halogen atoms, which each have two lone pairs, are slightly more complicated than those discussed above. As mentioned in the section on spin–orbit coupling (Chapter 6, Section 6.2), a single halogen atom will usually give two lone-pair peaks in the photoelectron spectrum, either because of spin–orbit coupling or because one halogen p orbital interacts more strongly than the other with the remainder of the molecule, or because both effects are operative. In a compound that contains two halogen atoms, four lone-pair ionization bands should be seen, although some components may overlap. Bands for chlorine lone-pair ionization that contain four components have been observed in the spectra of the dichloro-ethylenes by Lake and Thompson[22], and four distinct iodine

$$\underset{N=N}{\overset{CH_3 \quad CH_3}{\diagdown / }}$$ 3.6 eV

$\overset{CH_3}{\diagdown} N=N \overset{}{\diagdown}_{CH_3}$ 3.3 eV

$NH_2 \cdot CH_2 \cdot CH_2 \cdot NH_2$ 0.5 eV

(structure) -0.3 eV

(structure) -2.1 eV

(structure) 0.55 eV   t-Bu·S—S·t-Bu   0.64 eV

$\overset{O}{\underset{H}{\diagdown}}C-C\overset{H}{\underset{O}{\diagdown}}$ -1.6 eV

(structure) 0.25 eV

(structure) -1.22 eV

(structure S—S) -0.45 eV

(structure S—S)   0.41 eV

Figure 8.6.   Splittings between the lone-pair ionization potentials in some nitrogen, oxygen and sulphur compounds

bands are found in the spectrum of methylene iodide. The dichloropropanes and 1,4-dichlorobutane have been investigated[23]; their spectra contain broadened chlorine lone-pair bands, but in these instances the individual components are not resolved. The through-space and through-bond mechanisms must be expected to apply to halogen lone pairs just as to those of nitrogen, oxygen or sulphur, even though the appearance of the bands in the spectra is much more complicated.

8.3.2   Isolated double bonds

Apparently isolated π orbitals can interact by the same mechanisms as lone pairs and for them the through-space interaction is often referred to as *homoconjugation*, while *hyperconjugation* is one form of through-bond interaction.

Model compounds for the through-space interactions of π bonds are the cyclic molecules norbornadiene, barrelene and *cis,cis,cis-*1,4,7-cyclononatriene, of which the last is also the archetypal *homoaromatic* compound. In the spectra of all these molecules,

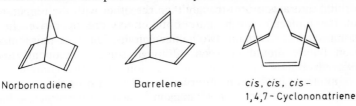

Norbornadiene   Barrelene   *cis, cis, cis –*
1,4,7 – Cyclononatriene

large splittings between the π ionization bands have been found[24-27] with the ordering predicted for predominantly through-space interactions. Typical overlap integrals for the non-bonded interactions in these and similar molecules in an HMO treatment would be about 1 eV, compared with 2–3 eV for normal double bonds. In barrelene and *cis,cis,cis*-1,4,7-cyclononatriene there are three equivalent π bonds, and when these are combined one of the orbitals obtained is doubly degenerate (e) and the other is single (a), as shown in the qualitative molecular orbital diagrams below.

When electrons are removed from the e orbitals, ^2E ionic states result, which are liable to Jahn–Teller distortions and to splittings

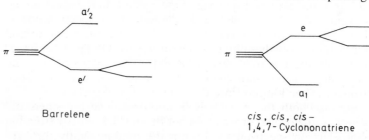

Barrelene

cis , cis , cis – 1,4,7- Cyclononatriene

in the spectra. The observation of such splitting in the second band of the photoelectron spectrum of barrelene and in the first band of the cyclononatriene, together with the greater intensities of the same bands, amply confirms the theoretical orderings. Another effect is observed in the spectra of barrelene and related molecules: as the number of double bonds is increased, the onset of the σ electron ionization bands moves to higher ionization potentials approximately linearly with the number of π bonds. This effect is rationalized by an increase in the 2s character of the σ bonds as more atomic p orbitals are taken over for π bonding. The replacement of hydrogen atoms by fluorine and the introduction of nitrogen atoms into aromatic rings have similar effects, shifting the σ levels more than the π levels to higher ionization potentials. The centre of gravity of the ionization system does move to a higher ionization potential as the number of double bonds, fluorine atoms or nitrogen atoms in a molecule is increased, but much less than does the onset of the σ ionization system. The π ionization band-shifts in barrelene and related molecules have been interpreted as evidence that through-bond interactions are also not negligible[26].

The observation of a splitting of about 0.95 eV between the π orbitals in *cis,cis,cis*-1,4,7-cyclononatriene is a most interesting result, as previous studies of the bond lengths, bond angles, nuclear magnetic resonance spectrum and heat of hydrogenation gave no evidence of homoaromaticity. The molecule has six π electrons and is identical with benzene except for the reduced overlap between alternate double bonds. Bischof, Gleiter and Heilbronner[27] showed theoretically that if the resonance integral between separate double bonds is given a value $m\beta$, where β is the resonance integral within the normal π bonds, the usual tests for aromaticity or delocalization will detect almost nothing unless m has a value greater than 0.3. The splitting of the photoelectron ionization bands, on the other hand, is directly proportional to m, and from the observed splitting of the π bands in the spectrum an m value of 0.26 was deduced. Photoelectron spectroscopy is therefore a much more sensitive test for the existence of orbital interaction than other physical measurements. On the other hand, the results must be treated with caution as they refer strictly to the ions and not the molecules. The conjugation may be much stronger in the ionized state than in the neutral species.

Because both the π orbitals in norbornadiene are singly degenerate, the orbital order could not be inferred directly from the photoelectron spectrum to confirm the predominantly through-space nature of the interaction. The proof of the orbital ordering is a very elegant example of a general method which Heilbronner[28] has proposed for the determination of such orderings. Isopropylidenenorbornadiene,

has almost the same dihedral angle between the two equivalent π bonds as norbornadiene itself and it has a new π bond, which, because of its symmetry, can interact only with the negative overlap combination of the two equivalent localized π orbitals. In the photoelectron spectrum of isopropylidenenorbornadiene[29], the higher ionization potential π band of the parent compound recurs at exactly its original energy. The first band in the spectrum of norbornadiene, on the other hand, is split strongly into two separate bands in the spectrum of its isopropylidene derivative. This effect is proof that the outermost π orbital in norbornadiene is the negative overlap combination, as required by the through-space interaction model.

The simplest model compound for the study of through-bond interactions of isolated π bonds is 1,4-cyclohexadiene, which has a large dihedral angle of about 160 degrees between the double bonds, and is of ideal symmetry for through-bond, hyperconjugative interaction. That the observed splitting of the π ionization bands in the spectrum of 1,4-cyclohexadiene is 1.0 eV[25], that is, greater than in norbornadiene (0.85 eV), is immediately surprising on a through-space interaction mechanism, as the π bonds are further apart. A proof that the symmetrical orbital combination has a lower ionization potential than the unsymmetrical combination, as consonant with a through-bond interaction, has been obtained by a similar method to that used for norbornadiene[28]. This result is also confirmed by a study of the spectrum of 1,4,5,8-tetrahydronaphthalene,

which contains two 1,4-cyclohexadiene rings.

The parameters needed to represent the ionization potentials of 1,4-cyclohexadiene correctly in an empirical calculation on the through-bond interaction model also led to a satisfactory representation of the photoelectron spectrum of the tetrahydronaphthalene[30]. The photoelectron spectra of many other molecules that contain apparently isolated double bonds have been examined and found to show splittings of the π orbital ionization bands, which are attributed to the two types of non-bonded interaction[31]. These interactions are not, however, restricted to lone-pair orbitals and π orbitals, but occur generally. This is an area in which experimental studies together with empirical molecular orbital calculations are greatly enriching the knowledge of molecular electronic structure.

8.4   Spectra of ions in liquids and solids

Since the radical cations produced by photoionization are generally very reactive, they are not common in condensed phases. The very familiar cations of aqueous solution chemistry are of *closed shell* structure, and the photoelectron spectra of the radicals (such as $NH_4 \cdot$) which would give rise to them are, regrettably, unknown.

The radical cations of photoelectron spectroscopy can, however, be produced in liquids and solids under special circumstances. These are:

(1) As transient species in high energy reactions–particularly in electrode processes in non-aqueous electrochemistry[32].

(2) In superacid media, such as SO_2/SbF_5. Many organic, particularly aromatic, halides dissociate heterolytically in such solutions[33]. A few molecules can be directly oxidized to form more or less stable cation solutions, the oleum solution of I_2^+ being the most accessible example[34].

(3) As components of charge-transfer complexes. Molecules of low ionization potential can become cationic partners in charge-transfer complexes with acceptors of high electron affinity[35].

(4) In rigid glasses, especially at low temperatures. Very many stable cation solutions can be made by ultraviolet or γ irradiation of suitable glasses containing the neutral molecules in solution[36].

The most wide-ranging comparison of photoelectron spectra with the electronic absorption spectra of the corresponding cations has been made for organic cations in rigid organic glasses at liquid nitrogen temperature, mainly by Hamill and Shida[36]. As in all the above cases, knowledge of the photoelectron spectrum is a vital prerequisite for the interpretation of the bands, and for their attribution to particular cations. The spectra generally contain one to three absorption bands in the visible–ultraviolet region, corresponding to transitions from the ionic ground state to the first few excited states seen in the photoelectron spectrum. Interesting details emerge from a quantitative comparison of band shapes and positions.

First, the (0–0) transitions in solution are almost always *redshifted* in comparison with the gas-phase band position predicted from the photoelectron spectrum. This shift is dependent on the solvent, and arises because excited ionic states are more polarizable than the ground state, and so can be better stabilized by solvation effects. Second, bands may be present in the absorption spectrum at energies where the photoelectron spectrum is empty, because of the different starting points for the two processes. Whereas photoionization populates only states with a single hole in an occupied orbital, absorption by the ground state ion can also populate states in which one electron is excited to a normally unoccupied orbital. Such non-Koopmans ('NK') states are just as numerous in ions as the states seen in photoelectron spectroscopy, and knowledge of their positions and characters is equally vital in ion chemistry. A beautiful example, in which the first excited state of an ion is of NK type, has been provided by Haselbach et al.[37] and is illustrated in *Figure 8.7.*

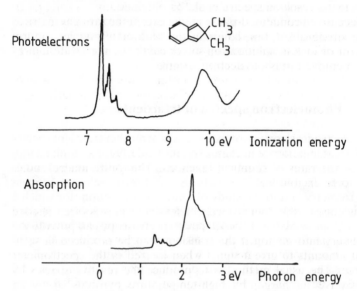

Figure 8.7. Photoelectron spectrum of 2,2-dimethylisoindene (gas phase) compared with its absorption spectrum in an *iso*-pentane-n-butyl chloride matrix at 77 K. The strongest absorption band matches the second band of the photoelectron spectrum (small red shift), but the weak first absorption band corresponds to formation of a 'non-Koopmans' state of the molecular ion[38]. Similar non-Koopmans states of naphthalene ion have also been recorded. (See ref. 54 of Chapter 3)

A third reason why ion absorption spectra may differ from photoelectron spectra is the occurrence of relaxation processes. In Chapter 7 we encountered the idea that cations may isomerize, and in Chapter 4 we saw that ions in orbitally degenerate states may be subject to Jahn–Teller distortions. If either an isomerization or a static Jahn–Teller effect occurs, the absorption spectrum of a cation need not resemble the photoelectron spectrum at all closely; several such cases are known[38,39]. These relaxation processes are often *activated* in glassy media, and their rates can be studied as functions of temperature or of photolytic irradiation. Less dramatic, but quite noticeable, differences also arise, of course, from the different Franck–Condon factors governing ionization and absorption transitions; a detailed study might provide additional information on ion structure, following the methods of Franck–Condon analysis mentioned in Chapter 5, if sufficiently resolved spectra could be obtained.

Because all condensed-phase media except the rare-gas matrices have strong absorption bands in the blue or ultraviolet, optical spectra of ions in solution can never cover the very wide energy range enjoyed in photoelectron spectroscopy.

8.5   Photoelectron spectra of transients

The electronic structure of free radicals and other transient species is of great importance in chemistry, particularly for an understanding of the rates of chemical reactions. The ionization potentials and ionic excited states of radicals are directly relevant to mass spectrometry and to the study of ionic decomposition, for which a knowledge of the energy levels of fragment ions is often needed but seldom available. Photoelectron spectroscopy can provide the necessary information if the transients can be produced in sufficient amounts to give a signal when ionized in the spectrometer source. The usual method is to produce the reactive species by microwave discharge, by high-temperature pyrolysis or by an atomic reaction in a flowing gas stream, which transports them as rapidly as possible to the ionization region. The raw spectra so obtained are generally very complex, because they contain contributions from the parent molecules and other reaction products, as well as the species of interest. The 'background subtraction' or 'spectrum stripping' problem is so severe that often only one or two bands can be attributed unambiguously to the transient species. Special modulation techniques[40] help, and careful systematic study of the effect of varying the formation conditions is almost always needed. The apparatus is usually built specially for this work, to allow rapid pumping, easy access to the source region, and rapid data acquisition. The last is very important, because highly reactive species often cause loss of spectral resolution and large-scale shifts within a rather short time.

Very many chemically unstable or labile species have now been studied by photoelectron spectroscopy, from free atoms such as H, N, O, Cl, I, Pb, through diatomic species such as S_2, PN, ClO and triatomic species like NH_2, CHO, HO_2, up to large organic radicals such as ethyl, phenyl, tropyl and phenoxy radicals. References to individual species are not given here, because they are easily accessible in two comprehensive review articles by Dyke and co-workers[41,42]. Besides the radicals, several reactive or short-lived closed-shell molecules have been studied extensively; examples are nitrosyl cyanide[43], NOCN, and fluorothiocyanate[44], FSCN. Another general class of transients is formed by excited species; until recently, only the metastable $O_2(^1\Delta)$ had been detected by photoelectron spectroscopy. With the increasing availability of high power lasers, the spectroscopy of electronically excited species and also of vibrationally excited molecules, is expanding rapidly.

A final group of chemically 'difficult' gas-phase molecules is represented by charged species, particularly the molecular negative ions. Their photoelectron spectra show states of neutral molecules, attained by photodetachment. Up to now the negative ions have been studied only in beams produced by mass spectrometers: such beams have very low density, and intense laser light is required to give useful photoelectron count rates. The work has been done mainly to determine molecular electron affinities[45] and, because of the low energy of the available intense lasers, only neutral ground states have been seen except in exceptional cases. The photodetachment of methylene negative ions to yield methylene radicals in singlet and triplet states was one such exceptional case[46], and it sparked off a renewed controversy on the relative energies of the CH_2 states[47]. If photodetachment could be done with helium light, it would reveal a whole range of neutral states, selected by the one electron rule. A new spectroscopy of neutral molecules might be opened up. If singly positive molecular ions could be photoionized in a like manner we would have a new spectroscopy of molecular doubly-charged ions; although efforts are being made in this direction, its attainment seems to be some way off.

8.6 Analytical applications

Photoelectron spectroscopy (PES) has not developed into a tool for general quantitative or qualitative analysis, although it is capable of being used for analytical purposes. The spectrum of air in *Figure 8.8* illustrates some of its qualities; each substance gives rise to many characteristic lines or bands which constitute a

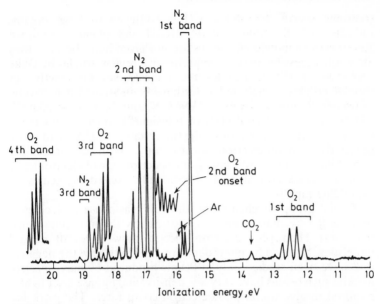

Figure 8.8.   Photoelectron spectrum of air. (From Betteridge, D. and Baker, A.D., *Anal. Chem.*, **42**, 43A (1969), by courtesy of the American Chemical Society)

fingerprint and their intensities are a quantitative measure of concentration. The overlapping of broad bands in the spectra of large molecules inevitably makes PES a poor technique for many compounds; it is most suitable for atmospheric and other light gases, and for compounds whose spectra contain sharp characteristic features. The lone-pair ionization bands of halogens and heteroatoms, such as sulphur, can provide suitable features, and some analytical work has been done on these lines. A particular advantage of PES over many other methods is that because the spectra are reflections of molecular *electronic* structure, they are often very different for different isomers, and even for conformers which differ only by restricted rotation about one or two bonds. The big differences in photoelectron spectra between isomers often arise from different possibilities for conjugation in the different forms. Evidently structural. isomers have completely different spectra, and those of geometrical isomers are also very different. *Figure 8.9* illustrates the difference between *cis-* and *trans*-isomers of di-iodoethylene[48], whose photoelectron spectra contain the same number of bands, but in distinctly different positions, and with different contours. The isomers which arise from rotation about single bonds, and the different stereochemical forms of ring molecules like cyclohexane, have spectra which differ more subtly, but often detectably. Several thermodynamic studies of conformer equilibrium have been made by the use of variable temperature photoelectron spectroscopy (VTPES)[49,50], in which temperature effects on the proportions of two isomeric forms are examined. This thermochemical application of analytical

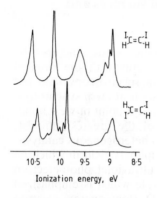

10·5 10 9·5 9 8·5

Ionization energy, eV

Figure 8.9.   The difference between *cis*- and *trans*-isomers in the lone-pair and π-electron region of the photoelectron spectra of the di-iodo-ethylenes. (After Wittel, K., Bock, H. and Manne, R., *Tetrahedron*, **30**, 651 (1974))

PES can lead to the determination of energy differences between the isomeric forms, as has been done, for instance, for thioanisole, methyl vinyl sulphide and dimethylhexahydropyridazine[51].

Another analytical application of PES has been found in the observation of gas-phase reactions. The first chemical reaction demonstrated in this way was that of ethane 1:2 dithiol[52]

$$HSCH_2CH_2SH \xrightarrow[\text{0.1 torr}]{\text{heat at}} CH_2\overset{\displaystyle S}{-\!\!-\!\!-}CH_2 + H_2S$$

Another reaction studied in some detail at different temperatures by PES is the cyanation of benzene by cyanogen–hydrogen cyanide mixtures, and the effect of heterogeneous catalysis upon it[53]. The spectra were used to detect the onset of cyanation, which was found to start at 1300 K in the absence of catalyst, but at only 700 K when the most effective $Cu–Al_2O_3$ catalyst was present. The thermal dissociation reactions of dithioacetic acid and 1,2,3-thiadiazole, both yielding thioketene, have also been followed by PES[54]. These examples demonstrate that the technique is a viable analytical method in specialized applications, and its possibilities should not be overlooked when other techniques run into difficulties. One speculative possibility which has not yet been investigated is that PES of chiral molecules (perhaps using circularly polarized light, electron angular distributions or electron spin polarization measurements) might distinguish optical isomers, or even provide absolute assignments.

8.7 Photoelectron spectroscopy of surfaces and adsorbates

The study of solids and their electronic band structures by photoelectron emission received an impetus with the original development of molecular photoelectron spectroscopy, and has undergone a second expansion with the application of synchrotron radiation sources. From the physico-chemical point of view bonding and behaviour of adsorbates are of the greatest interest, particularly because of their relevance to heterogeneous catalysis. The study of these topics is a multi-disciplinary field in which no single technique is pre-eminent; while ultraviolet photoelectron spectroscopy has played an important role which is emphasized here, other techniques such as LEED (low energy electron diffraction), EELS (electron energy loss spectroscopy), thermal desorption and X-ray photoelectron spectroscopy have contributed no less.

The depth from which electrons can escape from a solid without being scattered is a rapidly varying function of the electron energy, and also depends on the nature of the material. At very low electron energies mean free paths of 1000 nm are possible, meaning that bulk solid is sampled, while at higher electron energy (50 eV) the mean free path may be no more than 0.5 nm, so that it is essentially the surface layer that is examined. In the range of electron energies 5–20 eV, characteristic of ultraviolet PES, a depth of 2 to 3 nm is perhaps typical, but wide variations may occur. One major difficulty in the experiments is to keep control of the nature of the surface being studied under the always imperfect vacuum conditions. At a pressure of 10^{-6} torr (10^{-6} mBar, 1.3×10^{-4} Pa), a normal 'high vacuum', a new monolayer of ambient gas can be deposited in one second, and even at 10^{-9} torr a new monolayer appears in about fifteen minutes. In order to measure the spectrum of a clean surface, or a surface with an adsorbed layer of controlled density and composition, one must normally achieve a vacuum of 10^{-9} torr or better. This requirement obviously strains the capabilities of general purpose photoelectron spectrometers beyond their limit, and is a severe obstacle to the design of apparatus. Because there is no suitable window material in the vuv, any discharge lamp must be differentially pumped from its operating pressure of about 1 torr right down to ultra-high vacuum. Synchrotron radiation sources, which normally operate at 10^{-11} torr for the sake of long life of the circulating current in storage rings, have a notable advantage here.

An ingenious alternative solution, which has been suggested by Potts and collaborators[55] is to regenerate the desired surface continuously, and make the time between generation and spectrum measurement as short as possible. Clean metal surfaces can be obtained by cutting a thin layer off the bulk, or by evaporation, and continuously rotating devices can carry the new surface to the ionization region in less than a second, making surface studies possible even at 10^{-6} torr.

8.7.1   Pure solids

The photoelectron energy distribution produced by photoionization of a pure solid is a reflection of the electronic band structure. Ideally, the photoelectron spectrum might give the density of states in the different occupied electron bands directly, as the density of states at a particular energy in a full band corresponds to the orbital occupancy in molecular photoelectron spectroscopy. In fact, however, in ultraviolet photoelectron spectroscopy of solids the number of photoelectrons emitted at a particular ionization energy is also a strong function of the final state of the system, that is, of the outgoing electron energy. Photoelectron spectra must therefore usually be taken at several different photon energies before deductions about the band structure can be made. An example of a set of photoelectron spectra is shown in *Figure 8.10*, and a calculated density-of-states function is given for comparison in *Figure 8.11*[56]. A careful comparison shows that peaks in the density-of-states function do correspond to peaks or shoulders in the photoelectron spectra at the same energies relative to the Fermi level, but some of the experimental curves also contain additional peaks, and all have intensity distributions that are different from the calculated curve. The deviation is least at the highest photon energy, and it seems that this trend continues to higher energies. In X-ray photoelectron spectroscopy of metals,

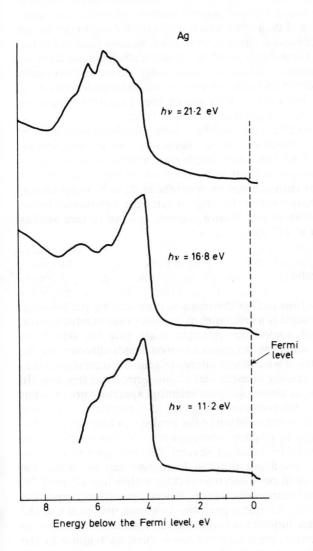

Figure 8.10. Photoelectron spectra of solid silver taken with light of three different wavelengths. The strong bands below 4 eV are d electron ionizations. (From Eastman[56], by courtesy of North Holland Publishing Company)

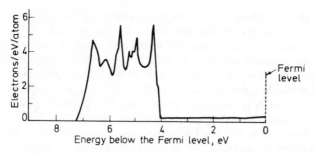

Figure 8.11.   Theoretical density of states of silver. (From Eastman[56], by courtesy of the North Holland Publishing Company)

the density-of-states function is reproduced directly in the photo-electron energy distribution[57] but at the high electron energies involved it is difficult to achieve the high resolution necessary in order to exploit this simplification.

The spectra in *Figure 8.9* were taken using resonance lamps, which obviously restrict the number of possible wavelengths. With synchrotron radiation sources there is no wavelength restriction, and more can be learnt from the wavelength dependent intensities of the different bands[58]. More interesting is the angular depend-ence of the photoemission, with respect to the crystallographic axes, since in principle such measurements allow the band struc-ture to be measured directly. While the band structure determina-tion involves detailed theoretical modelling, the symmetry prop-erties of the angular distributions may sometimes be directly related to the site symmetry of emitting atoms at or near the surface[59].

8.7.2   Adsorbed species

Owing to the small penetration depth for electrons of 10 eV ultraviolet photoelectron spectra of surfaces often contain relative-ly strong bands from adsorbates, despite the extremely small quantity of material that goes into a monolayer on a smooth substrate[60]. By choosing an ionizing wavelength at which the substrate ionization cross-section has a Cooper minimum, one can suppress some substrate bands considerably. Bands characteristic of the substrate are normally still the strongest in the spectrum; nevertheless they may not be identical to the pure substrate bands, because adsorption can change the band structure. The photoelec-tron spectrum of the adsorbate is also modified compared with the spectrum of the gas-phase species, both by effects of the bonding and by physical effects of the proximity of the surface. It is normally assumed that the chemical bonding effects are dominant, at least on the orbitals involved in attaching a molecule to the surface. The gas-phase He I spectrum of CO, for instance, contains three bands corresponding to $4\sigma^{-1}$, $1\pi^{-1}$ and $5\sigma^{-1}$ ionization. The 5σ orbital is localized mainly on the carbon atom, whereas 4σ is mainly an oxygen orbital; hence the disappearance of the $5\sigma^{-1}$ band from the photoelectron spectrum when CO is adsorbed on many metal surfaces[61] is interpreted to mean that the carbon end of the molecule is bonded to the metal, a deduction supported by much other evidence. The band probably disappears by being broadened and shifted on bond formation. When ethylene and acetylene are adsorbed molecularly on tungsten several of the bands shift in relative position, by comparison with the gas-phase spectra. The shifts in the π^{-1} ionization bands have been interpreted as consequences of $p\pi$–$d\pi$ bonding to single W atoms, similar to that in the metal carbonyls (p. 231); the molecules apparently lie with their axes parallel to the surface. There are also shifts in the σ^{-1} ionization bands, which were interpreted by comparison with MO calculations as indicating changes of hybridization from sp^2 to sp^3 and from sp to sp^2, respectively[62]. The reliability of such detailed deductions may, perhaps, be questionable, but they are indicative of the sort of detailed bonding information that can be hoped for in surface photoelectron spectroscopy.

Orbital energy and orbital character changes are actually very mild compared with the changes that frequently occur on chemisorption. Although CO is adsorbed molecularly on Ni, it chemisorbs dissociatively as C and O atoms on Cr and on most metals to the left of Fe in the Periodic Table. The atoms may diffuse into the bulk, or may appear as metal carbide and oxide in the surface layer[60]. Some of these chemical changes can be followed by ultraviolet photoelectron spectroscopy, but XPS is often more useful.

The most detailed deductions about the topography of surface species are made by study of the angular distributions of photoelectrons as a function of the ionizing light wavelength and polarization directions. This work, which rejoices in the acronym ARUPS (angle resolved ultraviolet photoelectron spectroscopy) absolutely requires the use of a synchrotron radiation source[63]. The angular distributions depend not only on characteristics of the adsorbed molecules and their orientations, but also on the kinetic energy of the electrons, the polarization of the light, the directions and strengths of local surface electric fields and on the extent of interference from electrons back-scattered from the surface itself. Readers will no doubt be able to think of other complications (image forces, diffraction effects....). Fortunately, the effect of these complications can be reduced, or circumvented, by tuning the ionizing radiation to *shape resonances* in the molecular ionization continuum. As explained in Chapter 3, such resonances may enhance the ionization cross-sections at particular energies. Because the resonances correspond to (temporarily) bound states of the electron, that is, to neutral molecule states, their production is governed by the dipole selection rules. Each shape resonance occurring in one particular ionization channel has a definite symmetry which can be discovered either by theoretical calculations or by study of X-ray absorption spectra. The orientation of the transition moment in the molecular frame is therefore known too—that is, whether the transitions are of parallel or perpendicular type. In CO, for instance, there is a strong shape resonance at 35 eV photon energy in the $4\sigma^{-1}$ ionization channel. It is a parallel transition ($\sigma_{(u)} \rightarrow \sigma_{(g)}$) and the photoelectron intensity should therefore be peaked along the molecular axis. Experimentally, the 35 eV peak in the $4\sigma^{-1}$ ionization cross-section is seen only if the electric vector of the ionizing light has a component perpendicular to the surface. There is no detectable resonance, though photoemission still occurs, if the electric vector lies in the surface plane. Furthermore, the angular distribution of resonance photoelectrons at 35 eV is found to be sharply peaked perpendicular to the surface, and agrees with theoretical expectation if the CO molecule itself is perpendicular to the surface. Thus, the orientation of the CO molecule on the surfaces of several metals is definitely established by ARUPS; the same methods apply to other adsorbates, but are not usually so simple.

Angular distributions of surface photoelectrons and photoelectron spectra at specific angles contain a wealth of information on the structure of the superficial layer, over and beyond the orientation of adsorbate molecules. By theoretical modelling and comparison with experiment it may be possible to establish the nature of the adsorption sites, for instance, but much depends on the quality of the theoretical model. Since photoelectron spectroscopy is primarily a probe of electronic structure, it is perhaps overstretched in trying to provide so much topographical information. If the surface topographies can be determined by other means, photoelectron spectroscopy should come into its own in characterizing the electronic changes that determine them, and which must lie at the heart of the special chemical and catalytic properties of surfaces.

8.8   Photoelectron spectra of liquids

Photoelectron spectroscopy of liquids could work just as well, in principle, as photoelectron spectroscopy of solids, and could reveal many details of surface electronic structure. The practical difficulties are severe, but a number of demonstrations have shown that they are not insuperable. The main difficulty is that most liquids exert so high a vapour pressure (even at their freezing points) as to cause electron scattering, which imposes a large differential pumping requirement to ensure safe operation of electron multiplier detectors. The high pressures inevitably also cause scale shifts, and these can be exacerbated by charging effects if non-conducting liquids are studied. Practical techniques for liquid handling have so far been either to form the liquid into a jet[64,65], or to transport a thin film of liquid to the ionization region on the surface of a fast-moving wire or disk[66]. The actual photoelectron spectra of liquids reported recently have all been obtained by the jet method, however, as the group specializing in the rotating disk technique actually measure total photoelectron yield as a function of wavelength, without energy analysis of the photoelectrons. This avoids the difficulty of electron energy analysis in a polluted vacuum, and has allowed fascinating studies of photoemission from ions in aqueous solution to be made.

True photoelectron spectra of liquid glycol[64] (1:2 ethanediol) and benzyl alcohol[65] have been reported, and also spectra of adiponitrile solutions containing various anions[67]. These spectra have been interpreted in detail by their originators. They all show intense peaks at low energy, caused by electron scattering and secondary ionization. The characteristic photoelectron bands are seen at the highest electron energies; the I$^-$ solution, for instance, shows doublet bands representing the spin–orbit split states $^2P_{3/2}$ and $^2P_{1/2}$ of the neutral I atom, formed by ionization of closed-shell I$^-$. It must be emphasized that these spectra refer to species at the surface: great care is needed in relating them to conditions in the bulk solutions. The data on benzyl alcohol were interpreted in terms of hydrogen bonding, which could be related to the surface tension and other properties. Some of the photoemission work has shown how sensitive liquid surfaces can be to contamination by common vacuum impurities (pump oil); the observations suggest the possibility of purposefully studying photoelectron spectra of Langmuir–Blodgett films, with their controllable alignment. This is one possible way of attaining molecular alignment in liquids, and so studying photoelectron spectra of orientated molecules.

References

1. Reviews on applications of PES: CARLSON, T.A., *Ann. Rev. Phys. Chem.*, **26**, 211 (1975); HAMMNET, A. and ORCHARD, A.F. in Day, P. (Editor) *Electronic Structure and Magnetism of Inorganic Compounds*, Vol 2, Chem. Soc., London (1972); BOCK, H., *Angew Chemie*, **89**, 631 (1977); WITTEL, K. and McGLYNN, S.P., *Chem. Rev.*, **77**, 745 (1977); GLEITER, R. and SPANGET-LARSON, J., *Topics in Current Chemistry*, **86**, 139 (1979); GLEITER, R., *Topics in Current Chemistry*, **86**, 197 (1979)
2. LEE, E.P.F., POTTS, A.W. and BLOOR, J.E., *Proc. Roy. Soc. London*, **A381**, 373 (1982)
3. RABALAIS, J.W., WERME, L.O., BERGMARK, T., KARLSON, L., HUSAIN, M. and SIEGBAHN, K., *J. Chem. Phys.*, **57**, 1185 (1972)
4. DYKE, J., FAYAD, N.K., JOSLAND, G.D. and MORRIS, A., *J. Chem. Soc., Faraday Trans. II.* **76**, 1672 (1980)
5. DYKE, J.M., JONATHAN, N. and MORRIS, A., *Int. Rev. Phys. Chem.*, **2**, 3 (1982)
6. EVANS, S., GREEN, J.C., GREEN, M.L.H., ORCHARD, A.F. and TURNER, D.W., *Disc. Faraday Soc.*, **47**, 112 (1969)
7. LLOYD, D.R. and ROBERTS, P.J., *Mol. Phys.*, **26**, 225 (1973)
8. HILLIER, I.H. and SAUNDERS, V.R., *Mol. Phys.*, **22**, 193 (1971)
9. CRAIG, D.P. and PADDOCK, N.L., *Nature, Lond.*, **181**, 1052 (1958)
10. BRANTON, G.R., BRION, C.E., FROST, D.C., MITCHELL, K.A.R. and PADDOCK, N.L., *J. Chem. Soc. A*, 151 (1970)
11. HOFFMANN, R., *Accounts Chem. Res.*, **4**, 1 (1971); GLEITER, R., *Angew. Chem.*, **86**, 770 (1974)
12. HOFFMANN, R., IMAMURA, A. and HEHRE, J.W., *J. Amer. Chem. Soc.*, **90**, 1499 (1968)
13. BISCHOF, P., HASHMALL, J.A., HEILBRONNER, E. and HORNUNG, V., *Tetrahedron Lett.*, 4025 (1969)
14. HEILBRONNER, E. and MUSZKAT, K.A., *J. Amer. Chem. Soc.*, **92**, 3818 (1970)
15. HASELBACH, E., HASHMALL, J.A., HEILBRONNER, E. and HORNUNG, V., *Angew. Chem.*, **81**, 897 (1969)
16. HASELBACH, E., HEILBRONNER, E., MANNSCHRECK, A. and SEITZ, W., *Angew. Chem.*, **82**, 879 (1970)
17. HASELBACH, E. and HEILBRONNER, E., *Helv. Chim. Acta*, **53**, 684 (1970)
18. GLEITER, R., HEILBRONNER, E. and HORNUNG, V., *Helv. Chim. Acta*, **55**, 255 (1972)
19. LINDHOLM, E., *et al.*, *Int. J. Mass Spectrom. Ion Phys.*, **8**, 85, 101, 215 and 229 (1972)
20. COWAN, D.O., GLEITER, R., HASHMALL, J.A., HEILBRONNER, E. and HORNUNG, V., *Angew. Chem.*, **83**, 405 (1971)

21. DAINTITH, J., DINSDALE, R., MAIER, J.P., SWEIGART, D.A. and TURNER, D.W., in *Molecular Spectroscopy*, Institute of Petroleum, London, 16 (1971)
22. LAKE, R.F. and THOMPSON, H.W., *Proc. R. Soc., Lond.*, **315A**, 323 (1970)
23. BAKER, A.D., BETTERIDGE, D., KEMP, N.R. and KIRBY, R.E., *Anal. Chem.*, **43**, 375 (1971)
24. DEWAR, M.J.S. and WORLEY, S.D., *J. Chem. Phys.*, **50**, 654 (1969)
25. BISCHOF, P., HASHMALL, J.A., HEILBRONNER, E. and HORNUNG, V., *Helv. Chim. Acta*, **52**, 1745 (1969)
26. HASELBACH, E., HEILBRONNER, E. and SCHRODER, G., *Helv. Chim. Acta*, **54**, 153 (1971)
27. BISCHOF, P., GLEITER, R. and HEILBRONNER, E., *Helv. Chim. Acta*, **53**, 1425 (1970)
28. HEILBRONNER, E., *Israel J. Chem.*, **10**, 143 (1972)
29. HEILBRONNER, E. and MARTIN, H.D., *Helv. Chim. Acta*, **55**, 1490 (1972)
30. BISCHOF, P., HASHMALL, J.A., HEILBRONNER E. and HORNUNG, V., *Tetrahedron Lett.*, **13**, 1033 (1970)
31. WORLEY, S.D., *Chem. Rev.*, **71**, 295 (1971)
32. ROBERTSON, P.M. in *Specialist Periodical Reports—Electrochemistry*, Royal Society of Chemistry (1972)
33. OLAH, G.H., *Topics in Current Chemistry*, **80**, 50 (1979)
34. GILLESPIE, R.J. and MILNE, J.B., *Inorg. Chem.*, **5**, 1577 (1966)
35. PIGNATARO, S. and ALOISI, G., *Z. Naturforsch.*, **A27**, 1165 (1972)
36. HAMILL, W.H. in Kaiser, E.T. and Kevan, L. (Editors) *Radical Ions*, Wiley, New York (1968); SHIDA, T., *J. Phys. Chem.*, **82**, 991 (1978); ANDREWS, L., *Ann. Rev. Phys. Chem.*, **30**, 79 (1979)
37. HASELBACH, E., BALLY, T., GSCHWIND, R., KLEMM, U. and LANYIOVA, Z., *Chimia*, **33**, 405 (1979)
38. BALLY, T., HASELBACH, E., LANYIOVA, Z. and BÄRTSCHI, P., *Helv. Chim. Acta*, **61**, 2488 (1978)
39. SHIDA, T., *J. Phys. Chem.*, **82**, 991 (1978)
40. JONKERS, G., deLANGE, C.A. and SNIJDERS, J.G., *Chem. Phys.*, **69**, 109 (1982)
41. DYKE, J.M., JONATHAN, N. and MORRIS, A. in Brundle, C.R. and Baker, A.D. (Editors) *Electron Spectroscopy*, Academic Press, London, 189 (1979)
42. DYKE, J.M., JONATHAN, N. and MORRIS, A., *Int. Rev. Phys. Chem.*, **2**, 3 (1982)
43. JONKERS, G., MOOYMAN, R. and deLANGE, C.A., *Chem. Phys.*, **57**, 97 (1981)
44. JONKERS, G., GRABANDT, D., MOOYMAN, R. and deLANGE, C.A., *J. Electron Spectrosc. Rel. Phen.*, **26**, 147 (1982)
45. JANOUSEK, B.K. and BRAUMANN, J.I. in Bowers, M.T. (Editor) *Gas Phase Ion Chemistry Vol II*, Academic Press, New York (1979)
46. ZITTEL, P.F., ELLISON, G.B., O'NEILL, S.W., HERBST, E., LINEBERGER, W.C. and REINHARDT, W.P., *J. Amer. Chem. Soc.*, **98**, 3731 (1976)
47. BAUSCHLICHER, C.W., *Chem. Phys. Lett.*, **74**, 273 (1980); SHIH, S-K., PEYERIMHOFF, S.D., BUENKER, R.J. and PERIC, M., *Chem. Phys. Lett.*, **55**, 206 (1978)
48. WITTEL, K., BOCK, H. and MANNE, R., *Tetrahedron*, **30**, 651 (1974)
49. SCHWEIG, A., THON, N. and VERMEER, H., *J. Amer. Chem. Soc.*, **101**, 80 (1979)

50. HONEGGER, E. and HEILBRONNER, E., *Chem. Phys. Lett.*, **81**, 615 (1981)
51. SCHWEIG, A. and THON, N., *Chem. Phys. Lett.*, **38**, 482 (1976); SCHWEIG, A., THON, N., NELSEN, S.F. and GREZZO, L.A., *J. Amer. Chem. Soc.*, **102**, 7438 (1980)
52. SCHÄFER, W. and SCHWEIG, A., *Z. Naturforsch.*, **30a**, 1785 (1975)
53. BOCK, H., HIRABAYASHI, T., MOHMAND, S., ROSMUS, P. and SOLOUKI, B., *Angew. Chem. Int. Edn.*, **16**, 105 (1977)
54. BOCK, H., SOLOUKI, B., BERT, G. and ROSMUS, P., *J. Amer. Chem. Soc.*, **99**, 1663 (1977)
55. POTTS, A.W., BRIGDEN, P.J., LAW, D.S. and LEE, E.P.F., *J. Electron Spectrosc. Rel. Phen.*, **24**, 267 (1981)
56. EASTMAN, D.E., in Shirley, D.A. (Editor) *Electron Spectroscopy*, North Holland, Amsterdam, 487 (1972)
57. HAGSTROM, S.B.M., in Shirley, D.A. (Editor) *Electron Spectroscopy*, North Holland, Amsterdam, 515 (1972)
58. GREEN, J.C., *Ann. Rev. Phys. Chem.*, **28**, 161 (1977)
59. SMITH, N.V., and TRAUM, M.M., *Phys. Rev.*, **B11**, 2087 (1975)
60. McKEE, C.S. in *Specialist Periodical Reports—Chemical Physics of Solids and their Surfaces*, Vol 8, Royal Society of Chemistry (1980)
61. GUSTAFSSON, T., PLUMMER, E.W., EASTMAN, D.E. and FREEOUF, T.L., *Solid State Comm.*, **17**, 391 (1975)
62. VORBURGER, T.V., WACLAWSKI, B.J. and PLUMMER, E.W., *Chem. Phys. Lett.*, **46**, 42 (1977)
63. PLUMMER, E.W. and GUSTAFSSON, T., *Science*, **198**, 165 (1977)
64. BALLARD, R.E., *J. Electron. Spectrosc. Rel. Phen.*, **14**, 331 (1978)
65. BALLARD, R.E., GUNNELL, G.G. and HAGAN, W.P., *J. Electron Spectrosc. Rel. Phen.*, **16**, 435 (1979)
66. WATANABE, I., FLANAGAN, J.B. and DELAHAY, P., *J. Chem. Phys.*, **66**, 4450 (1979)
67. BALLARD, R.E., JONES, J. and HART, D., *J. Electron Spectrosc. Rel. Phen.*, **26**, 31 (1982)

Appendix I
The names of electronic states in atoms, molecules and ions

Atoms

The name of an atomic state contains three pieces of information, which are written in the form of a *term symbol*:

$$^{2S+1}L_J$$

(1) The superscript on the left is the spin multiplicity, which has the value $2S + 1$ where S is the total spin angular momentum in units of $\hbar$. If $S = 0$ the multiplicity is 1, and we speak of a singlet state; if $S = \frac{1}{2}$ the multiplicity is 2, giving a doublet state; and $S = 1$ corresponds to a triplet state. S is the result of combining the individual electron spins, which each have an angular momentum of $\pm\frac{1}{2}$. If no electrons are unpaired the state is a singlet, if one is unpaired it is a doublet, and so on.

(2) The capital letter indicates the total orbital angular momentum, L, the result of combining the individual orbital angular momenta of all the electrons. The value of L is indicated by a capital letter following the convention:

$$
\begin{array}{ccccccc}
L = 0 & 1 & 2 & 3 & 4 & \cdots \\
S & P & D & F & G & \cdots & \text{alphabetic, excluding J.}
\end{array}
$$

If all shells are full, the individual orbital angular momenta cancel and we have an S state; if one electron is unpaired, L is equal to the orbital angular momentum, l, of that electron, 0 for an s electron, 1 for a p electron, 2 for a d electron, etc. When there are two or more electrons not in full shells, their individual angular momenta can combine in various ways, and several different atomic states arise from the same

259

electron configuration. The configuration p^2 outside closed shells, for example, gives terms ^1D, ^3P and ^1S. The details of how electron configurations relate to atomic states are to be found in textbooks of atomic spectroscopy[1] or valence theory[2].

(3) The right-hand subscript, J, is the value of the total angular momentum that results from combining L and S. J can have the values

$$L + S, L + S - 1 \ldots |L - S|$$

In a ^3P state, for instance, $L = S = 1$ and the possible J values are 2, 1 and 0, giving $^3P_2$, $^3P_1$ and $^3P_0$ terms. The energy difference between terms with different J values arises from the interactions between the magnetic moments generated by the electron spin and orbital motion, called spin–orbit coupling.

The term symbols described above are derived on the assumption that the spins of all the electrons in an atom combine to form a resultant S, and the orbital angular momenta of the different electrons combine into a resultant L. This is called the Russell–Saunders or LS coupling scheme, and it is valid strictly for light atoms only. In heavy atoms, and in states where two unpaired electrons are in orbitals of very different size, jj coupling may hold, in which the orbital and spin angular momenta of each electron first couple individually, and the resultant j values of the individual electrons combine to give J for the whole atom. Despite this, the Russell–Saunders terms are often used as convenient labels, even for states of heavy atoms.

Apart from the term symbol, the name of an atomic state sometimes contains the symmetry of the wave-function to inversion, indicated by another right-hand subscript, g (gerade) for even states and u (ungerade) for odd states. The g or u character of a state is determined by taking the product of the symmetries of the wave-functions of the individual electrons, using the rules g × g = u × u = g and g × u = u. The symmetry of s wave-functions is g, p wave-functions are u, d wave-functions are g again, and so on. The ground state of atomic carbon is $^3P_0$, and as this results from two p electrons it is $^3P_{0g}$. Atomic boron has one p electron and so has a $^2P_{1/2u}$ ground state. Finally, another optional extra in atomic state names is the value of the principal quantum number of the outermost shell, written before the term symbol to distinguish states of the same symmetry but different energies. The two metastable states of the helium atom that are most useful in Penning ionization have the electron configuration 1s2s, so the states are 2^1S and 2^3S.

Linear molecules

The electronic states of linear molecules (including diatomic) are named by using term symbols similar to those for atomic states. The multiplicity is shown as a left-hand superscript, the total orbital angular momentum Λ as a capital Greek letter, and the total electronic angular momentum Ω along the molecular axis as a right-hand subscript:

$$^{2S+1}\Lambda_{\Omega}$$

The convention for the Λ values is:

$$\Lambda = 0 \quad 1 \quad 2 \quad 3$$
$$\Sigma \quad \Pi \quad \Delta \quad \Phi$$

In centrosymmetric molecules, the g or u character of the electronic wave-function is indicated by an additional right-hand subscript, as in atoms. Σ states must also be distinguished into Σ^+ and Σ^- states according to the symmetry of the electronic wave-function to reflection in any plane containing the molecular axis. All closed shells give Σ^+ states, and a Σ^- state arises only when $\Lambda = 0$ is attained by cancellation of the orbital angular momenta of individual π or δ electrons. If a molecule in a particular state possesses a single unpaired electron, the term is a doublet, and the Λ value is equal to the orbital angular momentum of the unpaired electron, 0 for a σ electron, 1 for a π electron. The great majority of the ionic states produced by photoionization are of this type, so there is a direct relationship between the symmetry of the orbital ionized and that of the ionic state produced. Ionization of a σ_g electron from a closed-shell molecule gives a $^2\Sigma_g^+$ state, ionization from a σ_u orbital gives a $^2\Sigma_u^+$ state and ionization from a π orbital gives a $^2\Pi$ state. This rule does not apply, however, when molecules that already have unpaired electrons are ionized, because usually the resulting ions will have more than one unpaired electron. There will then be several ionic states corresponding to the different possible ways in which the angular momenta of the unpaired electrons can couple.

The term symbols for the electronic states of linear molecules indicate all the important symmetry properties of the electronic wave-functions, but are not sufficient to identify a state completely, as several states may have the same symmetry but different energies. An identifying letter is often written before the term symbol, sometimes with a tilde mark (˜), to give each state a 'personal' name. The ground state is always given the letter X (or X̃) and the excited states are usually named A, B, C, D, etc. in order of increasing energy. Lower-case letters are used to name states of a different multiplicity from those of the main series. Finally, the Ω value is seldom given for Σ states or singlets, where it is simply equal to S or Λ, respectively, and it is not usually quoted even for $^2\Pi$, $^2\Delta$ or higher states unless special attention is to be drawn to it. As examples of the names of linear ion states we can take those of I_2^+ ions. The occupied molecular orbitals of iodine, starting from the innermost, are $\sigma_g^2 \pi_u^4 \pi_g^4$, giving I_2 a $^1\Sigma_g^+$ ground state. Ionization from the outermost orbital gives ground state I_2^+ ions in the X $^2\Pi_g$ state, which is actually split strongly by spin–orbit coupling into X $^2\Pi_{3/2g}$ and X $^2\Pi_{1/2g}$. The next ionic states in order of energy are A $^2\Pi_{3/2u}$, $^2\Pi_{1/2u}$ and B $^2\Sigma_g^+$.

Non-linear molecules

The names of electronic states of non-linear molecules or ions contain the spin multiplicity indicated as a left-hand superscript in the usual way. The rest of the designation depends on the shape of the molecule, and indicates the symmetry properties of the total electronic wave-function. The orbital angular momentum symbol of atomic and linear states is replaced by a capital letter with various subscripts and superscripts, the Mulliken symbol for the irreducible representation to which the electronic wave-function belongs in the molecular symmetry group. The group theory needed to understand this in detail, and to deduce the appearance of wave-functions or orbitals from the symbols, must be studied in another textbook, such as that by Cotton[3]. The orbitals in a non-linear molecule are named with lower-case Mulliken symbols, so the relationship between the name of an orbital ionized and that of the ionic state produced is the same as for linear molecules. Ionization from an a_1 orbital in a closed-shell molecule produces an ion in a $^2A_1$ state. The names of the states and orbitals of linear molecules are, in fact, a special case of the general rule, as the symbols Σ_g, etc., are just the Mulliken symbols belonging to the symmetry groups for linear species.

The symbols are not arbitrary, and it is useful to recognize some of the main clues contained in them. The following are those that the author finds most useful:

A, B are non-degenerate representations, so A, B states and a, b orbitals are non-degenerate;
E states are doubly degenerate;
T (or F) shows a triply degenerate state;
A, A_1, A' or A'_1 in combination with g, if applicable, is the totally symmetric representation.

The individual designations X, A, B, C, etc., showing the energetic order of states of non-linear molecules are always augmented by the *tilde* (thus $\tilde{X}$, $\tilde{A}$, $\tilde{B}$, $\tilde{C}$...) to avoid possible confusion with the Mulliken symbols.

When a molecule has little symmetry, there may be very many states with the same symmetry of the electronic wave-function, so some means of distinguishing them is needed. For the purpose of identifying ionic states observed in photoelectron spectroscopy, the simplest solution is to use the name of the orbital ionized, a lower-case symbol, instead of the capital-letter state symbol. The orbitals in a molecule, whether it is linear or non-linear, are numbered sequentially within each symmetry type. The first orbital of a_1 symmetry in a C_{2v} molecule is called $1a_1$, the second $2a_1$ and the third $3a_1$, and simultaneously the b_2 symmetry orbitals are $1b_2$, $2b_2$, $3b_2$, etc. Normal bands in the photoelectron spectrum of any closed-shell molecule can therefore be identified unambiguously by the names of the orbitals from which ionization takes place instead of by the symbols for the ionic states produced.

References

1. HERZBERG, G., *Atomic Spectra and Atomic Structure*, Dover Publications, New York (1944)
2. MURRELL, J.N., KETTLE, S.F.A. and TEDDER, J.M., *Valence Theory*, John Wiley, London (1965)
3. COTTON, F.A., *Chemical Applications of Group Theory*, John Wiley, New York (1963)

Appendix II
Important constants and conversion factors

Constants

Symbol	Constant	Value
c	speed of light in vacuo	$2.9979 \times 10^{10}\,\text{cm s}^{-1}$
h	Planck's constant	$6.6256 \times 10^{-27}\,\text{erg s}$
$\hbar$	$h/2\pi$	$1.0545 \times 10^{-27}\,\text{erg s}$
e	electronic charge	$4.8030 \times 10^{-10}\,\text{e.s.u.}$
		$1.6021 \times 10^{-19}\,\text{C}$
m_e	electron rest mass	$9.1091 \times 10^{-28}\,\text{g}$
k	Boltzmann constant	$1.3805 \times 10^{-16}\,\text{erg K}^{-1}$
N	Avogadro number	6.0225×10^{23}
R	infinite Rydberg	$13.6053\,\text{eV}$
amu	atomic mass unit	$1.6604 \times 10^{-24}\,\text{g}$

Conversion of energy units

$1\,\text{eV} = 23.061\,\text{kcal mol}^{-1} = 8065.5\,\text{cm}^{-1}$
$1\,\text{eV} = 1.6021 \times 10^{-12}\,\text{erg molecule}^{-1} = 9.649 \times 10^{4}\,\text{J mol}^{-1}$
$1\,\text{cm}^{-1} = 1.23981 \times 10^{-4}\,\text{eV}$
$1\,\text{a.u. (Hartree)} = 27.2107\,\text{eV}$
At $\lambda\,\text{Å}$, photon energy is $12398/\lambda\,\text{eV}$

Units of wavelength

$1\,\text{Å} = 10^{-8}\,\text{cm} = 0.1\,\text{nm}$
$1\,\text{nm} = 10\,\text{Å} = 1\,\text{m}\mu\,\text{(millimicron)}$

Units of pressure

$$1\,\text{torr} = 1\,\text{mm Hg} = 1.316 \times 10^{-3}\,\text{atm} = 133.3\,\text{Nm}^{-2}$$
$$1\,\text{N m}^{-2} = 10\,\text{dyn cm}^{-2} = 7.5006 \times 10^{-3}\,\text{torr}$$
$$1\,\text{atm} = 1.01325 \times 10^{5}\,\text{N m}^{-2} = 1000\,\text{bar}$$

Index